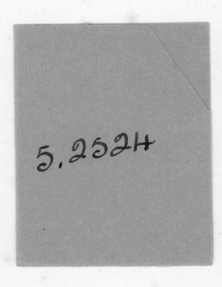

Strange World of
THE MOON

Frontispiece. The walled plain of Clavius, 146 miles in diameter, as seen through the 200-inch Hale reflector on Palomar Mountain. (*Page 59*)

Strange World of
THE MOON

An Enquiry into Lunar Physics

V. A. FIRSOFF

M.A., F.R.A.S.

523

HUTCHINSON OF LONDON

HUTCHINSON & CO. (*Publishers*) LTD.

178–202 Great Portland Street, London, W.1

London Melbourne Sydney
Auckland Bombay Toronto
Johannesburg New York

First published 1959

CONTENTS

PLATES

A map showing the positions of the larger features on the Moon mentioned in this book is given in Appendix II (page 216)

PREFACE

THE BOOK IS INTENDED as a popular volume, accessible to a layman without specialized knowledge, and for this reason it contains a good deal of background information, without which problems handled in it could not be properly understood. The unravelling of the mysteries of the Moon is, however, so fascinating a venture that it should appeal to any intelligent man or woman and there is enough in it to fire one's imagination.

Some of the arguments cannot be maintained without recourse to mathematics, for which purpose an *Appendix* has been provided. Formulae and complicated mathematical statements are completely excluded from the text.

The main subject of the book is the present condition of the Moon with special reference to the atmosphere, surface, and sub-surface structure, as well as the possibility of life there. The cognate selenological problems of the origin of lunar formations and the past history of our satellite do to some extent link up with the discussion of the present physical situation, but the suggestions or inferences made with regard to the former are not necessarily decisive for the latter, or *vice versa*: both may be true or false, wholly or in part, irrespective of each other.

In the treatment of the mathematical arguments in the *Appendix* I have striven to explain everything as fully as possible without unduly swelling its volume. Those who wish to check my conclusions or develop further the lines of research indicated should be able to find in the *Appendix* most of the relevant data.

In the preparation of this volume I have received some valuable assistance which it is a pleasure to acknowledge.

My gratitude is due to Dr. Charlotte Kellner, of the Imperial College of Science and Technology, for kindly advising me on the matter of diffusion coefficients (*Appendix*), to Mr. Patrick Moore for reading the first eight chapters of the typescript before publication and making suggestions, as well as generously lending me his own lunar note-book and helping me to obtain some of the reference works, to Dr. J. G. Porter, of the Royal Greenwich Observatory, for advice given on some special points, to the Director of the Meteorological Office for suggesting sources of information relevant for some of the problems, to Messrs. Dufay Ltd. for supplying colour filters for my lunar observations, and, last but not least, to the Publisher's Readers for their helpful remarks, anonymously made.

The opinions expressed in this book, however, are my own and, unless otherwise stated, do not necessarily reflect those of my advisers; nor are they in any way responsible for any errors of fact or judgment that the book may contain.

ix

Bibliographical references are appended at the end of each chapter. These are not exhaustive and list only the works actually consulted in the writing and referred to in the text. It would be quite impossible fully to cover the background reading I have done on the subjects in question and to this extent my debt to my predecessors must pass unacknowledged.

V. A. F.

1

DEAD OR ALIVE?

THERE CAN BE no doubt that the possibility of the conquest of interplanetary space which the recent advances in rocketry have placed
within the practical grasp of man and the wide publicity given to it
in the Press have greatly stimulated popular interest in astronomy and the
study of the Moon in particular. In response to it a number of books have
been written and published giving a good idea of the general knowledge of
the subject available at this date.

Yet, despite the modern charts, the wonderful detail of lunar photographs taken with the giant telescopes and the constantly mounting volume
of observational data, a sharp division persists in astronomical opinion on
the nature of the lunar world.

Is the Moon a museum piece from a geologically remote past, preserved
in the vacuum of space as though in a labelled glass case? Does nothing
happen in this mountain desert? Or are changes still going on there? Has
perhaps life secured a foothold on our companion world?

The question of whether the Moon is a dead or a living world has
become closely associated with two rival theories of the origin of lunar ring
mountains, the meteoritic and the volcanic. The reason for this is that if
these ring mountains are scars of meteoritic impacts on the surface they are
so large that they must have originated in a very remote past when
meteorites of sufficient size were still abundant. This again is lined up with
the planetesimal conception according to which the present planets and
their satellites are the result of gradual accumulation of fragmented
meteoric materials and bodies of asteroidal size called 'planetesimals'. Both
are hypotheses only, but hypotheses can exert a powerful influence on what
we do or do not see, and it will be appreciated that if changes are still going
on on the Moon it becomes doubtful if she could have kept intact the
marks of that remote time when planetesimals were hurtling down from
the sky.

To illustrate the problem, I will quote the views of two eminent astronomers, standing, as it were, at the opposite poles of the controversy.

In *Earth, Moon and the Planets*[3] F. L. Whipple writes:

'The Moon's surface, as we have viewed in the previous chapters, is
sublime desolation. The lunar plains are more barren than rocky deserts.
The lunar mountains more rugged than the terrestrial peaks above the
timber line. Lava beds of extinct volcanoes are more inviting than lunar
craters. Nothing happens on the Moon. Where there is no air there can be
no clouds, no rain, no sound. Within a dark lunar cave there would be

1

eternal silence and inaction. A spider web across a dim recess in such a cave would remain perfect and unchanged for a million years.'

Not so the late Harvard Professor W. H. Pickering, with a lifetime of diligent observational study of the Moon for a background: writing in *The 7th Report of the Section for the Observation of the Moon of the British Astronomical Association*,[2] he states:

'The view that the Moon is a dead unchanging world, although based on the most inadequate negative evidence, is so widespread and so firmly rooted in the minds not only of the general public, but of the astronomical world as well, that the united and practically unanimous opinion of all the greatest selenographers of successive generations has hitherto been able to make but little impression upon it. Maedler, Schmidt, Webb, Neison, Birt, Elger, and Klein, to mention but a few of the more prominent names, have all described changes upon the surface which could be ascribed to neither phase not libration, yet their careful and painstaking observations were accorded little or no weight during their lifetimes against the practically unsupported statement that no satisfactory evidence of change had ever been detected, this latter being made by men who had never devoted a single month of their lives to lunar observations. Indeed, the writer knows of no astronomer who has devoted sufficient time to the study of the Moon to be worthy of the name of selenographer who has not become convinced by his own independent studies that changes both periodic and non-periodic are actually at the present time taking place upon its surface.

'The arguments on the two sides of the case are extremely simple. The astronomers who are not selenographers declare that there is no atmosphere or water upon the Moon, and that, therefore, changes are impossible. The selenographers' reply is simply that they have seen the changes take place.'

And further on, likening the alterations in the dark lunar markings to the comparable changes observed on Mars:

'The only plausible explanation of the similar changes upon the Moon is that these changes are due to the same causes. If so, they involve the presence of air and water.'

Forty years have elapsed since these words were written, but it would be wrong to assume that the knowledge acquired in the interval has allowed us to solve the problem. It was merely shelved. The profession has largely abandoned the Moon, and to a less extent all planetary studies, to the amateur and devoted its energies to the more promising fields of stellar enquiry. In the words of the meteorist R. B. Baldwin, the Moon has become 'a subject anathema . . . because of its interference with other delicate observations'.[1] Thus if the amateur reported an observation which was out of joint with the established doctrine it could always be said that he lacked professional qualifications and his report was unreliable. The

2

professional himself, on the other hand, could seldom find time for the time-consuming observation of the Moon, and rested content with taking a few photographs or propounding theories.

This picture of the situation may be oversimplified but it is not untrue.

A further difficulty arose from the departmentalization of knowledge, leading to a situation where one specialist had next to no understanding of what another specialist was doing and was unable to correlate or properly assess his results. Another obstacle to progress lay in the lack of understanding of the true meaning of mathematical theory.

Mathematics is a wonderful tool of the mind, but it has its limitations. Mathematical reasoning can bring to light relationships and conditions which it would be impossible, or very difficult, to discover in any other way. Its conclusions are presented in the numerical form which permits comparisons to be drawn and the relative importance of various factors to be estimated. Yet a mathematical theory is a closed system of thought. Its inferences are potentially present in the assumptions made at the start, and if the assumptions are mistaken, incomplete or otherwise inadequate, however ingenious and correct the mathematical methods used, the outcome will be wrong, partial or otherwise inadequate. Worse, this may not be directly apparent.

As that ponderous but robust pillar of English common sense, Dr. Samuel Johnson, has said, 'there can be no security in the consequences when the premises are not understood'—and very often they are not.

The greatest difficulty of mathematical treatment of physical realities is the multiplicity of factors involved. If the relationship is a simple one, such as, say, of two masses moving under the influence of mutual gravitational attraction, the mathematical tool will be highly successful, though even this is an abstract situation, and when it comes to refinements the picture is not at all clear. When, on the other hand, we have such an entity as planetary climate to deal with, the complexity of the factors determining the situation defies mathematical formulation. One must pick and choose what appears to be the most essential and lay down theoretical conditions it is supposed to satisfy. In this way a model is created which bears a slight resemblance to actuality and may be vaguely instructive in general terms, but it provides no touchstone against which the reality of observations can be tested.

In physics the adequacy—not truth—of a mathematical hypothesis can be put to experimental test. In astronomy this is not usually possible.

In other words, one must beware of putting too much trust in integrals and differentials, impressive as these may look on paper. They are no sure guide to truth.

On the other hand, while there has been any amount of controversy on the subject of lunar changes reported by various observers, oddly enough, these reports do not seem to have ever been submitted to systematic investigation in the light of physics.

For this reason I have felt that such an enquiry into the physics of the Moon will be well worth while and the readers will find it developed step by step in the pages of the present volume. It would be foolish to regard this enquiry as complete. Many of the conclusions proposed here must of necessity be only tentative, but they are the fruit of application of established physical principles to the available observational data, and thus no idle flights of fancy, however unexpected they may seem.

REFERENCES

1. BALDWIN, R. B. *The Face of the Moon.* University of Chicago Press, 1949.
2. PICKERING, W. H. 'Lunar Changes.' *The 7th Report of the Section for the Observation of the Moon of the British Astronomical Association.* London, 1916.
3. WHIPPLE, F. L. *Earth, Moon and the Planets.* Churchill, London, 1946.

THE IMPORTANCE OF BEING A SATELLITE

A PART FROM THE SUN, which is a very ordinary star; meteors, which are metallic or stony bodies of irregular shape, ranging from dust particle to rock in size, circling the sun scattered along highly eccentric and somewhat haphazard orbits; the mysterious 'nebulous meteors' which may be swarms of matter of some kind and about which little is known; comets, which share the orbital characteristics of meteoric swarms and consist of unconsolidated aggregates of meteoric and gaseous matter of small mass but occupying enormous volumes of space; the Solar System contains a number of compact non-luminous spherical objects which may be described as 'worlds' in the same meaning as our Earth is a world.

Those worlds which revolve round the Sun in independent orbits are planets, while others making their circumsolar journey in attendance on another larger world, round which they circle as it moves along, are called satellites or moons. In the gravitational hierarchy they are a rung below the planets, more or less as a subtenant is below the tenant *vis-à-vis* the landlord. This is an important dependence, for it has manifold consequences for the structure and condition of the world in question.

A moon is necessarily a good deal smaller in mass and size than the planet it is attached to, for therein lies the root or their mutual relationship. Yet it would not be true to say that any moon is smaller in mass or volume than any planet. Mercury is one of the main planets of the solar family, but four out of the 31 known satellites exceed him in dimensions, if not in mass, while there exist thousands of small planetary bodies, known as asteroids or planetoids, which are in every way comparable to the smallest of the moons and at the tail end to the largest of the meteors, though planets in their own right, describing independent orbits round the Sun much as the Earth does. Indeed, the range of mass and size among both planets and satellites is so great that they may conveniently be subdivided into distinct classes.

The giant Jovian planets, Jupiter, Saturn, Uranus, and Neptune, could easily accommodate any of the smaller Terrestrial planets among their satellite systems, though in actual fact all their moons are a little less massive than the former. Mercury, Venus, the Earth, Mars, and Pluto make up in density for what they may lack in dimensions, and Pluto may prove to be a representative of yet another class of world as indicated by its very eccentric orbit, slow rotation of $6\frac{2}{3}$ days and possibly high density.*

* R. A. Lyttleton and lately G. P. Kuiper have suggested that Pluto may be an escaped satellite of Neptune.

The planetoids have already been referred to. Among the satellites we have a class of sub-planets, of which our Moon is one, and a large number of asteroidal satellites, which may even be captured asteroids, and which are exemplified by the tiny companions of Mars, some 5 and 10 miles in diameter respectively.

Any classification is an artificial system imposed upon nature by the orderly mind of man for the purposes of easier memorizing and understanding, and it cannot be applied too rigidly. One must always expect to encounter transitional cases which either fit into two or more pigeon-holes at a time or do not fit into any pigeon-hole at all. This is only one example of the process of simplification and abstraction on which all science is built. Yet our classification is based on real and vital differences on which the physical endowment of a world depends.

The Jovian planets are blanketed by heavy atmospheric envelopes, where hydrogen and its compounds (methane, ammonia) predominate, neutral helium being another important constituent of these atmospheres. There is some doubt as to whether these planets possess solid surfaces at all similar to the rigid cannon-balls of the Terrestrial group. The latter have thinner atmospheres of heavier gases; free hydrogen and helium are virtually absent, while nitrogen and compounds of oxygen, or free oxygen, occupy the pride of place. Here, too, there are differences depending on the mass and distance from the Sun, which affects the mean temperature of the world's surface. Venus and the Earth have comparatively copious atmospheres, whereas Mercury is surrounded by only a thin gas envelope, in which respect he stands close to the satellites of the lunar type. Asteroids and asteroidal satellites are incapable of retaining any proper atmosphere at all.

This is the result of the constitution of gases, where molecules are so far apart that there is practically no cohesion between them. Gas expands freely unless contained by an external pressure or the pull of gravity, which is a comparable force. In an 'ideal' gas, to which real gases approximate in certain conditions, there is no force of cohesion at all. The molecules dart hither and thither, impinge upon one another and rebound like swarms of ping-pong balls in a nightmare. This random molecular motion or agitation is apprehended by us as heat. Temperature measures the level of heat. If there is a difference in this heat level (temperature) of two bodies or gases in contact, heat will spill from a higher to a lower level until the difference is evened out. But the molecules of different gases have different weights, although within the same gas of uniform composition they are all alike. Now a heavy molecule moving with the same velocity as a lighter one will carry more energy—its heat level, or temperature, will be higher—so that in order to keep the temperature even it would have to move more slowly. In actual fact individual molecules will be moving with different velocities but there are enormous numbers of them and only the average effect counts. This is measured by their mean (or mean square-root) velocity.

It can be shown that the square of this mean molecular velocity in a gas varies inversely as its molecular weight (all molecules of the same chemical substance have the same weight) and directly as its absolute temperature. Thus, for instance, a molecule of oxygen is 16 times as heavy as one of hydrogen. Consequently, at the same temperature (on whatever scale) the oxygen molecules will on the average be moving only a quarter as fast as those of hydrogen. If, on the other hand, the *absolute* temperature of oxygen is raised to one 16 times as high as that of hydrogen the molecules of both gases will dart about with the same mean velocity.

Absolute temperature is the ordinary Centigrade, or Celsius, temperature but measured upwards from the absolute zero of $-273°$C. (in round figures), where the mean molecular velocity of all gases becomes zero and the concept of temperature loses its meaning. Absolute temperature, which is designated by degrees Kelvin, $°$K., as against degrees Centigrade, $°$C., is always positive.

To give an example, $-70°$C.$=273°-70°=203°$K., and it will be seen that $0°$C. corresponds to $273°$K. Temperature on the familiar Fahrenheit scale ($°$F.) is obtained by dividing the Centigrade temperature by 5, multiplying the result by 9 (or in the opposite order where more convenient) and adding $32°$. $0°$F, corresponds approximately to $-17°·8$C. (properly $17\frac{7}{9}°$) and so to $254°·2$K.

The absolute temperature, however, is so convenient in physical problems that the other scales are seldom used.

These are important points for understanding the vexed question of lunar atmosphere, on which conditions on the Moon's surface largely depend.

For when any lump of matter, large or sub-microscopic, exceeds what is known as the velocity of escape and is able to proceed unhindered it will leave the world to which it is attached for good and all. On the Earth this critical velocity is 7 m.p.s. and we all know that a rocket which has developed as much will be free from the Earth's gravitational bondage. This is the price of freedom. On the Moon less than $1\frac{3}{4}$ m.p.s. will suffice. Generally speaking, the velocity of escape increases directly as the world's radius and the square root of its density. Thus both mass and size play a part in the retentive force of gravity.

What is true of a rocket is also true of a gas molecule: if it exceeds the velocity of escape it will become a 'planet' pursuing an independent orbit round the Sun, provided that its path is unobstructed. Yet in the so-called normal conditions, which comprise the freezing point of water (the physicists take a pessimistic view of the weather) at sea-level, one

B

cubic centimetre of any gas contains on the average no less than 26,900,000,000,000,000,000 (this is usually written for short as $2 \cdot 69 \times 10^{19}$) molecules and the mean free path of an air molecule between two collisions is about $9\frac{1}{2}$ millionths of a centimetre. However fast our molecule may move, it will never be able to fulfil its 'ambition' of becoming a 'planet', will soon dissipate its excess of speed in collisions with its neighbours and be forced back into the average way of life.

In order really to rise into interplanetary space it would have first to gain the extreme heights of the atmosphere, where molecular collisions are so infrequent that they can be neglected for statistical purposes and the molecules may be said to be moving like some microscopic satellites in orbits, or substantial sections of orbits, round the Earth. This is the molecular 'spray' of the exosphere.

In any case, in the uppermost layer of the atmosphere some fast-moving molecules will now and again succeed in getting away from the Earth. By a reasoning based on such considerations Sir James Jeans[2] calculated that if the mean molecular velocity of a gas exceeds a quarter of the velocity of escape the whole atmosphere of this gas will be dissipated within about a thousand years. But should this ratio drop to one fifth, one thousand million years must elapse before the last molecule of this gas departs. Periods of time less than that are of little astronomical account, and accordingly one fifth of the velocity of escape has been taken as the limiting value for the mean molecular velocity above which a world could not have retained an atmosphere of a given gas up to the present day.

We will recall that the square of the mean molecular velocity is directly proportional to the absolute temperature and inversely proportional to the molecular weight. This leads to the not-too-surprising conclusion that the lighter gases will 'steam off' a world into space the more readily, this readiness increasing with temperature and decreasing with the retentive force of gravity. Thus Jeans has calculated that the Moon should not have been able to retain oxygen, nitrogen, or water vapour for astronomical periods, but ought to have preserved some of its carbon dioxide, sulphur dioxide, and other heavy gases.

As a matter of fact, Jeans's original calculations contain an error.[4] His atmospheric model also differs considerably from the real atmospheres, which necessitates a further correction, and in the case of water the molecular weight at low temperatures is in doubt[1,3] and it is only a vapour, not an ideal gas as assumed. I will return to these matters in Chapter 13. But the fundamental conception is sound.

In other words, the temperature is of crucial importance to the existence and composition of the atmosphere round a body of small retentive power, and the atmospheric temperatures of the Terrestrial planets and all bodies below them in mass derive solely from the Sun.

8

At our distance from the Sun, which also holds good for the Moon, every square centimetre exposed vertically to unobstructed sunshine for one minute will receive just under two gram-calories of heat, that is to say, if it were able to retain all this energy, this would be sufficient to raise the temperature of one gram of pure water through two degrees Centigrade per minute. This is the so-called Solar Constant, which actually varies a little, as the rate at which the Sun radiates energy is not quite steady. But it is affected much more drastically by the distance from the Sun, for the energy emanating from a point in the Sun may be represented as an extremely narrow pyramid or cone (solid angle), the cross-section of which corresponding to the Solar Constant is at the Earth's mean distance from the Sun (93 million miles) equal to a square centimetre. At twice this distance the same energy will cover a cross-section of twice the same width and an area four times as large; in other words, the Constant for that distance will be only a quarter of ours. Generally, the Constant for any given distance will be inversely proportional to the square of that distance, as will readily be appreciated once it is realized that the same energy must always suffice for a square whose side increases in proportion to the distance.

Thus theoretically the closer an astronomical body is to the Sun the hotter it will be. In actual fact, however, its temperature will depend on various factors.[6] The most important of these is the amount of light and heat it absorbs, or—conversely—reflects, for the reflected part of the light and heat cannot contribute to raising its temperature. This reflected part, measured as a fraction of the whole amount taken as a unit, or else as a percentage of it, is called *albedo*. Rotation and inclination of the axis will expose different portions of the surface of the globe to the rays of the Sun at different angles and for different periods of time, which greatly affects the distribution and variation of temperature in different latitudes, as exemplified by the climatic zones and seasons of the Earth. The atmosphere, too, is a very important factor. It reflects back part of the light and heat brought by the sunrays and absorbs a further part of it, so that only a proportion of the Constant (on the Earth about 50 per cent) reaches the ground. The winds, scattering and conduction, all help to spread the available amount of heat more evenly over the globe. Finally, certain gases, and carbon dioxide, water vapour, methane and ammonia in particular, energetically absorb invisible heat rays, including the 'obscure heat' radiated by the ground at its comparatively low temperature, which prevents its escape into space by night. It stands to reason that where the atmosphere is thin or absent these effects will be weak or absent. One may also add here, slightly out of context, that the atmosphere provides a shield against the constant bombardment by small meteors, which are slowed down and vaporized by friction in our air, and probably even in the very thin air of the Moon.

Generally speaking, solid bodies are much more efficient absorbers of heat than gases, so that in the lower atmosphere the temperature of the air is determined primarily by that of the ground and the ascending currents of air warmed up in contact with it. In this way the temperature at ground level influences the rate of escape of gas. I have, however, already referred to certain gases which are especially effective as absorbers of heat and will be warmed up as a result, their molecules becoming more agitated.

Carbon dioxide behaves not unlike the phosphorescent substances which absorb light and later re-emit it in a longer wavelength, but the phosphorescence of carbon dioxide is all in the invisible infra-red part of the spectrum. It re-radiates some of the absorbed 'obscure heat' in the lower infra-red. Oxygen, on the other hand, in all its forms, absorbs strongly at the opposite invisible end of the 'optical window' (part of the spectrum accessible to the eye) the likewise invisible ultra-violet rays, which are harmful to living tissues. In absorbing these rays the normal oxygen molecule composed of two atoms is transformed into ozone, which contains three atoms, and in still shorter ultra-violet both are broken up into single ionized (electrically charged) atoms. In recombining at night these oxygen—and to some extent also nitrogen—atoms emit a radiation responsible for the faint luminescence of the night sky. However, this absorption intensely agitates the oxygen atoms, which is the same as raising their temperature, and, since this happens at high levels in the atmosphere, leads to an increased rate of escape of this gas.[4]

I have dwelt on this atmospheric problem at some length because of its great importance for the conditions on a world's surface, and more particularly for the possibility of life existing upon it, and I will return to the lunar atmosphere at the end of the book.

From this discussion it emerges clearly that satellites, even of the large Moon class, are not well placed for retaining an ordinary atmosphere of any density, unless they be very cold, which differentiates them sharply from the massive planets.

Yet the low force of superficial gravity which characterizes the satellite status has other vital consequences. Satellite orbits, with a few exceptions, mainly in the asteroidal class, lie close to the governing planetary bodies in the sphere where the latter's attraction is not only powerful but shows a perceptible drop in intensity over a distance of even a thousand miles or so corresponding to a satellite's diameter, which is astronomically speaking negligible. As a result of proximity to the planet the satellites complete their revolution round the planet in a period which may be referred to generally as a 'month' and forms only a fraction of the planet's 'year', while in some cases it is more like our day in duration, so strongly are they gripped by the gravitational pull of the planet, which the centrifugal force of their motion must counterbalance. But the fall in the intensity of the planet's pull over

10

the Moon's diameter is no less important, for this difference in gravitational attraction at the point nearest to and farthest away from another celestial body is the force that raises the tides. The Moon's mass is 81 times smaller than the mass of the Earth and she is comparatively far away, yet she still rules our oceans. The planetary tides raised on the satellite bodies are immensely more powerful and affect their whole structure. In any case great friction is, or was, generated in any parts of them that are or used to be liquid, and this, combined with the tidal stresses in the solid parts, quickly slows up their rotation until it coincides with the length of the month, so that the satellite always presents the same half (apart from minor wobbles) to its master. This is a peculiar feature of all the inner moons of planets and also of the planet Mercury, which lies so close to the Sun that the tides raised by the latter have had a comparable effect.

However this may be elsewhere, the lunar day and month are of the same length, which results in a very peculiar regime that we will examine in Chapter 11.

Tidal action must needs have played an outstanding part in the past history of the Moon, as it possibly has even in that of the Earth; but a low surface gravity has a more direct influence on the large-scale relief of the ground and on the intimate texture of the rocks.

On the Earth 14¾ pounds weigh down on every square inch of the ground, while running water, winds, rain, and snow fret at its unevennesses, steadily grinding them down in the never-ceasing process of subaerial denudation. On the Moon atmospheric pressure must always have been negligible; while such instances of erosion on the terrestrial lines as her face appears to show (and this is in dispute) prove conclusively that this, too, can never have contributed much to the shaping of her features, though other forms of erosion may have been active there. These circumstances must have greatly affected the uppermost 'skin' of the lunar globe.

The virtual absence of ordinary subaerial denudation is not the only cause of the ruggedness of lunar mountains. Higher gravity alone has a restraining effect on the mountain-building forces by making the rocks heavier and more difficult to raise. Its action does not stop at the surface; it extends to the very centre of the globe. The full consequences of this fact have been only partly explored, but it is clear that the interior of the Moon has experienced less compression than the interior of the Earth. At one time it was thought that all planets and satellites were of the same chemical composition at birth, and if their densities were now different this was due partly to the loss of the lighter elements by the smaller masses when these had been still very hot and partly to internal compression. Yet Mercury with a mass smaller than that of Mars is considerably denser than the latter. The more massive Jupiter is twice as dense as Saturn, which is again less dense than the smaller masses of Uranus and Neptune, while Pluto

11

with dimensions between those of Mercury and Mars threatens to prove a good deal denser than the Earth. In fact, the distribution of densities both in the Solar and in the satellite systems is clearly related to the distance from the governing body, indicating what may be described as centrifugal separation of substances according to weight. In any case, the older view has become untenable, and it is reasonably certain that the lower density of the Moon, which is only 60 per cent of the mean density of the Earth, implies a greater abundance of light materials, especially near the surface This, too, could not have been without influence of the lunar relief.

The compressibility of solids and even liquids is indeed small, so that their density will not be greatly increased even by the tremendous pressures obtaining in the depths of planetary globes (pressure does affect crystalline habit and so density). Gases, on the other hand, respond readily by a change of volume to both temperature and pressure. Magma, or molten rock, contains large amounts of gas, mainly water and carbon dioxide, in solution, which it gives off in cooling.

When magma surges upwards towards the surface under the pressure of the overlying rock layers, part of the gas is liberated and forms bubbles in it. In intrusive igneous rocks which have consolidated deep below the surface of the Earth such gas bubbles, or druses are few, if sometimes large, but the nearer to the surface the rock has set the more 'bubbly' it becomes, until the lavas which have cooled under atmospheric pressure assume the spongy (scoriaceous) structure of pumice. Pumice floats in water.

On the Moon, where there is practically no atmospheric pressure, even the restraining force of those $14\frac{3}{4}$ pounds to the square inch is lacking and the gases in the cooling magma will have been able to expand, hindered but feebly by the gravity one sixth of ours acting on what is probably intrinsically lighter material. Moreover, owing to the ineffectiveness of the denuding forces, the rocks will remain substantially at their original level.

Lately it has been questioned (Urey, Gold) whether the surface or even the interior of the Moon has ever been molten. Thus the surface formations may have been produced by sintering, or chemical binding of the practically unaltered meteoric material by the gases percolating from below. This hypothesis, however, does not alter the fundamental picture I am painting here. The present-day meteorites are certainly of secondary origin and have been produced by the break-up of larger masses, whether by collision or other means. They are as compact as terrestrial rocks formed at considerable depths, but meteoric matter of very low density is known, and the primordial meteoric material will have accumulated in free space under negligible gravitational strain. It is from such matter that the Moon will have aggregated on this view and the resulting structure of the surface formations would be a kind of rock foam.

In any case, the porous nature of lunar rocks has been generally recognized, though it is often overlooked when numerical estimates are made and little effort has been made to visualize the degree and the consequences of this porosity. From what has been said above the lunar mountains appear to be more like meringues than like our granite peaks in texture and are enabled to withstand the wear and tear of ages mainly because there is no wind and no liquid water to bring them down. If exposed to terrestrial conditions, they would be obliterated very rapidly.

This alone is sufficient to show that the Moon is a world very different from ours; but the consequences of the peculiarities of her structure and surface conditions do not end here. Before, however, we proceed to consider these in detail, it will be instructive to cast a glance on the probable past history of our satellite, in so far as this is known or can reasonably be conjectured, for the present is only a cross-section in the process of continual change, of which it forms an inseparable part. Nor can this examination be undertaken without at least passing acquaintance with the telescopic appearance of the Moon. This has been described in detail in other works,[5,7,8] to which the reader may advantageously refer, but a brief survey is nevertheless indispensable.

REFERENCES

1. ALLEN, H. S. '*Molecular Frequency and Molecular Number.*' *Philosophical Magazine*, April, 1918.
2. JEANS, J. H. *The Dynamical Theory of Gases.* Cambridge University Press, 1925.
3. KENT, ANDREW. *Chemistry—Scientific Thought in the Twentieth Century.* Watts, London, 1951.
4. KUIPER, G. P. (Ed.). *The Atmospheres of the Earth and Planets.* 2nd Edition. University of Chicago Press, 1952.
5. MOORE, PATRICK. *Guide to the Moon.* Eyre and Spottiswoode, London, 1953.
6. VAUCOULEURS, GÉRARD DE. *Physics of the Planet Mars.* Faber and Faber, London, 1954.
7. WILKINS, H. P. *Our Moon.* Muller, London, 1954.
8. WILKINS, H. P. and MOORE, P. *The Moon.* Faber and Faber, London, 1956.

3

THE EARTH'S FAIR CHILD OR A FOUNDLING?

AMONG THE SATELLITES of the Solar System the Moon occupies in many ways an exceptional position. Ganymede, the largest member of Jupiter's family, amounts in mass to barely one twelve-thousandth of the ruling planet. Titan, the pride of Saturn's system, and incidentally the only satellite that is definitely known to possess a considerable atmosphere, is 4,700 times less massive than the latter. Triton, the heaviest if not the largest of all moons, is a companion of Neptune, a body 290 times greater in mass. The diameter of Triton is not accurately known but is in the region of 3,000 miles as against Neptune's 27,600 miles. In the other two cases the ratio of diameters is roughly 1 : 30.

Our Moon, on the other hand, with a diameter of 2,160 miles, is not conspicuously dwarfed by the Earth's 7,900 miles, and from the distance the two will look very much more like a double planet than a planet with a satellite. In mass, the Earth's preponderance is more marked, as she is fully 81¼ times more massive than the Moon; even so, the Moon would fit much better into the family of a giant world like Jupiter or Saturn than into that of so small a body as the Earth.

Nor is this the end of the anomalous features.

Apart from Triton, which may be a captured planet of the Pluto group (Lyttleton), the inner satellites of the other planets circle them very close to their equatorial planes. Indeed, they used to be held to have been torn out of the primitive planet or protoplanet's body at some early stage of formation by the combined action of rapid rotation and the tides raised by the Sun in its unconsolidated mass. This view has been disproved[7,10] and indeed it is something of a mystery how the flat solar gravitational field could have achieved as much at the distance of Neptune, though it might be argued that at that time Neptune was pursuing a very eccentric orbit, rather like the orbits of many comets, which recede to great distances from the Sun at one end and approach to within a few million miles from him at the other.

Satellites may also have originated as independent condensations within the same primordial cloud from which the planet was born. In this case, their revolutions and the planet's rotation being the outcome of the common rotation of the cloud, their orbits would tend to approximate to the equatorial plane of the planet.

This writer has suggested a somewhat different, though cognate, mechanism to account for the birth of a satellite from a planet, or rather protoplanet.[3] Rotation enters into this, too, for the contracting preplanetary mass would have whirled faster and faster round its axis as its outlying portions settled towards its centre of gravity. If sufficiently large, as would be the case of the Jovian planets, this mass would also have become very hot, possible hot enough for some nuclear reactions to take place. Simultaneously, however, its outer regions were cooling rapidly and at a certain moment sealed off the radiations from the interior by a doubly compressed envelope of cool opaque gas and its condensations, which may still be the present condition of Jupiter and Saturn. The escape of heat from the interior being thus blocked, a local or general overheating of gases beneath the thickening envelope would occur and result in an enormous eruption or eruptions, mainly in the equatorial region where the force of gravity was weakened most by the centrifugal effect of rapid rotation.

An eruption of this kind may be described as something intermediate between that of a nova and a volcano, either an envelope or one or more 'bubbles' being emitted. It does, in fact, look as though the Great Red Spot of Jupiter was produced in a similar way by an eruption that lacked sufficient force to eject the material from the planet's interior beyond its atmosphere, in which the 'bubble' remains embedded as a half-formed satellite.[3]

Such an eruption, whether localized or general, would involve the inter-action of the ejecting radial force, initial rotation and gravity—possibly also magnetic attraction—as proposed in Alfvén's cosmogonical conception in a different context. As a result, in the absence of a strong resistant medium, the ejected material would tend to collect in the equatorial plane in a ring or fragments of rings, the initially heaviest matter being closest and the lightest farthest away from the planet.

The interaction of the rotary and radial movements would work, through internal friction, towards condensing the ring more and more, and if sufficient mass were present spherical bodies would form round the nuclei produced by impact and chemical bond. The reason why the rings of Saturn have failed to condense into satellites lies in the fact that they are too close to the planet, within the sphere where tidal action is too strong to permit permanent condensations to exist. The limiting distance from the planet within which a large satellite cannot survive is known as Roche's Limit. A very small satellite body could exist within the limit, for the dis-rupting tidal force increases with the diameter, and, in fact, the rings of Saturn are composed of minute satellites, which are simply snowballs, with the possible exception of the dark, innermost Crepe Ring.

In the case of an eruption where most of the energy came from the heat of the diffusing gas, with rotation playing but a subordinate part, the lightest atoms or molecules would have travelled farthest from the source. As a result the atomic weight, reflected in the present mean density of the

15

condensates, would diminish outwards. This situation is found both in the system of Jupiter and among the planets of the Solar System from Mercury to Saturn, inclusive. The relation between the mean density and the mean distance is, moreover, very nearly linear in both cases.[3]

If, on the other hand, the explosion came primarily from the centrifugal force of rotation all *ejecta* would be moving with substantially the same velocity, in consequence of which the heaviest of them would possess the greatest angular momentum and would proceed and eventually settle farthest from the source. A very similar effect would be obtained in the case of eruption in a resisting medium.

This arrangement is clearly exemplified by the satellites of Saturn and the solar planets beyond Saturn.

The strong polar flattening of Saturn's globe which measures rotational distention and the existence of rings appear to support this view, while the smaller mass would account for the lower gas pressure and the lower heat of the eruption than in the case of Jupiter. Saturn, however, is 95 times as massive as the Earth, and it would be idle to invoke this mechanism for explaining the existence of the Moon. The Earth could not possibly have given birth to a satellite of such size in the suggested way. We are, of course, still left with Jeans's and Jeffreys's abandoned alternative (*see* p. 19) that the Moon was torn out of the rapidly spinning liquid spheroid of the proto-Earth at the perihelion (point nearest to the Sun) of her orbit by the solar tides intensified by resonance.[7]

However, on this view, too, the main force which had caused the disruption would have been the centrifugal force of rotation in the equatorial region, so that one would expect the orbit of the Moon to lie close to the equatorial plane. The assumption that the Earth was at any time a ball of liquid magma is not nowadays in universal favour, but even if it were the Moon's orbit, instead of approximating to the plane of the Earth's equator, would still be forming an angle of barely 5 degrees with that of her orbit, which stands off the equatorial plane by $23\frac{1}{2}$ degrees. This would seem clearly to connect the Moon with the Sun rather than the Earth, and, in fact, this solar affinity goes a good deal farther.

Unlike any other satellite, the Moon completes her revolution round the Earth outside the sphere of the latter's gravitational predominance. Solar and terrestrial gravity draw level with each other at the distance of 161,800 miles from the centre of the Earth, whereas the Moon never comes any nearer it than 221,463 miles. She follows, in fact, not a satellitic but a planetary orbit coincident with the orbit of the Earth, which perturbs the Moon to the extent of making her half-swing about the Earth in a kind of flat scallop. To a terrestrial observer each scallop appears as a closed curve, the Moon going completely round, but this is due to the superimposition of the Earth's simultaneous progress round the Sun. From the latter, on the other hand, the scallops remain open, always curving away, like those of a tea-cloth seen from inside.[5]

Thus on the orbital evidence the Moon does not seem to be the Earth's child at all but a foundling, who once was an independent planet, a point that is not altogether irrelevant for the estimated condition of the lunar surface.

There exists, however, evidence of a different kind: the orbit of the Moon is subject to tidal evolution.

What may be loosely termed the 'amount of spin' or 'quantity of rotation' is called angular momentum and measured by the product of the mass of the moving body or particle into its linear velocity at any moment and its distance from the focus of revolution, or axis of reference. This angular momentum can be distributed variously between the parts of a closed system but it cannot be altered except by the intervention of an extraneous force; on the same lines as one cannot pull oneself out of the bog by one's own ears. We have, in fact, already encountered the problem of redistribution of angular momentum in a condensing body, where the shortening of the distances of its parts from the axis of rotation resulted in increasing their linear speeds and so accelerating the rotation of the body as a whole.

The Earth–Moon system is also closed within itself and its angular momentum consists primarily of their revolution round the common centre of gravity and their respective axial spins. The sum of the angular momenta represented by these rotary movements remains constant and when any one of them is intensified the other or others must be correspondingly slackened. Such redistribution of the angular momentum within the Earth–Moon system occurs through the agency of tides. Tides cause friction which slows up axial spins and the angular momentum lost in this way is transferred into orbital motion. Mention has already been made of the strong planetary tides which brake the axial rotations of the satellites, reducing these to the tied-up condition, where the satellite orbits the planet, always turning the same half towards it, as though tied up to it with a string. But there is also reciprocal action, only that owing to the comparatively small mass of the satellites it is very slow.

The Moon, however, is an exceptionally large satellite as compared with Mother Earth and our day grows one second longer every 120,000 years. Simultaneously the Moon is speeded up in her orbit, which makes her recede from the Earth, and thus she has a longer path to cover, so that the length of the month is likewise on the increase. Yet our day and month are slowly converging at the same value, and, no other forces being present, would, according to Jeffreys, become equal after 50 thousand million years, when the Moon's mean distance from the Earth had increased from the present 240,000 miles to 340,000 miles.[1,5]

It is further reasoned that, once this has happened, solar tides will continue to slow up the rotation of the Earth, and by a converse process the Moon will draw closer once more until she has passed Roche's Limit and is completely sundered by the Earth's tidal pull. Here a blood-curdling picture is drawn of the fiery rain of lunar fragments descending upon the Earth. Yet absolutely no dynamical reason exists for anticipating a catastrophe of this kind, for even if the Moon had been shattered to pieces these pieces would still be participating in the original orbital movement and so would continue to circle the Earth, eventually to spread out into a ring. Individual fragments might become slowed down by collisions and crash like meteors into our atmosphere, but the process would be gradual, and, I am sorry to disappoint the readers of H. A. Bellamy, nothing much would happen.

Furthermore, the Moon moves not only round the Earth but also, even mainly, round the Sun. Orbital velocity is inversely proportional to the square root of the distance. In one half of her orbit round the Earth, as seen from the latter, the Moon is on the same side as the Sun; in the other half she is on the opposite side and farther away from him than is the Earth. Consequently, on the Sunward side the Moon will be moving a little faster than the Earth relatively to the Sun, and vice versa. If the resulting acceleration and deceleration exactly balanced up no mischief would follow; but they do not, because the intensity of the solar gravitational field rises the more steeply the nearer the Sun we are. Thus there is an appreciable excess of acceleration over deceleration, which causes the orbit of the Moon round the Earth to be blown out away from her in the direction of the orbit of Mars.[5]

Nor is this quite the end of the story.

As the eccentricity of the Earth's orbit is on the decrease the effect is intensified and the Moon is receding as a result. There are good reasons to believe that the eccentricity of the terrestrial orbit was still larger in the past, so that the Moon's orbit will have been broadened out from this cause alone. In the remote geological ages the orbit of the Earth may have undergone even greater changes, which would automatically have reacted on the Moon. If the changing month had at any time become commensurable with the synodic periods of Mars or Venus there would have been cumulative planetary perturbations, which could have either driven the Moon away from the Earth or brought her back. Other forces may also have intervened. A full discussion of the problem would be of great mathematical difficulty and does not appear to have ever been attempted.

On the other hand, G. H. Darwin and H. Jeffreys have reconstructed backwards the theoretical course of the tidal evolution of the lunar orbit. Starting with the present tidal interaction between the Earth and the Moon, they have arrived at the point where the two would have been in actual contact. At that time the Earth would have been turning once round in 4 hours. This has given rise to the idea that the Moon was born out of the molten Earth just about the time her crust was beginning to consolidate and the lighter granitic rocks formed the first continents, set in an ocean of plastic basalt, over which the proper oceans were still suspended as steam. To clinch the issue, the Pacific Ocean is pointed out as the scar left by the nascent Moon—in fact, a kind of navel.

W. H. Pickering[6] has calculated that:

'A body the size of the Moon would equal a section of the Earth's crust having an area equal to the terrestrial oceans and a uniform depth of 35 miles. Since the mean depth of the ocean bottom may be taken at about 3 miles below the continental surface, this would indicate that a floating crust 35 miles in thickness was floating to a depth of 32 miles on the Earth's liquid interior.'

He does not appear to think it very probable, and possibly he might have spared himself the trouble of these computations if he had considered that the Moon would have met immediate disaster at birth owing to having found herself inside Roche's Limit. Thus on top of the dynamical improbability of the suggested genesis, we have to account for the mechanism which allowed the scattered fragments of the Moon, spread in a ring round the proto-Earth's equator, to have moved away to a safe distance, whereas we have just been told that these fragments would *instantly* crash down to earth, which, after all, is the more likely contingency.

In fact, in *Earthquakes and Mountains*[4] (pp. 142–3) Sir Harold Jeffreys sums up the situation thus:

'The friction at the boundary of the core would dissipate the energy of the tide so rapidly that it could never reach an amplitude more than about 1/20 of the radius, which would be far too small to give instability; and it seems, according to Nölke, that the velocity of the detached mass would be so small that it would at once fall back into the primary. The rotation would not be rapid enough to produce disruption without assistance, and it seems that we cannot suppose the moon to have been part of the earth at any time since the latter had a distinct individuality.'

The collision with an asteroid, as has recently been suggested (Bergquist), could not possibly have provided the required momentum.

To evade this difficulty it has been suggested that the Earth and the Moon have never been one, but arose as two separate bodies from the same primordial mass, and the tidal evolution began when they were about 11 thousand miles apart and the day–month was about 6 hours.[1]

It must, however, be added that there are no definite reasons for believing that this ever happened, whereas there exist definite reasons for holding the opposite view.

Before we proceed with this argument, it will be interesting to form some

19

idea of how long it would take the tidal action of the Earth to reduce the speed of the Moon's spin to its present value. A thoroughly reliable estimate would require a far greater knowledge of the constitution of the Moon than we now possess. By making different assumptions Moulton and Jeffreys have arrived at somewhat divergent conclusions. The first estimates that the tidal action of the Earth will be 480,000 times as effective in slowing down the rotation of the Moon[8] as that of the Moon is in reducing the Earth's spin; the second puts the same ratio at 17,000.[1] However, the discrepancy is not really so great as it might at first sight seem.

To be on the safe side, let us further reduce Jeffreys' figure to 12,000. We know that the day lengthens by one second in about 120,000 years. Consequently, if the same rate of change is assumed in the past—which is an obvious under-estimate, for the Moon was at one time closer to the Earth than she is now and tidal action was more powerful—the lunar day would increase by one second every ten years. The month contains about $2\frac{1}{2}$ million seconds, so that 25 million years, a geologically short period, would have sufficed, even on this unfavourable assumption, to reduce the Moon to her present status. If Moulton's figure is taken instead, the required time is cut down to 625,000 years, which is less than the geological history of Man.

If, however, the Moon was an independent planet captured by the Earth in a comparatively recent past, she would originally have been moving in a very eccentric orbit, not unlike that of Nereid, the recently discovered satellite of Neptune. If the Moon's original orbit lay outside that of the Earth, that is nearer to Mars, as her comparatively low density might indicate, then her point of closest approach to the Earth—and this could have been very close—would lie on the Sunward side. Here she would be subjected to drastic tidal action, reducing her speed of rotation and increasing her orbital velocity; but at the other end of her orbit she would suffer considerable solar deceleration, tending to bring her closer to the Earth. As a result of these two tendencies the orbit of the Moon would become more and more circular and her axial spin more and more nearly equal to her declining period of orbital revolution. The process could be relatively rapid.

Geological data give no definite indication that the length of our day altered appreciably since the beginnings of life on the Earth, but it need not have done so on the above hypothesis. On the other hand, the alternative views postulate considerable reduction of the rate of diurnal spin of the Earth as a result of the Moon's tidal action. Now Mars turns once round in about 24 hours. He has no moon of a size that could have slowed down his rotation even by a few minutes during the whole geological time, though he has, of course, been subject to the influence of solar tides, rather less than the Earth owing to his greater distance from the Sun and shorter diameter, but rather more in proportion owing to his smaller mass. It may, therefore, be assumed that Mars has been slowed down in his rotation by solar tides to the same extent as the Earth. If, as appears not unlikely, they both started off with approximately the same rate of spin, it is remarkable that they are still turning round at the same rate despite the tidal action of the Moon. (Periodical fluctuation in the radio 'noise' from Venus indicates that this planet, too, turns round once in about 24 hours though it has no satellite at all.) Would this mean that through most of her existence the Earth was free from it? It is impossible to give a definite answer to this query, the more so as alternative explanations exist.

Thus, Urey has suggested that the moment of inertia of the Earth may have been reduced by a process of differentiation of the materials contained in the upper portions of the globe, as a result of which the day could have been shortened from about 30 hours to its present value. A different mechanism has been invoked by Holmberg. According to him the atmospheric solar tide may tend to keep the period of rotation steady. The smaller solar tide is here more important owing to its regularity and through the coincidence of the pressure effect with the atmospheric expansion due to heating during the day, energy is supplied to the Earth's spin. The resonance occurs for a period of about 24 hours, so that it is no coincidence that the Earth's rotation has settled at this figure. Indeed, if there are no significant changes in the constitution of our atmosphere this period should be maintained indefinitely by Holmberg's 'heat engine'.[12]

On the other hand, there is geological evidence for changes in the composition and possibly the mass of the atmosphere, so that the Earth may have rotated in the past in a different period, though, as already indicated, no very drastic changes would appear to have occurred.

It will, however, be seen that if the Earth's rotation is pegged down to its present period, the effect of lunar tides on the length of the day will have been effaced or concealed and the tidal evolution of the Moon's orbit need not have been paralleled by the lengthening of our day. This leaves room for very considerable orbital changes in the past, and I will show later on why such changes should have taken place.

The American geologist J. E. Spurr has submitted the features of the Moon to detailed analysis, which is so far unsurpassed, applying to their interpretation the knowledge acquired and the methods developed in the study of terrestrial formations, with such adjustments as appeared necessary to him. The results of his investigations are collected in four volumes, jointly entitled, *Geology Applied to Selenology*.[8] These do not make easy reading, not only because of the abundance of technical terms, many of which are introduced by the author on the way, but also because he writes as he thinks, which leads to frequent repetition and occasional revision of the earlier views. Nevertheless, his conclusions command respect. On page 238 of Vol. III of *Lunar Catastrophic Theory* he says:

'The moon's "capture" by the earth seems theoretically inevitable. [He uses the term 'capture' only in the meaning of the slowing down of the Moon's rotation, which originally is assumed to have been much shorter than the month, to its present length, and otherwise postulates a terrestrial origin of the Moon.] The end would arrive, sooner or later; and the moon would permanently face the earth as it does.

'. . . When the rotation came to a halt [it will be understood that he speaks of rotation relatively to a terrestrial observer], the moon had become a fairly solid sphere: the surface, so far as we can divine, seems to have been a wrinkled but not greatly accidented one.

'The sphere was already ancient. In its fluid phase it had separated or differentiated into a thin siliceous uppermost layer, some tens of miles in present maximum thickness, and a basic residual magma, which extended to a great depth, if indeed not to, or close to, the center; and much of the superficies and probably all of the deeper basic interior had become solidified.'

[This model of the lunar globe is based on that accepted for the Earth, with a thin layer of siliceous granitic rock, about 20 miles thick on the average, called Sial—*Si*licon and *Al*uminium—followed by 'glassy' plastic basalt Sima—*Si*licon and *Ma*gnesium—as the main chemical elements, wrapped round a nickel–iron core, called Nife from *Ni*ckel and *Fe*rrum (iron), which accounts for most of the Earth's mass.[9] It will be noticed that, to satisfy the lower mean density of the Moon, the sial is made thicker in proportion to the smaller diameter of the Moon, while the nife is largely dispensed with, in Spurr's model. Even so I suspect that this model is far too terrestrial, a point to which I propose to return in another chapter.]

'This solidified sphere', writes Spurr, 'was brought to a halt, which seems to have been a definite one; at any rate, this halt initiated, with relative suddenness, a cycle of activity in the moon, especially marked on the surface, where alone we can apprehend its records.'

And on p. 241:

'It was a story of violent activity, of a succession of catastrophic happenings, brought on, as it seems probable, by the halting of the moon's considerable speed of rotation by capture by the earth.

'. . . And the lapse of time which preceded the (rotational) capture of the moon by the earth is, in perspective enormous. It would involve the period of more active rotation, which was perhaps the spin acquired when it left the earth, at a stage when both were fluid. . . .'

Spurr vitiates his reasoning by trying to adapt it, quite unnecessarily, to the hypothesis of tidal fission of the proto-Earth, but evidently is not aware that on this hypothesis, although the length of the lunar day altered, it was always equal to that of the Moon's orbital revolution, so that there was no 'rotational capture'. Nor does he appear to have troubled to calculate the time required to bring the Moon's axial spin down to a point where she always turned the same half to the Earth. As we have seen, the period necessary for this could in no case exceed 25 million years, which is not long by geological standards, and if the 'lapse of time which preceded' it is 'enormous', the Moon clearly could not have been the satellite of the Earth then, for a total period of about 2,000 million years is under review.

Further, Spurr points out that the face of the Moon shows two systems of great surface fractures, or faults, lying about 30 degrees from the two poles and trending from west-south-west to east-north-east. This is explained by him as a result of the halting of the Moon's rotation, during which her north pole shifted south, while the outer crust was wrenched to the east and then swung back. Curiously, the face of the Earth, too, shows a similar structure, with the same general trend—the Highland Boundary Fault. Much of the Earth being under water, it is not known whether this Fault has a counterpart in the southern hemisphere, to make the parallel complete, but the spiral distribution of the continents suggests a twisting force. The poles of the Earth would also seem to have shifted place on at least three occasions, in the Cambrian, Permian, and (lastly) Quaternary Periods, bringing ice and cold to previously warm lands.[9] In the Permian glaciers overflowed India and South Africa; in the Quaternary Ice Age north-western Europe and north-eastern American were mainly affected, showing that the North Pole moved south, just as it did on the Moon. Would there be a correlation between these crustal movements on the two companion worlds? It is easier to ask the question than to give an answer, but if the Moon had been lost and recaptured more than once in the course of the past ages recorded in our rocks many a point which has baffled the geologists might be explained.

In the Tertiary Britian enjoyed a hot climate. Tropical animals and plants flourished. Then came the great volcanic disturbance. The bowels of the Earth were convulsed, seas changed their boundaries, continents were engulfed and mighty mountain ranges heaved up, mainly in the southern part of the northern hemisphere. On the Moon, too, at the unspecified date of capture—last capture?—proportionately even greater changes took place. The crust rose in a huge dome, then foundered, producing Mare Imbrium—in the southern part of the northern hemisphere.

The terrestrial volcanoes had quietened down, but some mighty force made the crust of the Earth slip (the rotational stability of the axis of a mass as large as the Earth is enormous) and the position of the poles wobbled, causing a series of glacial and interglacial periods known as the Great Ice Age. From this upheaval the new world and the civilization of man were born. Was the Moon our godmother?

If so, and I suspect that the answer is 'yes', the salient features of her face are geologically young. Indeed, the American geologist, Joseph Barrell, estimated on the basis of the rate of 'heat erosion' (the disintegration of rocks due to rapid changes of temperature), which he thought should be higher on the Moon than in our deserts, that 'measured by the scale of terrestrial chronology, the great craters of Tycho and Copernicus, each 65 miles in diameter, may be as recent at least as the younger Tertiary. . . .'[2]

This estimate may be questioned in view of the porosity of lunar rocks. It has further been shown by Blackwelder that the presence of water is very important for heat erosion (exfoliation) on the Earth and in the absence of water rocks are very little affected even by the sharpest fluctuations of temperature.[10] Yet, on all evidence, erosive processes operate on the Moon and the craters mentioned by Barrell appear suspiciously clear-cut and undamaged to be very old.

My own investigation shows[12] that there exists on the Moon a triple grid of surface fractures (Plate II), some of these accompanied by faulting and thrusting (horizontal displacement of rocks), perpendicular to each other within each grid, the grids being of different ages. Other features of the Moon appear to be closely related to these fracture grids, which falls into line with the three periods of crater formation proposed by Spurr,[8] and the question arises whether these in turn are not connected with the great terrestrial mountain building periods (orogenes) and ice ages caused by the displacement of the polar axis within the globe of the Earth (or slipping of the crust relatively to the poles). If we go on to consider the changes in the Moon's diameter associated with each crater-building period, which must have reacted upon the period of rotation and so on the orbit, the definite possibility presents itself of three 'captures' of the Moon, related to the great periods of disturbance on both companion globes (Cambrian, Permo-Carboniferous, and Tertiary). Their mountains would thus be the children of their marriage, which would account for the virtual absence of mountains, whether of the chain or crater type, from the surface of the 'bachelor' planet Mars.

The cycle would be: approach of the Moon, rapid decrease of her rotation, disturbance of the surface equilibrium on both planets leading to mountain formation and volcanic activity—on the Moon enormous exhalation of gas and shrinking of the globe, which in turn accelerates the rotation of the Moon, repelling her from the Earth through tidal interaction (see *Appendix*)—thus the Moon regains partial independence and passes through a quiescent period at a distance from the Earth, but is gradually drawn back again—her rotation is stemmed once more and the cycle is repeated.

REFERENCES

1. BALDWIN, R. B. *The Face of the Moon*. University of Chicago Press, 1949.
2. BARRELL, JOSEPH. *On Continental Fragmentation and the Geologic Bearing of the Moon's Surficial Features*. U.S. Government Printing Office, Washington, 1929.
3. FIRSOFF, V. A. *Our Neighbour Worlds*. 2nd Edition. Hutchinson Scientific Publications, London, 1954.
4. JEFFREYS, HAROLD. *Earthquakes and Mountains*. Methuen, London, 1935.
5. MOULTON, F. R. *Celestial Mechanics*. Macmillan, New York, 1902.
6. PICKERING, W. H. *The Moon*. Doubleday, Page and Co., New York, 1903.
7. RUSSELL, N. H. *The Solar System and Its Origin*. New York, 1935.
8. SPURR, J. E. *Geology Applied to Selenology*. Vols. I–IV. Science Press, 1944; Rumford Press, 1948; Business Press, 1949.
9. STEERS, J. A. *The Unstable Earth*. London, 1932.
10. JEFFREYS, HAROLD. *The Earth*. 3rd Edn. Cambridge, 1952.
11. FIRSOFF, V. A. 'On the Structure and Origin of Lunar Surface Features.' *Journal of the British Astronomical Association*, Vol. 66, No. 8, 1956.
12. 'Geophysical Discussion.' *The Observatory*, Vol. 76, No. 892, 1956.

4

THE TELESCOPIC PANORAMA

THE MOON is a small world and the diameter of 2,160 miles gives her a volume equal to 1/49 of the Earth's. Yet whether we explore her vicariously through a telescope or at some future date directly, it is her surface rather than her volume that will concern us first and foremost. This equals about 1/14 of our planet's total superficial area, or approximately 10 million square miles. Moreover, most of the terrestrial globe is under water, only 57,500,000 sq. miles being dry land, while the Moon has no seas. Thus she has over 1/6 of the total combined area of our continents, counting Antarctica, to offer to the explorers who first make a successful landing among her rather forbidding mountain landscape. For this is rough ground, largely impassable to any landborne transport even at first sight, and it may well prove still more impassable than it looks. It will certainly take longer than the lifetime of one generation to explore only the familiar half of the Moon facing the Earth. On the other side, we should have to do without maps and extensive surveying would have to be carried out from circumlunar space-ships before any surface expeditions could venture forth.

As already noted, the satellite mode of spinning makes the Moon turn once round herself each time she circumambulates the Earth. If this were not so and she did not turn at all, as some people imagine, we should be looking at her opposite half after each half-revolution. As things are, however, we can only see substantially one half of the Moon's surface. Substantially only—for while her axial rotation proceeds at a uniform pace, her orbital velocity varies with the distance from the Earth (approximately inversely as the square root of it), so that she now outruns her spin, now lags somewhat behind it. This causes the 'Man in the Moon' to wobble from side to side with regard to the man in the Earth, which will be readily noticed even in a small telescope if one watches the features at the limb (edge) of the disk, or compares a collection of lunar photographs taken at different times. The polar axis of the Moon makes an angle of 6½ degrees with the normal to the plane of her orbit, as a result of which the 'Man in the Moon' also nods his head by this amount as the Moon moves round. All these *librations*, as such wobbles are called, are slightly enhanced by the effect of perspective. The Moon is so close to us that when she sets or rises we overlook about a degree of arc beyond the limb she shows when at the zenith, where she appears only at lower latitudes. Indeed, the geographical position of the observer and the Moon's apparent path in the sky, which depends on the season of the year and on the inclination of the Moon's

26

orbit to the Earth's orbit (roughly 5 degrees), also contribute to the visibility or otherwise of the limb features.

In sum total we can see some 9 per cent over and above the allotted half of the Moon's surface. These edge-views suffer greatly from foreshortening, and the high mountains, of which there are many near the limb, get in the way. There exist, however, other means of detecting and locating invisible detail of the averted half, of which H. P. Wilkins has even produced a provisional chart.[7] Disappointingly, perhaps, the other side of the lunar globe does not promise to be greatly different from this one. Yet there may be some room for a few surprises.

The reason is that the Moon is not a perfect sphere. In fact, the Danish astronomer Hansen once propounded a theory that she was egg-shaped, the pointed end facing the Earth, and that all the air and water had escaped to the blunt side, the difference of level between the two being as much as 30 miles. This idea was 'debunked' by Newcomb but not quite annihilated.

Neither lunar gravity nor the density of the lunar air would alter much over a distance of a few miles, but in a marginal case even a small difference in these quantities might have far-reaching consequences, and the tidal bulge of the Moon is a reality though it is nothing like so large as was proposed by Hansen. It betrays itself by certain irregularities in libration. If the Moon were a perfect sphere a libration of, say, 6 degrees west would produce a longitudinal displacement of all features and of the central meridian by this angle and their positions could be easily calculated. Yet the observed positions show systematical deviations from those obtained from theory. The surface of our companion world is very rough and this alone affects the situation, but even when the changes in the positions of lunar features due to libration have been referred to the 'mean surface', that is to say, to the surface obtained by levelling down all the mountains and filling in all the hollows with the material gained in this way, the differences persist. Various measurements of these have been made by lunar observers and all of them indicate that the centre of the earthward hemisphere is upraised by about a mile and a half.[1,5] If there is a corresponding difference of mean levels on the other side, as one must expect, the middle portion of the invisible part of the Moon will be about 3 miles nearer the centre of the lunar globe than its visible counterpart. As stated, this will have very little effect on atmospheric density, but it may affect the relief of the ground, while the circumstance that the invisible half of the Moon knows no eclipses, with the great temperature changes these bring, may have had some influence on this, too.

In this connection one may also mention the possibility of uneven distribution of mass within the lunar globe. If this has never been molten, as suggested by Urey,[8] the heavier materials will not have become concentrated towards the centre and there may be considerable gravitational anomalies on the surface. On the other hand, a rapid temporary heating at the core resulting in the gassification of matter in this region could have produced a zone of lower density near the centre (Firsoff), in which case superficial gravity on the Moon may be appreciably higher than, now thought and any asymmetry of shape will lead to more marked differences in the intensity of gravitational attraction.

The interesting point about the lunar bulge is that it is 17 times larger than theory allows. Jeffreys has calculated that the present tidal couple acting on the Moon would suffice to produce a bulge only 125 feet above the 'mean sphere' (this is something different from the 'mean surface' and denotes a perfect sphere of the same volume as the real Moon); and even if we make various allowances for the possible peculiarities of lunar rocks it appears certain that the Moon was once subjected to enormously greater tidal stresses than she is now.[1,5]

The story does not end here. Librational irregularities indicate a polar flattening which makes the polar diameter of the Moon about a mile shorter than the equatorial diameter at right angles to the line joining the Moon with the Earth—again in the 'mean' position—this diameter being itself one third of a mile shorter than the diameter measured along the latter line, though these figures are subject to some doubt. Now polar flattening is caused by the centrifugal force of rotation and, other things being equal, is inversely proportional to the square of its period. It also increases with decreasing density and is, further, affected by the distribution of mass inside the body, for, as will be readily understood, the more mass there is close to the surface the greater its centrifugal pull. With the present slow rotation, combined with the assumption that the Moon is only slightly denser towards the centre than in her surface layers, the formula for polar flattening (or *oblateness*), which will be found in the *Appendix*, gives a polar diameter about 90 feet shorter than the mean diameter of the Moon. By taking the tidal action of the Earth into account, Jeffreys gets a figure almost exactly twice as large as this. Even so, however, it is 30 times less than the value obtained from observation, despite the fact that the south pole of the Moon is crowded with great mountain massifs, and her north pole, though depressed by comparison, also stands above the level of the maria.

This can only mean that the Moon acquired her present shape at a time when she was rotating very much faster than now, that, to put it in a different way, both her tidal bulge and polar oblateness are 'fossil'. If tidal action is left out of account the present polar flattening could be produced if the Moon turned once round in $3\frac{1}{2}$ days, and a little faster if her density shows a marked increase towards the centre, which, though, does not seem very likely. If twice my figure for the maximum permissible oblateness is taken, as calculated by Jeffreys, the required period of rotation will go up to 5 days. Assuming identity of the periods of rotation and orbital revolution, this would correspond to a reduction of the lunar orbit to about a third of its present radius (semi-diameter). Indeed, Jeffreys concludes that this was the distance of the Moon from the Earth when the present 'fossil' bulge had set.

Yet there exists no compelling necessity for making this assumption and the whole reasoning is based on another unspoken assumption—that there have been no alterations in the shape of the Moon due to internal causes. This, as we shall see later, is a highly questionable point. In fact, the distortion of circular features due to the shrinkage of the lunar globe is greatest near the equator and decreases towards the poles,[6] so that the Moon has been, so to speak, taken in at the belt and was once much flatter at the poles than now. In the absence of any definite chronological scale it is impossible to synchronize these processes so as to apportion their individual contributions to the total effect, and there may be other factors requiring inclusion. In other words, this is a problem that cannot be adequately solved by simple theory. Still, it can be stated with absolute confidence that the Moon did at one time rotate very much faster than she does now and that the evidence of her shape would point to a period of rotation not greatly different from our day, which, indeed, one would expect if she had been an independent planet. This conclusion may not be without bearing on the present position.

Having started off, so to speak, 'on the wrong face', we must now abandon the realm of plausible hypotheses for the minor uncertainties of direct seeing.

As the Moon's distance from the Earth's centre varies between 221,463 miles and 252,710 miles so does the apparent diameter of her disk oscillate about its mean value of 31 minutes of arc. This, however, has little effect on the visibility of her surface features, which is affected far more by the phase, altitude above the horizon and more generally the transparency of our atmosphere, of which the former is but a special instance.

With a magnification of 360 diameters, which is within reach of a medium-sized telescope, the face of the Moon will spread out over some 180 degrees, that is to say, nearly over the whole of the sky if all of the disk could be seen at once instead of only a portion at a time. Larger instruments admit more light and allow higher powers to be used (for the brightness of the image declines in proportion as the square of linear magnification increases and increases as the square of the aperture). Yet in lunar and planetary study a linear magnification of 1,000 marks the practical limit, beyond which the unsteadiness and impurity of the air nullify the advantages of increased diameter. The aperture, represented by the diameter of the object lens or mirror, suffers from a similar limitation, for the larger it

29

is the larger is the area of the sky it uses to gather its light from and the less likely this is to be in good condition all over at once. Moreover, the greater brilliance of the image produced by a large telescope, important as it may be for photographic purposes, is not necessarily an undiluted boon to the eye, though practised observers become largely immune from this inconvenience at some cost to their eyesight.

For these reasons the effectiveness of large telescopes is often questioned by planetary astronomers. (Possibly many of them are amateurs who can afford only smaller instruments and like to think that these are as good for their purposes as the largest ones, which in British conditions may often be the case.) Much valuable planetary research has certainly been done with modest means. The famous selenographers, Beer and Madler, used a 3¾-inch refractor. Wilkins[7] has compiled his famous 300-inch map of the Moon with reflectors between 6 and 15 inches in diameter. Yet, since he has had access to some giant telescopes he has found that these have been unjustly derated.

In theory, a thousandfold magnification should bring us within about 250 miles of the Moon. Objects 500 feet in diameter and streaks and lines of less width should be accessible to the eye. In practice, however, such minor detail only 'flashes out' occasionally, perhaps for a fraction of a second when the air is exceptionally steady. It requires skill and experience to capture and accurately record such a flitting glimpse, and individual preconceptions tend to creep in to 'help' in the mental reconstruction of what has been observed. One day instantaneous photography may come to supplant the individual eye. So far, however, despite the great progress made since the first lunar photograph taken in 1850 by Bond, who used the daguerreotype process, it still lags far behind a skilled observer in descrying and representing fine surface detail, which becomes blurred and largely blotted out by the atmospheric tremors during the time of exposure. Moreover, an observer who is a good and accurate draughtsman (this excludes the 'modern' artist!) can combine in his drawings the repeated experience of many separate moments of best seeing, which a photographic plate can never achieve. A series of instantaneous exposures in a film may provide a comparable effect, or at any rate a check on the observations, but this remains to be seen.

Such are the lights and shadows of the visual study of the Moon, whose central portions have been repeatedly mapped. And yet even here minor features continue to be discovered by diligent students, so that the question is often asked whether any of them are still being formed at the present date. I will return to this in Chapter 7. Meanwhile we may concentrate on the general aspects of lunar topography, without some knowledge of which our further deliberations will become increasingly difficult to follow.

Even the naked eye discloses a good deal of detail on the Moon. Some

Lick Observatory

PLATE I The oblique rays of the Sun pick out the relief in this waxing crescent photographed with the 36-inch refractor at the Lick Observatory. The larger mare near the middle is Foecunditatis; the smaller hexagonal one below it is Mare Crisium. *(Pages 31, 35)*

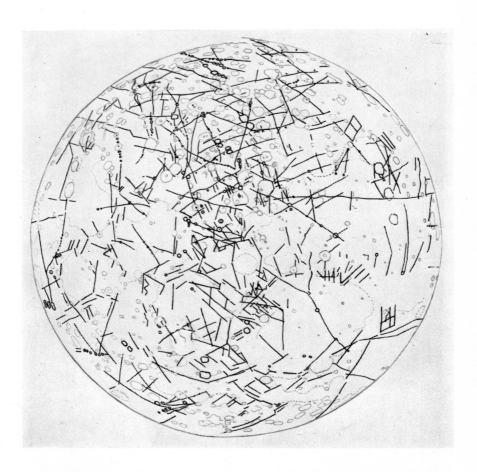

PLATE II A tentative chart of the lunar tectonic grids, based on the identification charts of Sky Publications' *Moon Sets*. The two half-Moon photographs to which these refer differ in libration, so that they cannot be made to match in the region of the south pole, where the outlines of the craters and other formations are displaced from their true positions relatively to one another. Grid lines, whether fractures, faults, crater chains or ridges, are shown in full black. The larger chain craters are represented individually. Where the ground is noticeably higher on one side of a fault than on the other, the higher side is indicated by small crosses. *(Pages 24, 41)*

PLATE III Full Moon showing a slight polar phase in the south, which is uppermost in the plate (following the usual astronomical convention). This photograph was taken with the 36-inch refractor at the Lick Observatory, California. *(Pages 31, 41)*

The positions of the principal features mentioned in this book may be found by reference to the name map in Appendix II, page 216

In the Lunar Altai
240x . 6½in. spec.

"Plan"

"Elevation"

V. A. firsoff

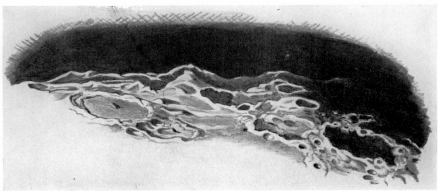

PLATE IV Lunar mountains drawn by the author direct from telescopic observation. *Above:* the lunar Altai. *Below:* the Leibnitz Mountains, near the south pole of the Moon, seen on the morning terminator at the gibbous phase, northern libration projecting the peaks on to the skyline. (Drawn 31 May, 1955, 20 h. 10 m. to 20 h. 25 m. G.M.T., from observation with a 6½-inch reflector, powers ×240 and ×360). *(Page 39)*

fortunate individuals are said to be able to see a few of the largest lunar mountains without optical aids. Still, it took Galileo's primitive 'optick tube' to establish their identity. But no exceptional keenness of sight is required to discern the pattern of dark and light areas, which repeats itself at each phase, and at full Moon has variously been construed as a broad grinning face, a man with a dog, a donkey or rabbit with long ears, an old-fashioned beauty with flowing hair admiring herself in a mirror (she favours a gibbous phase immediately after the full), or a girl reading a book in an uncomfortably inverted position. The South Sea islanders fancy in the Moon of their skies, where, the south pole being uppermost, the girl assumes a more natural posture, the dark image of a mythological crab,[3,4] which has just swarmed up into the visible part of the globe, and personally I find this particular representation of the dark lunar maria the easiest to follow. (See Plates I and III.)

The Latin name *mare* (pl. *maria*), meaning sea, dates from the pre-telescopic times when the dark patches on the Moon were thought to be water and the bright ones land. The medley of fanciful names given to the latter by the early selenographers has not survived, which is rather a pity, for these nameless tracts must now be referred to by awkward circumlocutions. The maria, however, still bear their ancient misnomers. Having supplemented our eye with a pair of binoculars, we shall see that the crab has edged up into the lunar disk from the east-north-east, in what is known as the second quadrant, and here his body lies. In the east Oceanus Procellarum (Ocean of Storms) sprawls in amorphous foreshortening. Next to the west, and the most crabby part of all, lies the dark oval of Mare Imbrium (Sea of Rains), which is of capital importance in all selenological thinking (selenology is the lunar counterpart of geology). Northwards, beyond a long strip of light-coloured land pierced with the eye of the crater Plato, Mare Frigoris (Sea of Frost), with its dependencies, straggles—again greatly foreshortened—and deputizes for the crab's legs. The south-eastern claw of the crab is curved down towards his head. It issues from the Ocean of Storms, is jointed in the south by the small rounded Mare Humorum (Sea of Humours), while its pincer is formed by Mare Nubium (Sea of Clouds) and is half-opened towards the light-shaded ground near the prominent ring mountain Copernicus, with its bright halo, and the very dark spots of Sinus Medii (Gulf of the Middle). The latter, together with the comparable enclosure of Mare Vaporum (Sea of Vapours), farther west, compose the head of the crab.

The first quadrant, in the north-west, harbours most of the unmistakable great claw, the first segment consisting of the rounded Mare Serenitatis (Sea of Calm). The second segment is the Mare Tranquillitatis (Sea of Quiet), and the two jaws (which also make the head and the book of the reading girl, or the rabbit's ears) consist of the Mare Foecunditatis (Sea of

31

Fertility) and the Mare Nectaris (Sea of Nectar). Detached, in the north-west, is the small oval of Mare Crisium (Sea of Crises). There are also small marginal maria, on the brink of the visible hemisphere, more or less conspicuous according to the libration, but of little importance for our purposes.

If you have now absorbed the compass bearings of the quadrants you will soon see that the Sun is supposed to be rising on the Moon in the west and setting in the east, which, of course, is nonsense, since the Moon rotates the same way as the Earth does. It is odd that so few people remark upon it, which goes to prove, if proof were needed, that most people at most times prefer to repeat what the Joneses say to using their own brains. This is an extremely valuable feature of human behaviour from the point of view of coherence of societies, but, as a Scandinavian proverb puts in, one can get too much even of a good thing. However, in the present case the designation of the quadrants follows the terrestrial convention. The 'west' side of the Moon corresponds to the west side of our sky, only that our view of the Moon is antipodal—it is, in fact, a mirror image.

The Moon and the Earth complement each other in the phase. When the Moon appears as a crescent from the Earth the Earth will be gibbous as seen from the Moon, and she is new at full Moon. But a lunar observer facing south will still have the east on his left and the west on his right.

Full phase is not the time when vertical relief shows to advantage. If we use higher power we shall be able to make out here and there a bright ring enclosing a darker pool: this is one of the lunar ring mountains, or craters. But we could not have guessed as much with any certainty without previous knowledge. We may surmise, and as it happens rightly, that the bright 'land' stands somewhat higher than the 'seas'—indeed, the difference of level is several thousand feet, and there may be a suspicion of roughness about some parts of the former. This is, however, no more than a suspicion and on the whole the Moon under moderate magnification appears at this time to be a smooth sphere, rather like a marble that has been bashed about and acquired a multitude of white spots where the glass has been cracked or bruised. From some of these spots rays fan out irregularly, as though splintering had occurred, though more detailed inspection will soon show that this is too simple an explanation.[2]

The most prominent of these ray systems is centred on a bright oval within a dark narrow ring. This is the crater Tycho in the vicinity of the south pole, where the whole surface appears as though it had been rudely chalked. Some of the rays run to considerable distances, over 'sea' and 'land' alike, as far as the Sea of Nectar and beyond, giving the Moon a superficial resemblance to a peeled orange—which has often been remarked upon.

This is a shadowless picture if we see the full face of the full Moon. More often than not, however, we are not in line with the Sun, so that, though the Moon is technically full, she shows a polar phase, a thin sickle of shadow encroaching somewhat on either one of the other pole. If so, the mountains near it will spring into prominence and we shall be able to admire some of the stupendous mountain rings of the Moon, contracted to narrow ellipses by perspective.

The dark and light-coloured areas are fairly evenly balanced, most of the former being in the north-east, while the south-west of the disk is distinctly lighter and higher. Thus the second quadrant is nearly all 'sea' and the fourth nearly all 'land'. At a more favourable phase we may note the rather worn appearance of the mountains round the north pole as against the rougher, fresher structure of the south, by comparison with which the north pole is generally depressed. This parallels the terrestrial distribution of low and high ground, though the 'seas' of the Moon do not, for on the Earth there is far more water in the southern portion of the globe.

Scrutiny at other phases, when the unevennesses of the ground cast long shadows, will soon dispel any doubt about the nature of the maria. They are not seas but vast plains, wrinkled and uneven, sometimes vividly recalling under oblique lighting the skin on boiling milk, and here and there pitted with hollows or broken up with mountain peaks and rings. Yet the shadowless panorama of the full Moon did not lie and our comparison with the Earth is not futile. There must be important differences not only in the relative altitude but in the composition of the lunar 'land' and 'sea'. Indeed, if the Earth had lost her waters and consequently her mantle of vegetation, she would present to the lunar observer, when at full phase, a general aspect not unsimilar to that of the Moon. The land masses would consist mainly of light-coloured acid granitic rocks and products of their decay cemented into sedimentary formations; but the deep ocean beds, composed of the duskier basalt of the sima, would form vast dark plains, comparatively smooth, or only lightly wrinkled. The presence of sedimentary rocks, which are expected to be substantially absent from the Moon,* would somewhat obscure the picture, but its main outlines should not be seriously affected.

This is due to the effect of specific gravity on the vertical stratification of the Earth, combined with isostasy. Not only did the lighter rocks naturally tend to rise above the heavier ones at the early stages of consolidation of the surface; but even now the surface crust, 20 or 30 miles thick, is buoyed up on a semi-molten plastic mass, into which the heavier basic formations subside to greater depths than the lighter acid ones. As erosion proceeds the latter are gradually worn down, which reduces the pressure exerted by them on the subjacent plastic mass and the land rises to keep it even. This,

---

* It has been suggested by T. Gold that the maria may, in fact, be areas where dust produced by erosion has accumulated and become largely compacted into rock.

however, requires simultaneous subsidence elsewhere, and the accretion of mass from below is mainly in the form of the heavy formations, so that it cannot continue indefinitely, and in the end the old denuded land must subside below the level of the sea. In the absence of energetic superficial erosion this mechanism of isostasy in its terrestrial form cannot operate on the Moon, and it could never have played there an equally important part as it has on the Earth. Yet the vertical distribution of the light-coloured *lunarite* and the dark *lunabase*,[6] the names proposed for the two types of lunar rock by Spurr, reflects a similar stratification on the basis of specific gravity.

The precise relation of these rocks to their opposite numbers on the Earth is not known and one must resist the temptation of equating them simply with our granite and basalt respectively, to which many selenologists yield. This would not matter very much if a mere quantitative shift in the scale of gravity and composition were involved, but I will try to show later on that some fundamental differences in the forces that have shaped the mountains of the Moon may become obscured as a result.

REFERENCES

1. BALDWIN, R. B. *The Face of the Moon*. University of Chicago Press, 1949.
2. MOORE, PATRICK. *Guide to the Moon*. Eyre and Spottiswoode, London, 1953.
3. PICKERING, W. H. *The Moon*. Doubleday, Page and Co., New York, 1903.
4. RUDAUX, L. and DE VAUCOULEURS, G. *Astronomie*. Larousse, Paris, 1948.
5. RUSSELL, H. N., DUGAN, R. S. and STEWART, J. Q. *Astronomy*, Boston, 1926.
6. SPURR, J. E. *Geology Applied to Selenology*. 4 Vols. 1944–9.
7. WILKINS, H. P. *Our Moon*. Muller, London, 1954.
8. UREY, H. C. *The Planets*. Oxford University Press, 1952.

THE MOUNTAINS OF THE MOON

A T FULL MOON the Sun is shining vertically down on her face; he is directly behind us, so that we can see only what he sees and he can see no shadow. But at half Moon, or quarter phase, our gaze and his make an angle of 90 degrees with one another, and when this angle is larger the Moon becomes a crescent. The larger the angle the smaller is the illuminated part of the disk and the more of the shadows we see in proportion. Long shadows exaggerate surface relief, making a mountain of a molehill, if not quite literally, and bringing out every nook and cranny which were not betrayed by shadows at full phase. (See Plate I.)

This is the more true as the softening effect of atmospheric scattering is, except for isolated doubtful instances, substantially absent from the Moon. Thus in a typical case a lunar shadow looks ink-black and sharp, without a discernible brightening up at the edge. Owing to this the height of a mountain on the Moon can often be determined with greater ease than of one on the Earth. It is enough to measure the length of the shadow in terms of the diameter, correct this for spherical perspective, determine the altitude of the Sun above the theoretical lunar horizon, and the problem reduces itself to obtaining one short side of a rectangular triangle when the other short side and the adjacent angle are known. There is, however, one important difference between the terrestrial and lunar heights: the former are referred to the mean level of the sea, but no such convenient level of reference exists on the Moon, so that the heights are usually given above the surrounding country. Sometimes reference is made to the 'mean surface' of the Moon, but this is a wholly abstract concept without any visual counterpart.

It is, nevertheless, not quite true to say that lunar shadows have no penumbra. The Sun is not a geometrical point but a disk about half a degree of arc in width and he does to this extent look round the edge of any obstacle. Thus lunar shadows must needs have a hazy edge from this cause alone, and this edge will widen as the shadows grow longer, being at its widest on the dividing line between night and day, where a kind of 'dawn' will result. The sunrise is rapid enough, but even so the heights do not suddenly spring into full brilliance, being at first only half lit. Furthermore, light is scattered not only by gas or dust but also by large bodies, in fact, it is scattered by them much more effectively, except that they soon eclipse one another when the Sun is low. Yet any high mountain that has caught the light will shine like a kind of moon on the surrounding country, which can be seen plainly in the mountainous regions of the south pole.

STRANGE WORLD OF THE MOON
STRANGE WORLD OF THE MOON

The whole question of lunar shadows must be viewed with regard to the total brightness of the illuminated portion of the disk. At night, when observations are made, the eye is adjusted to receive and register minute gradations of lighting; but the Moon is in full sunlight, so that the contrast is dazzling. In fact, the disk of the full Moon seen in a large telescope with a low magnification becomes quite unbearably bright. In these circumstances the half-tones are often completely imperceptible, even where they undoubtedly exist. In order to be able to see them, one must eliminate the rest of the sunlit disk. W. H. Steavenson interposed behind the eye-piece a dark (transparent) screen pierced with a pin-hole, which allowed him to isolate the dark interiors of large craters. In this way he was easily able to see the shadows cast by the central peaks in the light reflected by the sunlit walls opposite: these shadows pointed towards the Sun.

For the same reason all but the brightest stars become invisible when close to the sunlit limb of the Moon. Nor would an observer on her surface see the sky sprinkled with stars, as this is usually shown in space-travel books, when out in sunshine. He could, however, easily see most stars from a mountain shadow or through a tube, as the lunar sky is dark by day. It is generally believed that one can see the bright stars in broad daylight even on the Earth, once the brilliance of the surrounding scene has been eliminated—for instance, when looking up the shaft of a mine. This belief, however, is optically and physiologically unsound.*

The appearance of any portion of the lunar surface varies greatly with the phase, that is to say, with the position of the Sun in the lunar sky and so with the length and direction of the shadows. The shadows of the invisible objects, below the threshold of telescopic resolution, also contribute to the effect, as do the reflections from the small prominences, such as boulders, which may cause a seemingly smooth area to vary greatly in darkness and general appearance depending on the phase and libration. Yet, curiously, some of the darkest portions of the surface achieve their greatest intensity under a vertical Sun, which is inexplicable by geometrical causes alone.

These are refinements. The mountains of the Moon stand out most clearly when close, though not too close, to the terminator, as the boundary terminating the illuminated part of the disk is called. Near the quarter phase the southern highlands in particular are so pitted with hollows that under moderate magnifications they look exactly like a crumpet. Even with a map it is not easy to find one's way among the minor detail of this maze. As the power increases the scene assumes a dark magnificence and when it is realized that the smallest pit will exceed a mile in diameter and the rings round the large ones are mountain ranges many thousands of feet high one is touched with something like reverential awe.

* *Observatory*, Vol. 76, No. 890, p. 36.

Circular or oval outlines occur in terrestrial topography. The Sea of Japan and the Yellow Sea look suspiciously like a pair of rather worn lunar craters, say, Julius Cæsar. The island arcs of northern Pacific show a distribution of high ground very similar to the mountain ramparts of the lunar maria and may even be due to the action of very similar factors (conical fracture),[14] which has also been traced by Wilson and Scheidegger in several great mountain systems.[16] The Gulf of Mexico, too, is crater-like in shape. Hungary is a plain ringed by mountains, and a few other instances may be picked out indicating comparable arrangement. The difficulty with all these large features, however, lies in the powerful action of ice and water and/or the presence of the sea, which mask the true original relief.

In French West Africa, on the other hand, there exist well preserved rings of volcanic origin, known as Richat structures, up to 30 miles in diameter, which would seem to form exact counterparts of the lunar craters.[15] We have 'calderas of collapse', such as Volcano Bay in Japan, large crater lakes, of which Bombon in the Philippines is an example, and, of course, the volcanoes proper. Only that, with a few exceptions, such as the Hawaiian craters, these look nothing like a typical lunar ring and are also very much smaller on the average.

However this may be, the circular features of the Earth make a modest contribution to her appearance, nor do they seem to have been much more conspicuous in the past geological ages so far deciphered. Our mountains have been produced chiefly by the folding of the crust along broad arcs and irregular lines, with some contribution from vertical displacement of the strata through uplift or subsidence, sometimes accompanied by fracture or faulting, and minor horizontal shifts of the strata across the fault-line, known as overthrusts. In every case their appearance has been subsequently modified by erosion, without which they would have assumed the form of gentle upswellings with occasional steep scarps where the cohesion of the strata had given way. There are also remnant mountains, like those of Britain, produced by the vertical movement of the land and its subsequent dismemberment by streams and glaciers.

The structure of the lunar surface differs considerably from these terrestrial patterns. Circularity, or rather polygonality close to circularity, is the prevalent trend. There are rings everywhere, sometimes in groups, but mostly scattered without any clear pattern. Maria, too, as already indicated, are composed in quasi-circular lines, locally affected by super-imposition of later crateriform structures or land movements. Here and there these vast plains are traversed by straggling wrinkle ridges, which show a remote likeness to the foldings of the Earth's crust. Yet these ridges are low and suggest a flow of viscous, plastic matter, such as half-solidified lava, so that they are probably the work of different forces. There are some

37

plateaux and circular updomings, recalling their terrestrial counterparts, and, perhaps surprisingly, some examples of remnant mountains, subdued and broken down by some erosive (denuding) forces. Such are the Riphaean Mountains in Mare Nubium and the Carpathians, north of Copernicus, the conspicuous ring formation near the apparent centre of the great eastern 'sea' complex. Farther north, the Sea of Rains (Mare Imbrium) displays a number of isolated blocks of high ground, as well as steep, more or less conical peaks, jutting straight up from the plain, such as Pico and Piton, which recall the ice-smoothed nunataks of Greenland, and must also be classed as remnant mountains, probably produced by the destruction of large ring formations when the mare first came into being.

The mountains that, superficially at least, appear closest to our forms are the great chains that half ring the Sea of Rains in the west and have been christened from north to south, Alps, Caucasus, and Apennines. The last-named chain has a total length of some 600 miles and its highest point, Mount Huyghens, attains nearly 20,000 feet above the neighbouring country. Towards the Sea of Rains the Apennines drop in a stupendous scarp, paralleled by tell-tale lines of concentric subsidence which result in a terraced approach to their foot from the east. Away from the Sea of Rains the mountains spread fanwise in more or less radial ridges gradually diminishing in height, with hardly any secondary valleys, such as would soon have been produced by our streams. The ridges are rough and craggy and the valleys are mainly due to subsidence along tectonic fractures, a type of formation not unknown on the Earth. The 70-mile Alpine Valley must almost certainly have had a similar origin, but its regular outline, smooth floor, and isolation make it conspicuous. The Caucasus and the Alps are lower and less compact than the Apennines, the Alps particularly assuming the form of an irregular jumble of high peaks and short ridges.

Other maria have their border heights, too, but nowhere equally well developed or preserved as in the selenologically younger Mare Imbrium. About 50 and 200 miles south-east of Mare Nectaris two scarps or ranges of worn ancient appearance straggle through the vast crater-lands of the fourth quadrant in concentric curves which are not quite parallel to the present mare and would seem to indicate that this was preceded by two nearly coincidental but much larger 'seas'. The outer of these two ranges bears the name of Altai and still attains locally to 13,000 feet above the surrounding ground. The vanished mare these mountains may have bordered would have been comparable to Mare Imbrium itself. There exists a trace of another ancient mare-bed near the north pole[8] as well as signs to show that Copernicus and the Carpathians were once the floor of a vanished mare.*

* V. A. Firsoff: 'Palaeography of the Nubian and Imbrian Plains, *Journal of the British Astronomical Association*, Vol. 67, No. 4, 1957.

These are some indications of the long history which has preceded the present shape of things on the Moon.

In the south and also in the east, the visible hemisphere is edged by powerful mountains, of which the Leibnitz and the Doerfel Mountains near the south pole far surpass not only the Lunar Apennines but even our Himalayas, attaining heights estimated to exceed 35,000 feet. These mountains, however, are rather different in character from the straight-forward Apennines. They form ranges indeed, especially the Leibnitzs, but these ranges are coincident with the walls of some large ring complexes of exceptional depth and steepness,[6] which run in lines.[10] Thus we have as it were a superimposition of two different systems: the linear and the circular, the combination of which has not yet received a satisfactory explanation, unless the mountains have been extruded by the upward pressure developed by the subsidence at the centre of the rings. A great rift may also have been formed under the tidal action of the earth on the confines of the visible hemisphere, possibly intensified by the crustal movements following on the change of the speed of rotation; and this rift, now hidden, may be the source of these remarkable features. By the rule of compensation it is permissible to surmise that a vast mare plain exists somewhere beyond the south pole.

At crescent phase the summits of the Doerfel and Leibnitz ranges appear in the telescope as a string of pearls bordering the dimly earthlit 'old Moon' and Wilkins and other observers, including myself, have seen the 'pearls' linked by a thin thread of light.[5,9,12] This was twilight, whether atmospheric or due to reflections from the peaks themselves it is difficult to tell. Yet the peaks at the edge of the Moon looked bluish to some observers which I can confirm from my own colour study, and this might indicate the presence of gas, possibly rising from the suspected great fault. In any case, here is one of the mystery regions of the Moon. (See Plate IV.)

Faults and clefts are, indeed, a salient feature of many lunar areas, especially those bordering on the maria. There is a fine complex of them near the centre of the visible disk: the Triesnecker, Hyginus, and Ariadaeus Clefts. The last-named, at the south border of Mare Vaporum, is 170 miles long and cuts through several minor ring-complexes. The Hyginus Cleft splits in half the crater of this name. Generally speaking these crevices show small regard for surface formations and will cut right through massive walls of large craters as though they offered no resistance, which may be an indication of the comparatively insubstantial texture of lunarite, although fractures formed during our earthquakes have equally little regard for mountains. The surface of the Moon is literally criss-crossed by small cracks, like a mudflat which has dried up in the Sun. Some clefts gape open to depths exceeding 1,000 feet, but most have been sealed by material seemingly surging from below, and, like the Sirsalis and Ariadaeus Clefts,

D

form only shallow ravines that appear as white lines under vertical illumination. Near the poles, and the south pole in particular, there exist vast systems of intersecting fractures, which Spurr calls the 'polar grid'.[8] These fractures, however, would appear to have been filled with some material, which may be siliceous, surging from below, so that they actually stand out above the surroundings in the manner of terrestrial volcanic dykes where the dyke rock is harder than the country rock and has, consequently, not yielded to erosion to the same extent as the latter. In the opposite case we have a depression, not unsimilar to, say, the Sirsalis Cleft.

This is an interesting point, for wherever terrestrial lava could flow freely out of the fracture, as it does in Iceland, it has spread out on the surface as a sheet. The present appearance of our dykes, whether upraised or depressed, is due to differential erosion and in most cases the dyke was buried far below the surface of the ground and became exposed only as this surface had been denuded (worn away). This is hardly the interpretation one would apply to the Moon on the conventional reckoning. Some erosive forces there must be at work, as is shown by the steady destruction of the old ring mountains, and this may possibly account for the 'polar grid'. But why has the material, which would seem to have filled the large clefts, never risen to the top?

Observing at Pic-du-Midi with a power of 1,026 diameters, Gilbert Fielder saw the floor of the Ariadaeus Cleft convex in shape, which was subsequently confirmed by the examination of photographs taken at this observatory. This suggests an upthrust of matter from below, halted in its tracks before the surface was reached.[11] This would be understandable if the lava were heavier than the surface rocks, an important point to bear in mind.

A fracture caused by vertical movement of the land may result in a fault, the ground being higher on the one side of the fracture than on the other.

The most spectacular 'vertical' lunar fault is the Straight Wall or Railway near the crater Thebit, in the Sea of Clouds (Mare Nubium). It is some 60 miles long and the difference of levels attains 800 feet, so that in favourable lighting it is within easy reach of a small instrument. But there are many other faults on the Moon, for instance, in the Apennines and more generally on the confines on the maria, where concentric and radial faulting is often present, as it also is in larger ring complexes.

A fault, of course, need not be, and seldom is, vertical; more often than not it slopes, or hades, more or less steeply. If the ground has risen along the slope we have a direct fault; if on the opposite side—a reverse fault. With a gentle hade the latter will become an overthrust. A fracture accompanied by a horizontal displacement of the ground, without or with little change of level, on its two sides relatively to one another is a shear fault, exemplified in the St. Andreas Fault, which gave rise to the San Francisco earthquake in 1906.

Overthrusts, of which the Highlands of Scotland provide some classic examples, are present also on the Moon, though they have long remained unrecognized. They manifest themselves not only in the difference of levels across the dividing line but also by the deformation of the intervening features, due to shearing stress, and sometimes by the overlap of neighbouring craters, which have been bodily pushed over each other, as Purbach has over Regiomontanus. I have found a number of overthrusts in the third and fourth quadrants.[13]

On the Earth the faults are usually levelled down and sealed, and it requires 'detective' work to uncover them by the tell-tale non-conformity of strata appearing at different levels on the two sides, or the distribution of earthquake tremors. On the Moon they are easier to make out, though here, too, sealing, landslips, and obliteration by encroaching craters have occurred. More, many of the minor and major faults or fractures are associated with or pass into chains of small and even large craters, as in the case of the oblique faults in the region of Ptolemaeus, south-west of the Altai Mountains and most conspicuously in the so-called Rheita Valley in the fourth quadrant. This is significant, if not altogether unexpected.

As already mentioned in Chapter 3, in my study of the Moon I have established a complex network of these semi-concealed faults, crater-chains, and tectonic fractures, which envelopes the whole visible surface of the Moon and is clearly subdivided into three grids of different ages, composed of lines roughly at right angles to each other. (Compare Plates II and III.) These grids fit in closely with the distribution of the maria, some prominent craters and the general lie of the land. They result in the shattering of the entire surface of the lunar globe into polygonal rock blocks, presumably wedged against each other and supported by some medium or other at a lower level.[13] An inclined fault may give rise to conical fracture and the diameter of this at the ground level depends on the depth at which the fracture originates. Marginal extrusion of lava may occur, resulting in something like a walled plain, or a mare. The veteran English astronomer and geophysist Sir Harold Jeffreys[14] favours this explanation of the lunar ring features. Geological structures of this kind are known on the Earth.

This, however, carries us a little ahead of the story.

If there are two parallel faults the land may have either slipped down or risen the same way on both sides, producing a stepped configuration, as in the case of the terraced inner slopes of the large ring mountains; or else the movement between the faults may have been in the direction opposite to that outside them. If the intervening portion stands above the surroundings we have an upthrow or horst; and, conversely, if it lies below the latter this is a downthrow or graben. Thus the Alpine Valley is probably a graben and the Apennine ridges are essentially horsts. Some circular downthrow is certainly present in the large craters.

41

Lunarite would seem to be so stiff and brittle as to resist folding to the breaking-point, which may be the reason for the absence, apart from wrinkle ridges, of the true folded mountains on the Moon.

Gashes converging towards Mare Imbrium have almost totally obliterated the Haemus Mountains, which divide Mare Serenitatis from Mare Vaporum. The highlands about Ptolemaeus and to the south of this large flat-bottomed ring, along what Spurr calls the 'Centrameridional Horst', that is to say, an upswelling of the ground bounded by faults, some 300 miles wide and forming part of the tidal bulge, are also seamed with similar features. These are usually referred to the Imbrian system,[2,3,8] but the issue is not clear, as they parallel the main axes of Mare Imbrium and the Serenitatis–Tranquillitatis depressions and have probably originated in the thrusts coming from these directions. The deformation of the craters in this region closely parallels the gashes and shows the existence of crustal shortening at right angles to them, which would confirm this view.[4]

The meteorists, who maintain that Mare Imbrium was initiated by a tremendous explosion (*vide* Chapter 6), attribute these features to masses of rocks projected with circular velocity from the centre of this explosion hurtling horizontally along the ground. There are grave objections to this hypothesis and, as I have shown, there is no convergence of these so-called 'radial valleys' at any one centre, whether in Mare Imbrium or elsewhere. G. P. Kuiper and G. Fielder,[3] however, have examined these depressions and found in them large masses of rock and huge boulders which would seem superficially to support the explosive hypothesis; but it is more likely that these masses represent simply the collapsed rims of the overthrusts when the stiff lunarite rock was splintered and pushed over by the pressure coming from the two systems of maria. Such developments are well known from the Highlands of Scotland.

Lunar clefts include another controversial group of formations which Pickering termed 'river-beds',[7] and the most conspicuous of which is Schroeter's Valley in the vicinity of the bright crater Aristarchus.

These have a winding course and increase in width in one direction, with a pear-shaped crater at the broader end. The subject is discussed in fuller detail in Chapter 15.

Yet, interesting as these various features are, it is time to return to the craters and ring mountains, which hold the key to the present appearance of the Moon and to many secrets of her past.

There is great disparity of size and general features between lunar ring forms. One can establish an *almost* continual progression from the largest circular mare to the smallest craterlet, with which the surface of our satellite is so thickly strewn. Parts of the initial mountain rampart which must have been ringing the 700-mile-wide Sea of Rains have been swamped and destroyed by the neighbouring Ocean of Storms and Sea of Clouds, as is the case with some overlapping or contiguous craters; but enough of this rampart is left to show that the mare is substantially a vast depression ringed by mountains. The oval Mare Crisium with a longer diameter of 335 miles is not too far a cry from the largest 'walled plain', still classed as 'crater'—the 180-mile-wide Bailly in the third quadrant. Bailly, however, has a light floor.

Thus, as often happens, a link is missing between the maria and the ring mountains, leaving the question open, whether they are different degrees of one and the same thing or the difference between them is one of kind. Near the east limb there is a 200-mile Mare Orientale, with a dark floor and a crater-like rampart, and this may be a transitional formation, but, unfortunately, it can be seen only in extreme foreshortening during a favourable libration and is very difficult to study. (See Fig. 1.)

55·7·13 − 2:50 U.T.   v. a. f.

Fig. 1. Maria Orientale and Veris at favourable libration. (200 ×, Amber, 6½in. spec.)

There are craters, large and small, having dark level lunabase floors, but they occur close to maria; in some cases the remnants of the central peak can still be made out, and it is reasonably clear that the dark floor is a secondary feature, due to flooding with the material directly or indirectly derived from the mare. As already pointed out, Bailly and the 146-mile Clavius, next after it in size, have rough interiors of light-coloured lunarite. The craters inside the maria, which have obviously been formed after them, do not differ in structure from the similar formations found elsewhere.

The mountain rim of Mare Imbrium resembles that of a crater in sloping gently on the outside, but the interior scarp is much steeper than in typical craters, even of the largest size, where it usually falls a good deal short of 30 degrees. In Mare Nubium the mountain girdle is conspicuous by its absence, nor is it at all developed round Oceanus Procellarum, which would appear to have been subsidences without peripheral uplift.

With very few exceptions, the best known of these being Wargentin, which is filled to the brim and forms a kind of table mountain, the interior of a ring mountain lies considerably below the level of the surrounding country. In the largest ring forms, which usually present a worn ancient appearance and have been much encroached upon by minor craters, the floor is nearly level, and this is why they are often referred to as walled plains or bulwark plains. With the greater curvature of the Moon and, consequently, a closer horizon, a person standing inside one of these giants

43

would be unable to see the surrounding mountain enclosure. This enclosure is both comparatively and absolutely lower than in the smaller ring forms of fresher appearance, and it is often breached and deformed. Yet, even quite apart from the effect of age, the ratio between the diameter and the height of the ring alters with size. Up to the diameter of about 80 miles the depth of the hollow and the height of the rim may be said to increase, at first rapidly, then more gradually, but beyond this point there is no apparent increase and even a recession,[2] which, however, is probably in part due to the fact that all the largest craters belong to an earlier age and thus have suffered by encroachment and such denuding forces as have affected the older formations of the Moon. Both the depth of the crater (which term does not necessarily denote identity with a volcanic vent but is simply the Greek for bowl) and the height of its rim show a considerable range of variation within any given diameter. The formations lying close to the limb cannot be accurately measured and there are some gigantic rings near the south pole; but the deepest known crater is Newton, also in this region. It is 85 miles wide and over 29,000 feet deep, the rim standing up to 13,000 feet above the surrounding mountain-land.[6] Wilkins[9] has observed a minor crater which appears to be 'bottomless', the internal shadow not disappearing even under a vertical Sun, but it is badly placed for observation and the impression may be due to some unknown peculiarities of internal structure.

There exists an approximate rule formulated by Schroeter that the material of the ring above the external level would just suffice to fill up the depression inside it. Hence it follows clearly that the smaller craters must be comparatively the more deeply trenched. Curiously, the alterations due to age appear to respect Schroeter's rule, for not only does the rim diminish in height but also the floor of the crater rises, which is difficult to account for except by the levelling down (denudation) of the neighbouring ground, combined with accumulation of sediments within the enclosure, and/or by an isostatic adjustment beneath the surface. Both forces may be present.

Copernicus (Plate XII), 56 miles from crest to crest of the ring, is a giant among the younger craters, though moderate in the general classification. Lying in the central portion of the disk, with few neighbours and no rivals among these, it is beautifully located for observation. The crater is 11,000 feet deep and its rim stands 3,300 feet above the neighbouring country. The rim is jagged, buttressed and terraced on the inside, where repeated faulting and subsidence appear to have taken place. It is thus the result of circular downthrow, or what Spurr calls 'grabencrater'.[8] This appearance is typical but becomes less and less pronounced as the diameter of the crater declines and below 10 miles the terraced effect disappears, the internal slopes become smoother and the height of the rim more uniform. Also the shape alters. Copernicus is rather like a broad saucer, with a group of peaks in the centre—another typical feature of the well-preserved crater, lacking in the large walled plains and in the rare dish craters, which though recent in other characteristics show no central rise. In smaller craters the central mountain is usually single and becomes less and less prominent, always well below the rim in height, which is the general rule without exceptions. Sometimes the central mountain is replaced by a central craterlet, and in some cases, the most prominent of which is Alpetragius, the two features are combined (there are also concentric craters), the craterlet being at the summit of the mountain. The smallest craters, however, do not appear to possess central peaks, which may or may not be due to the difficulty of seeing such minor detail. They are like egg-cups sunken in the ground. There also exist crater pits, where the rim is practically or totally absent. These are found among the minor objects and appear to be of seleno- logically recent age, signifying a decline in the crater-building activity.

The reality is somewhat more complicated than this and D. W. G. Arthur[1] distinguishes among smaller craters bowl-craters, craters with inverted cone interiors, indicating the existence of an either actual or past sink-hole at the centre, ring craters with small bright floors and ring craters with small dark floors. For general purposes, however, the description given above is accurate enough.

At the bottom of the scale are the small blowhole craters, or craterlets, which often occur in chains, well represented in the neighbourhood of Copernicus. In the southern uplands there are similar chains of somewhat larger craters, a mile and more in diameter, which suggest a kind of 'burrowing' from below. Occasionally these craters are packed so close together that they overlap and form a continuous rift. The sides of some clefts display tell-tale circular scoops, and the Hyginus Cleft emerges under higher magnification as a continuous crater-chain. Craterlets are also associated with cracks, wrinkle-ridges, which sometimes pass into cracks, thus being a sign of structural weakness in the outer surface, and with domelike heights found in several localities, such as Mare Imbrium and Mare Frigoris.

In the maria one also comes upon flattened rings and 'ghost craters', which have no vertical existence, but are distinguishable under a high Sun by their lighter colouring. Both are interpreted as ancient ring forms submerged under a flood of lunabase.

Some craters of extinct volcanoes on the Earth are coated with a white layer of volcanic ash, as is e.g. the 1½-mile crater of Nimrud in Turkey,* and the interiors of many newer-looking lunar craters are noticeably brighter than the rest of the landscape, or even brilliantly white under vertical illumination, which may or may not be due to the same cause. Sometimes the light-coloured matter extends beyond the ring, forming a compact or

* Alfred Harker in *Philosophical Magazine*, January 1918.

45

diffuse halo, from which long rays and streamers may issue in some or all directions. The character of these rays varies, too; some are scattered and patchy, others—very long and regular—passing impartially over high and low ground, as though unaffected by its configuration. These rays do not become visible until the Sun has reached a certain height above the horizon, whence it is inferred that the effect is due to some powdery or finely divided material accumulated at the bottom of small hollows.

These rays are one of the most puzzling lunar features.

Small craters with dark haloes likewise exist and are particularly numerous in the region of Copernicus.

Generally speaking, the bright haloes, rays, as well as some dark markings and the mysterious dusky radial bands on the walls of many ring complexes, show interesting alterations with phase, alterations which it is difficult to explain by the effects of light and shade alone. These, however, belong to Chapter 9.

Still, as already stated at the beginning of the present Chapter, the chiaroscuro can change the appearance of many lunar regions almost beyond recognition, and the shadows cast by small objects below the threshold of resolution play in this an important part. The effects can usually be best explained by multitudes of small cup-like depressions in the lunar rocks.

REFERENCES

1. ARTHUR, D. W. G. 'The Classification of Smaller Lunar Craters.' *J.B.A.A.*, Vol. 64, No. 1, 1954.
2. BALDWIN, R. B. *The Face of the Moon.* University of Chicago Press, 1949.
3. FIELDER, GILBERT. 'A Study of the Valley System Radial to Mare Imbrium.' *J.B.A.A.*, Vol. 66, No. 1, 1955.
4. FIRSOFF, V. A. 'Some Comments on a Recent Paper by Gilbert Fielder.' *J.B.A.A.*, Vol. 66, No. 4, 1956.
5. MOORE, PATRICK. *Guide to the Moon.* Eyre and Spottiswoode, London, 1953.
6. NEATE, A. N. 'The Lunar Formation Newton.' *J.B.A.A.*, Vol. 62, No. 6.
7. PICKERING, W. H. *The Moon.* Doubleday, Page and Co., New York, 1903.
8. SPURR, J. E. *Geology Applied to Selenology. III: Lunar Catastrophic Theory.* 1948.
9. WILKINS, H. P. *Our Moon.* Muller, London, 1954.
10. WHITAKER, E. A. 'The Lunar South Polar Region.' *J.B.A.A.*, Vol. 64, No. 6, 1954.
11. FIELDER, GILBERT. *Note on the Bottom of the Ariadaeus Rille* (mimeographed). Manchester University, 1956.
12. FIRSOFF, V. A. 'Lunar Occultations Observed in Blue Light.' *J.B.A.A.*, Vol. 66, No. 7, 1956.
13.   'On the Structure and Origin of Lunar Surface Features.' *J.B.A.A.*, Vol. 66, No. 8, 1956.
14. JEFFREYS, SIR HAROLD. *The Earth.* 3rd Edn. Cambridge University Press, 1952.
15. MOORE, PATRICK. A lecture delivered at the Manchester University, 1956.
16. *The Observatory*, Vol. 76, No. 891 (p. 45), 1956.

6

METEORITES OR LUNAVOES?

VARIOUS SUGGESTIONS have been put forward to explain the origin of the lunar ring forms. In recent years, Ingolf Ruud, of Norway, observed that craters could be produced in a yielding layer spread on an expanding sphere, say, paste on a rubber ball, whence he concluded that the explanation of the lunar ring mountains must be sought in the contraction of the surface over the comparatively unyielding interior.

The idea is not without its points, but it fails to account satisfactorily for the various features of the Moon and more particularly for the existence of central peaks in most ring formations. The latter is indeed the stumbling-block of many conceptions.

In France a similar hypothesis has been proposed by A. Fillias, who, however, assumes expansion of the lunar interior in relation to the surface, a far less likely contingency.

W. H. Pickering, Boneff, and others have favoured the tidal conception in one form or another and this, as we shall see later on, probably contains some truth. Here the scene is set in a distant past when the Moon was closer to the Earth and only partly solidified. It either rotated relatively to the surface of the Earth or its distance from the Earth varied owing to an eccentric orbit. However this may be, powerful tides were set up in the subjacent mass of lunar magma, which surged forth to the surface at high tide, spread out in circular pools, then was again sucked up underground at low tide, leaving behind a solidified ring on the confines of the pool. The ring mountains, with their frequently multiple ridges and terraces, would have been formed by the repetition of this process and the central peak would be a volcanic cone marking the last stages of the dying activity as the Moon receded from the Earth, with the consequent slackening of the tides, the crust of the Moon grew stronger and the supplies of underground lava became less copious and less easily accessible.

By the same token the size of the ring mountains decreased steadily until only small craters were formed.

Nor has there been any lack of wilder flights of fancy.

Thus S. E. Peal and Hans Hoerbiger share the honours of upholding the view that our satellite is completely ice-bound and the craters are pools produced by 'internal sources of heat', which have frozen up since, the girdling rampart being the result of precipitation of the rising vapours round the edges. Beard and Davis maintained that the ring mountains are simply coral atolls left behind by a long-vanished ocean that once used to spread over the whole surface of the Moon, which is perhaps even jollier.

Ocampo, on the other hand, sees in the pock-marked face of our companion world a grim memento of what may become of the Earth after a protracted atomic war.

Sad to say, these views have had a cool reception and the main trends of selenological thought have followed different lines.

When I once showed the Moon in the telescope to a small boy he immediately exclaimed, 'Bang! Bang!', which was his way of expressing the idea that the craters have been produced by explosions of some kind or other, or—let us say more guardedly—the action of a central force, which need not necessarily have been violent, although most selenologists have actually thought in terms of explosion, whether volcanic or meteoritic.

The volcanic idea, being the more natural of the two, came early, and the possibility that the ring mountains have been formed by falling meteorites was first broached by the German astronomer P. von Gruithuisen in 1823. It was popularized by the English astronomical writer, R. A. Proctor, in 1873, though he abandoned it in later years. Lunar observers generally and most British and Continental astronomers have pronounced in favour of the volcanic, or rather plutonic, interpretation, which is less rigid and allows of variation and modification; while the meteoric or meteoritic conception has struck root on the other side of the Atlantic. Recently R. B. Baldwin put it on a more scientific basis in his book, *The Face of the Moon*,[1] published by the University of Chicago Press in 1949, and H. C. Urey[22] in America and T. Gold[16] in Britain have further elaborated his arguments.

The greatest difficulty of the volcanic hypothesis, especially in its straight original form, lay in the enormous dimensions and to a less extent in the appearance of the lunar craters. Beside these most of our volcanoes were mere pin-holes. True, Pickering[8] lists a nameless crater in Kamchatka, Mount Asosan in the Kyu-Shyu islands of Japan, and Lake Bombon, in the Philippines, all of which are about 15 miles in diameter. The Volcano Bay is an even larger volcanic subsidence, some 25 miles across, and in the preceding chapter a few still more extensive candidates have been referred to. There are some extinct volcanoes in East Africa which closely recall lunar forms and one of these, Ngorongoro, is oval with a minor diameter of 12 miles and a major diameter of 13 miles. The Hawaiian volcanoes, too, though smaller, are of comparable appearance. Even more suggestive are the so-called Richat structures, recently discovered in the Adrar Mountains of Mauretania (French West Africa).[19,21] These are of two types: single-walled crater-like depressions with diameters ranging from 500 to 1500 metres; large circular areas up to 50 km. (32 miles) in diameter, showing a concentric arrangement of alternating valleys and ridges (as in the large lunar rings). The latter have been ascribed to the destruction by erosion of domelike geological structures produced by intrusions of molten magma.

Thus the objections based on either the size or the appearance of the lunar forms are not really valid, though it remains true that such formations are comparatively rare on the Earth and in the latter case could not have arisen without the intervention of denuding forces acting on strata of different hardness, in a region of low rainfall.

Typically, however—to pursue the line of reasoning of the meteorists— the crater floor of a terrestrial volcano is elevated above the surrounding country, which is particularly true of the Far Eastern examples if the great oceanic depths in their vicinity are taken into account. The interior bowl of a lunar ring, on the other hand, is almost invariably depressed below the level of the neighbourhood. With the possible exception of the great rings in the south polar region, the inward slopes of the lunar craters are gentle by comparison with their terrestrial counterparts. This may be due to the greater tensile strength of terrestrial rocks, which combines with stronger gravity to produce a more abrupt subsidence, but this explanation is admittedly not very convincing.

The usual volcano on the Earth is a steep cone crowned with a comparatively small vent, rarely in excess of one mile in diameter. Similar features exist on the Moon, though it is not definitely known that their nature is identical. They are also rather inconspicuous, just as our volcanoes would be, if transferred into the lunar surroundings. (See Plate V.)

To solve this problem, the nineteenth-century British selenographers Nasmyth and Carpenter[7] proposed the central-fountain hypothesis. According to this, the ring round a lunar crater was formed by the accumulation of material projected from a central vent against reduced gravity and negligible resistance of the thin atmosphere. Indeed, some of the large ring mountains display central peaks with craterlets at the summit, which lends colour to this submission. Baldwin[1] spares no effort to demolish this old-fashioned and long-abandoned conception. He points out that external slopes, or glacis, of lunar rings are too gentle for this genesis. The inclination is usually about 5 degrees, whereas the angle of repose of scoria and volcanic ash on the Earth is 40 degrees to 45 degrees and, contrary to his statement,[17] would be the same on the Moon, as it does not depend on gravity. This, in other words, would be the slope of a ring formed by a steady central dry fountain. However, even this is not necessary, for, assuming that the speed of ejection varied, a multitude of concentric ridges would be produced and their coalescence could easily result in a gentle outer glacis. Furthermore, a ring of this kind could have been formed by very liquid lava. The outward slopes of the Hawaiian volcanoes are inclined at only about 8 degrees. Other materials with similar properties could likewise be found, so that we are more or less where we started in the first place.

In any event, such considerations and the huge size of the walled plains have influenced some selenologists to abandon the volcanic theory.

Large meteorites are very rare, but a few cases are known where they have been of sufficient size to produce upon impact substantial craters. One of these, Coon Butte, in Arizona, measures three-quarters of a mile in diameter. Fragments of meteoritic nickel–iron have been found in abundance in and about the bowl, the meteoritic origin of which has been established beyond doubt by drilling operations. Discovered more recently is the Ungava Crater, in the Province of Quebec, in Canada. This is about two miles across, with a bounding rampart standing 300 feet above the surrounding country.[2] In Orange Free State, in South Africa, there is a peculiar Vredefort 'structure', 75 miles wide, within which the land rocks have been crushed and shattered by some force which does not appear to have been volcanic.[1] Yet no meteoritic material has been found there either, so that it cannot be definitely said that this is the result of an enormous meteoritic explosion.

However, the important point is, what was not realized at first, that the meteorite does not dig a crater by the mere mechanical force of impact but by the violent release of compressed and overheated gases beneath it. T. Gold[4] has recently calculated that with the impact velocity of the order of 50 km. per second the temperature attained will be about 10 million degrees Centigrade. Thus we would have an explosion comparable to that of an atomic bomb. This has not been the case with terrestrial meteorites, apart perhaps from the Siberian meteorite in 1908 and the hypothetical Vredefort affair; but, of course, Gold assumes that the Moon neither has nor ever had an atmosphere of any kind. This may be going too far. It is, nevertheless, true that a meteorite, even if falling obliquely, will still produce a circular pit. Otherwise all meteorites would have been required to fall vertically down on the face of the Moon, which is an impossible assumption.

Thus, it is reasoned, the ring mountains may have been formed in the same way as our small meteoritic craters, but at a remote age, soon after the consolidation of planetary bodies, when interplanetary space abounded in large meteoritic masses, left from the original planetogenic cloud. In the absence of erosion (Gold assumes a slow erosion by short-wave radiations),[4,16] the scars of these mighty blows would have been preserved more or less intact through hundreds and thousands of millions of years; whereas their contemporaries on the Earth have been entirely effaced by the ensuing geological transformations. For this reason the meteoritic hypothesis has become closely associated with the view that the Moon is an unchanging world.

Yet supporting geological evidence was strangely lacking. On this reckoning meteoritic impacts should have been both the more frequent and the more powerful the farther back we moved into the geological past, and some traces of them ought to have been preserved in the records of our rocks. None, however, was found. In recent years Boon and Albritton undertook a systematic search for these fossil meteoritic craters and found a number of so-called 'crypto-volcanic' structures, of which the Vredefort formation is the largest example, bearing witness to a large-scale disturbance due to some unspecified force.[1] Yet, while it is possible that these vast concussions or explosions were meteoritic in origin, there exists no evidence in support of this view. (See also examples in Plate VI.)

With the recent war material for a background, Baldwin[1] draws a comparison graph from the bomb pits, through the known terrestrial meteoritic craters, to the smaller lunar ring forms of newer appearance, in terms of a relationship between the logarithms of their depth and diameter. All these formations are shown to observe rather well a simple quadratic equation, whence he concludes that their shapes are consistent with an explosive origin. As much is implicit in Schroeter's Rule, which states that the material of the ring standing above the level of the neighbouring ground will approximately fill in the central hollow. Yet the bang could equally well have been volcanic. In fact, Jeffreys points out that water rising towards the lunar surface from the deeper layers would explode violently on reaching the low-pressure level and that no other mechanism is required to account for the explosion.[17] The relationship is also wholly compatible with repeated eruption and in the preceding chapter I have indicated that isostasy could produce exactly the same result. Patrick Moore[20] has applied this reasoning to the Richat structures (the smaller ones which are indubitable volcanic vents) and finds that their dimensions are in full accord with Baldwin's formula and much closer, in fact, to those of a typical lunar crater, such as Theaetetus, than the terrestrial meteoritic pits, which entirely knocks the ground from under Baldwin's thesis.

Moreover, on Baldwin's own account, the larger ring mountains, that is exactly those with which the protagonists of the volcanic hypothesis have had some trouble, no longer obey his equation and the points corresponding to them are scattered anyhow about the curve. The agreement is equally unsatisfactory for the terrestrial calderas of collapse examined by him. He does not, however, stop to consider the possible agreement between these two nonconformist groups, which both behave in much the same way. There is another point which casts doubt on the validity of his argument. Craters over 10 miles in diameter, which are included in his calculation, show distinct signs of central subsidence, which becomes multiple as the diameter increases. Thus, if they still satisfy the explosive relationship after the subsidence they clearly could not have done so before this took place; or else some other force, such as isostasy, is present which tends to maintain the ratio despite the increase in depth. If so, this force alone should suffice to secure the agreement without any explosion at all. Furthermore, it is very difficult to see why and how meteoritic explosion should result in subsidence, which necessitates the existence of a hollow beneath the crater. In Pickering's experiments[8] there was always a cavity under the little craters forming in cooling iron slag; and one would expect as much on the volcanic assumption. The hollow could result from the effusion of lava, ejection of solid matter, or escape of gases, or, alternatively, from the washing out of soluble materials; but the thrust of an exploding meteorite could only compact the underlying rocks, collapsing any pre-existing hollows and thus making subsidence all the less likely.

Nearly all ring mountains of newer appearance display central peaks in various stages of disintegration and these peaks have been a great headache to the meteorists, especially as most, if not all, of the best-preserved specimens are crowned with small craters. On the volcanic interpretation this is a thing to be expected, and G. P. Kuiper, whilst postulating the impact origin of the ring mountains, has yet been constrained by his own study of the Moon's surface with the 82-inch McDonald reflector to assume volcanic character for these features.[18] This makes one ask if the meteoritic journey was really necessary, after all, and he has, accordingly, been attacked with some show of feeling by H. C. Urey for this dangerous deviation.[24]

Baldwin tries to dismiss the summit craterlets, of which he lists a dozen, as accidental, for, according to his calculation, taking the average distribution of these features on the Moon for a guide, this would be the number to be expected. Alas, over 40 summit craters are now known! Moreover, these features, as well as the central peaks themselves, would appear to suffer rapid destruction by some forces, at present conjectural, which heavily tilts the balance.[16] His calculations include numerous blowholes, which are volcanic in his own view; but perhaps the most damaging evidence comes from the absence of such crater pits from the slopes of the central peaks, which offer a much larger cross-section to the falling meteorites than do the small areas of the summits.

Gold[16] tries to circumvent the difficulty by suggesting that in an ultrasonic explosion the material immediately below the focus of the explosion would not be removed, leading to the formation of a central peak, for which, though, there exists no present supporting evidence, and, further, that the meteorite, having been slowed down to sonic speed, would dig a hole in the peak thus produced and make a crater pit; but no explanation is provided for the miracle which had allowed the meteorite to survive the 10,000 million-degree detonation immediately beneath it. One would expect it to be completely vaporized and the whole argument looks like special pleading.

Having put the ground density of the lunar air at one ten-millionth of ours, Baldwin[1] concludes that about two meteorites will penetrate it to strike each square mile of the Moon's surface every day. This would mean that at the present rate every square yard will get six direct hits in a million years. Regarded from the point of view of personal risk to an exploring

Earthling, this bombardment may not be serious, but it should result in appreciable erosion over geological periods, even though the lower mass limit of these meteorites is only one gram, or about one-third of an ounce.

If we now recall that the youngest features of the Moon are supposed to be hundreds of millions of years old, the absence of meteoritic scars on the walls of lunar ring mountains noted by Wilkins,[12] and the generally fresh appearance of some of them become difficult to understand. It would seem that, on the one hand, Baldwin under-estimates the density and shielding power of the lunar atmosphere, and, on the other, the age of these formations has been greatly exaggerated.*

Yet meteorites do penetrate our atmosphere, so that some of them must also pierce the atmosphere of the Moon. La Paz calculates that a ten-pound meteorite hitting the Moon will produce a flash visible with the naked eye, and, taking the average frequency of such objects, there should be about 10 such flashes every year, as well, of course, as a great many telescopic ones.[5] Nevertheless, a naked-eye flash does not seem ever to have been observed, and reports of telescopic flashes are few and doubtful. Baldwin contends that a meteorite will penetrate the porous lunar rock to several times its thickness before exploding, so that the flash will be obscured by the dust and debris blown up by it, which may be true. I have seen a white flash, which with a magnification of 30 diameters and an aperture of $1\frac{3}{4}$ inch had the naked-eye brilliance of a star of fourth magnitude, may have lasted for about a second and left behind it a brief bluish after-glow, close to the small crater Lyot inside the walled enclosure of Ptolemaeus. Very similar observations have been made by others, so that the flash was probably real; but in looking at a brilliant surface one does occasionally see spurious ones which have no existence outside the eye.

However, there can be no doubt that some meteoritic craters exist on the Moon and that there also is a slow meteoritic erosion, which over millions of years may produce considerable effects.

To return to the main trend of the meteoritic theory of lunar ring forms, Baldwin[1] gives the following dramatic description of the birth of Mare Imbrium (p. 119–20):

'Downward the meteorite plummeted from the north-east, gradually gaining velocity. Probably it did not even glow from the effects of the nearly absent lunar atmosphere. Then it struck the surface and quickly disappeared beneath, leaving a small sharp hole to mark its passage. For only an instant, however, did the calm prevail, for then all hell broke loose, soundlessly, on a scale to shame the infernos dreamed of by little men. A great section of the crust, several hundreds of miles across, domed up, split rapidly and radially from the central point. Surface layers peeled back on themselves like the opening of a gigantic flower, followed quickly by a

* *See* also Chapter 3.

stamen of dust and fragments spreading rapidly in all directions without the roiling turbulence imparted by an atmosphere.

'The unfolding of the initial dome had a shielding effect and thus created a null zone surrounding the great pit. Most of the matter lifted from the crater was deposited in this protected area, raising a broad and low rim of mountains. Higher-velocity fragments, spewed forth horizontally, smashed great furrows into the moon's face during the succeeding 20 minutes, furrows radiating outward from the explosion focus. . . .'

To cap this description, he states blithely, 'Any unmeteoritic hypothesis represents a fanciful extrapolation beyond anything known on the earth'. And the largest undubitable meteoritic crater on the Earth is two miles across! The Mare Imbrium is pictured in Plate VII.

I have pointed out elsewhere that the explanation of the so-called 'radial valleys' round Mare Imbrium proposed here is not feasible for a simple dynamical reason.[14] The focus of the explosion being underground, any fragments thrown up by it would emerge moving at an angle to the ground, so that if they had attained circular velocity that alone could allow them to move *horizontally* along the surface of the Moon they would, in reality, describe elliptical paths and land at steep angles in various parts of the visible and invisible hemisphere. The closer to the focus of the explosion the landing point, the steeper would be the angle of fall. Circular velocity will result in a circular orbit only if it is gravitationally horizontal.

Otherwise, however, apart from the mechanism of impact of a 10-mile asteroid invoked by Baldwin, the domelike uplift and the subsequent collapse of the land, followed by an outflow of basic lava, which overran 400,000 square miles or so, do not substantially differ from the picture painted by the vulcanist Spurr.[10]

Urey dissents from Baldwin on some essential points.[22] He assumes that the surface of the Moon was at the time close to the melting point and the impact was just enough to turn the scales and bring about superficial liquefaction. A superficial liquefaction it would have to have been according to him. For if the lower layers beneath the surface had been molten, 'one wonders why the surface did not sink as it formed'. Molten rock, he contends, would have lower density than solid rock, which may be true enough if this rock is compacted, but I have already shown why there is every reason to believe that the surface rocks of the Moon are highly porous and, therefore, have a very low specific gravity, whatever the material they may actually consist of. Besides, lava flows occur on the Earth and the crust does not sink. This argument rests on the unnecessary assumption that the Moon was molten as a whole and not only up to a certain depth below the surface.

Gold has conclusively disposed of Urey's idea that liquefaction of the surface could have resulted from impacts. He writes:

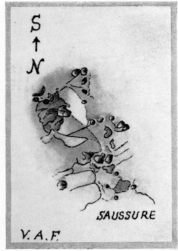

Above: A cratered peak on the Moon in the neighbourhood of Saussure, drawn from telescopic observation by the author. Note the similarity with the terrestrial formation in the upper photograph on the left

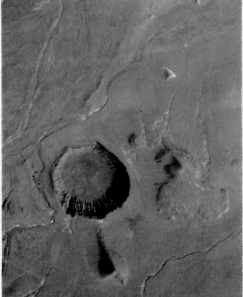

Left: Photographs of volcanic formations in the Crater Highlands, Tanganyika, taken from a height of 25,000 ft. The flat-bottomed crater in the lower picture bears a marked resemblance to many lunar craters, e.g. Abulfeda, and has a diameter of approximately half a mile. (*Director of Lands and Surveys, Tanganyika.*)

PLATE V Terrestrial volcanic structures compared with similar forms on the Moon.
(*Page 49*)

PLATE VI *Above:* The Deep Bay crater in Saskatchewan, Canada. It is about six miles in diameter and appears to be of meteoric origin. (Composite photograph by the *Royal Canadian Air Force.) Below:* The volcanic crater of Ololmoti, Tanganyika, from a height of 25,000 ft. It is about five miles in diameter. (*Director of Lands and Surveys, Tanganyika.*)

(*Page 51*)

'Liquefaction would have to be due to the transport into the material of the energy made available at the impact. The transport by conduction of heat cannot account for more than a very thin layer of liquefaction. However much heat is supplied externally to a piece of material, its surface cannot be maintained at a temperature higher than the one at which it vaporizes. . . . The depth below the vaporization surface to which enough heat for melting can be conducted in the brief interval of the order of seconds during which heat is supplied in the case of an impact explosion . . . does not exceed some centimetres for any material.' (Monthly Notices of the *R.A.S.*, Vol. 115, No. 6, p. 596.)

One may add here that the very low conductivity of lunar rocks would have seen to making this liquefied layer exceptionally thin.

Shock waves are another possibility whereby heat could be transported, but the energy here diminishes in accordance with the inverse square law and is soon whittled down, so that this alternative is likewise unworkable for areas the size of Mare Imbrium. Gold himself postulates a sedimentary origin of the maria,[16] which will be considered in the next chapter.

To return meanwhile to the volcanic, or rather plutonic, theory, the central-fountain hypothesis had to be abandoned and in its present form the plutonic theory has departed considerably from the straight analogy with the fire-belching mountains of the Earth. It rather harkens back to the bubble hypothesis proposed by Robert Hooke in 1665. According to this, when the surface of the Moon was still in plastic semi-molten state gases liberated from the magma heaved up enormous bubbles in its cooling skin, and as these bubbles burst and subsided rings were formed round the edges, much as the bubbles in boiling porridge produce upon bursting temporary craters which, though, do not get a chance to set, as the more viscous and rapidly cooling lunar rings are supposed to have done.

In this form the hypothesis is not tenable, but on the present plutonic view, developed by Tomkins, Loewy, Puiseux, Spurr, and others, the ring mountains of the Moon have been produced by underground intrusions of magma rich in gases, which heaved up the overlying rocks into circular domes; the upheaval was followed by the escape of gases and caving in of the dome. Such intrusions, called laccoliths, are known on the Earth. I have mentioned the Richat structures; whilst nearer home, for instance, the granite mountains of Arran are the dismembered stump of an eight-mile wide laccolith intruded in Tertiary times.[3] It is not definitely known whether the intrusive magma succeeded in piercing the overlying strata and opened a volcanic vent, or remained sealed in a blind *puy*. Both types of structure exist. On the Moon, too, there are numerous domes,[5,12] many of which in Mare Imbrium, where they are usually about 40 miles in diameter.[10] Some are topped with small craters, and at least on one occasion (a dome inside the walled plain of Darwin) the dome is seamed by strange parallel

E

depressions, probably due to cracking and subsidence, resembling the marks made on a mud-pie hit with a stick. Several low domes will be seen in the drawing of Posidonius and Chacornac reproduced in Plate VIII.

The sealed domes may represent the last stage of the volcanic upheaval in the maria, when these were already strongly crusted over with congealing lunabase, sufficiently yielding to heave up without fracturing, yet too tough to be pierced by the gases from below; or else they may be new ring mountains which have not yet completed their evolutionary course. Usually, however, the gases are assumed to have broken out with more or less violence. In some cases solid matter and even huge blocks of rock up to 4 miles across (Aristillus) were ejected by the central explosion, followed by water, ash, and pulverous materials; but gas would seem to have formed the lion's share of these eruptions. The escape of gas appears to have continued long after the central subsidence had been initiated and in some instances may be going on to the present day, although only on a small scale*. A few ring mountains display a secondary central upswelling, of which the convex floors of Hevel and Petavius are the most striking examples. The interior of the great walled enclosure of Schickard is also slightly convex. Concentric craters likewise exist.

Tycho, Theophilus, Copernicus, and some other craters of the post-mare, or Teleoselene (Spurr), age belong to the eruptive type which is fairly close to the terrestrial volcanoes. On the whole, however, lunar vulcanism appears to have been of a quiescent kind, similar to that of our geysers or mud volcanoes rather than to that of the fire-and-smoke-belching Vesuvius, and in order to underline this distinction J. E. Spurr[10] has introduced the term *lunavo* (*luna*r *vo*lcano). This, incidentally, would be consistent with the low heat of the lunar interior postulated by Urey.[23]

The eruptive features are probably best illustrated by a group of craters in the western part of the Sea of Rains, and notably by Aristillus, Autolycus, and Timocharis; while it is interesting to observe that the older ring or Archimedes, now a flat-bottomed walled plain, must have possessed the same character in its prime. In any case, a portion of the ancient surface to the south of it which has escaped foundering in the mare shows traces of radial grooves, typical of the other three lunavoes.

To return to the latter, the rings occupy the centres of singularly regular gentle domes and are surrounded by collars of coarse bouldery material, ten to twenty miles wide, which indicates low velocities of projection, followed by lighter deposits which are traversed by regular systems of radial gullies. In the case of Aristillus, the largest of the three, these gullies extend up to about 50 miles from the crater, and proportionately less with

---

* A gas eruption from the central peak of Alphonsus was observed in November 1958 by N. A. Kozyrev with the 50-in reflector of the Crimean Astrophysical Observatory. Spectrograms were taken, showing the presence of C_2 and C_3, as well as many unidentified absorptions.

the smaller lunavoes. Spurr[10] interprets them as proper channels of radial drainage, worn out by the torrential rains pouring down from the steam clouds emitted by the erupting lunavo. For liquid water to exist in bulk, an atmospheric pressure of at least about 5 mm. of mercury* would be necessary and this would have been provided by a temporary atmosphere, or 'atmodome', of gas escaping from the crater. Still farther out and probably representing the last stage of volcanic activity, stretch the light rays. Spurr interprets these as volcanic ash, emitted mainly from the small craterlets within or on the outer slopes of the enclosure; but Pickering[8] thought that at least some of them might be snow, which would be consistent with the predominantly geyser-like action of these volcanoes and the fall of pressure below the point allowing liquefaction. I will return to this subject in another chapter.

Baldwin[1] and other meteorists maintain that all these features were produced in one swoop by an exploding meteorite. This, however, is rather difficult to visualize, and the variety of form and composition points to a prolonged time sequence. Moreover, the velocities of ejection in a meteoritic explosion would be too high to account for the existence of coarse and fine debris close to the crater. On the meteoritic view, the rays are supposed to consist of 'rock flour', that is to say, finely ground rock, such as is found at the bottom of terrestrial meteoritic craters. There is, indeed, some little evidence in favour of this interpretation. In my colour study of the Moon I have found that many, though by no means all, rays resemble lunabase in fundamental colouring, which is yellowish-green-grey, though there is, of course, a great difference in tint, the rays being almost snow-white by comparison with the maria. The latter often recall glass in texture and have been found to polarize light somewhat like obsidian, a glassy lava of a predominantly greenish hue, though sometimes red or black. If crushed, it would be nearly white and yet betray the original colouring when viewed through monochromatic filters. This result could, however, be obtained by other means; while certain ray and halo systems are distinctly bluish, which has already been noticed by Pickering.[8] (Gold,[16] assumes that lunar dust would be dark more or less as a *deus ex machina*.)

Yet, whichever line we follow, the theory of simple ejection of the ray matter by a central force does not appear to be tenable.

Various explanations have been proposed[13] but all of them are open to objection and the nature itself of the rays is in doubt. On one view the bright-coloured matter is located at the bottom of small hollows, owing to which the rays cannot be seen until the Sun has risen to a certain altitude (8–9° for large rays according to A. P. Lenham). The observation made by Wilkins that the bright rays sometimes appear dark under a low Sun would support this interpretation.[25] But then the limb rays are clearly visible both

* *See* Chapter 15.

when illuminated vertically by the Sun, i.e. at quarter phase, and horizontally, i.e. near full phase. Thus the rays would appear in this case to be elevated above the surface. In some cases accumulation of ray matter along low ridges has been observed (e.g. south-west of Proclus). Yet this is not a general rule and does not solve the problem.

The main difficulties of the ejection interpretation are: (1) the rays do not necessarily, nor even often, trend into the parent crater, and both those of Tycho and Proclus are tangential to the ring walls; (2) the rays are often preferentially directed, sometimes only a single long streamer issuing from the crater; (3) they are frequently obstructed by quite low obstacles, which shows that the matter was moving more or less horizontally at a low level.

The tangential distribution could be obtained if an oblique jet of gas carrying the ray material were issuing from the inner boundary of the crater glacis, where cracks and craterlets are often present, and then hitting the rampart at an angle. The effect can be illustrated by directing a jet of water obliquely at the inside rim of a pudding-basin. But a low-level horizontal projection over distances of hundreds and even thousands of miles (Tycho) is not easily accounted for in this way. Electrostatic (Pickering) and magnetic forces may have intervened, but this does not properly belong to the present chapter.

Tycho is surrounded by a dark halo and at least some of the rays appear to be picked up and continued by small craters on the way, as though the material rising from them was overtaken and carried away by the main stream. In the case of Proclus, Aristarchus, Kepler, Copernicus, and many other rayed craters the dark halo is largely or totally absent and there is great diversity in the different ray systems. Tycho is also wreathed with radial gullies, which show in this case little regard for ground relief and thus could hardly be drainage channels. Another peculiarity of Tycho is that it is ringed by a zone peppered with small pits as though it had been sprayed with some corrosive liquid ejected from the crater. At insufficient resolution this tends to give the surroundings of Tycho a blurred appearance.

The rays of Copernicus, which are of a darker hue, interpreted by Spurr as that of basic volcanic ash, show a very different habit from the straight streamers of Tycho or Proclus. They do not trend into the crater either and are generally discontinuous, or linking up into diffuse loops.

Spurr[10] gives a graphic description of the situation, which is substantially correct:

'The general pattern is much like that of snow thinly drifted by a strong wind across a black frozen lake. They are essentially an aggregation of white comet-shaped or boat-shaped smears, each of no great length, the prow towards the crater. There are many of them, like snow or sand blown by a constant wind, striking some slight obstruction and spreading out in a long narrow widening tail behind this protection.'

Even the low wrinkle-ridges are sufficient to deflect some of these rays, so that they could not have possibly originated in a meteoritic explosion, or indeed any explosion. The expulsion of gas must have been a slow gradual process and the gas was cold and heavy, so that it did not rise high above the surface, merely spilling outwards from the crater in a steady atmospheric flood.

This quiescent activity is characteristic of lunavoes. The great domes were deflated, as it were, by slow-puncture rather than a big bang: an eruption was an exception, not the rule. In a few cases, however, considerable outpourings of lava would seem to have occurred, rather on the lines of the quiet Hawaiian volcanoes. Lava has filled up Wargentin to the brim and overflowed the ring, spilling over the adjacent country. Copernicus and Lambert show fingerlike flows of lava. But the most remarkable flood of lava issued from the small crater Fontenelle A near the north pole. Spurr estimates the maximum width of this lava flow at 80 miles. Eratosthenes, on the other hand, would seem to have sent forth a flood of mud.[10]

The meteoritic hypothesis requires that the ring mountains should follow no natural alignment, and Baldwin[1] is emphatic about this. Yet a casual glance at the face of the Moon will suffice to refute this contention. There is a whole row of huge ring mountains along Spurr's Centrameridional Horst. Even more striking is the Langrenus–Petavius chain near the western limb of the Moon. These magnificent formations are closely comparable in size, evenly spaced and yet date from very different periods of selenological history, which puts an impossible strain on the meteoritic interpretation. Residual crater chains can be made out in Mare Nubium and Mare Imbrium, but mostly as ghosts only, with the exception of the enormous rings associated with Hoerbiger, whose western halves are still quite unmistakable.[15] There are also Flamsteed, Letronne and Gassendi in the third quadrant.

It is passably clear that this result could have been produced by repeated outbursts or inflations along a deep-seated tectonic fracture. Jeffreys suggests a slightly different process, already referred to, of conical fracture and marginal effusion,[17] which would result in roughly circular or polygonal subsidence without a central mountain. The Hoerbiger craters appear to belong to this class and so, too, does Clavius, which is well preserved, has escaped flooding with lunabase, yet shows no trace of a central peak. (Clavius is illustrated in the *Frontispiece*.)

There are also quite incontestable crater pairs. In these the two craters appear to be contemporaneous and of very similar appearance, but usually somewhat different size. Their alignment is either meridional or makes an angle of about 30 degrees with the present north–south line and may correspond to the original direction of the Moon's rotational axis. The significance of these directions is further underlined by the fact that they also coincide with the main axes of the great maria systems and thus must clearly be related to the forces that presided over their birth. Spurr suggests that these were due to the tidal action of the probably closer Earth on a rapidly rotating Moon, which presupposes capture (*see* also Chapter 7). In the meridional pairs the northern crater is invariably larger than the southern, a tendency which becomes less and less pronounced as we move south and is eventually reversed, not, however, until we are well beyond the equator in the high southern latitudes. This, too, may be connected with the movement of the lunar poles.

The meridional pairs are the more conspicuous and generally younger than the off-meridional system, represented mainly in the fourth quadrant, where the doublets sometimes become triplets and quadruplets. Aristoteles and Eudoxus, Aristillus and Autolycus, Agrippa and Godin, Metius and Fabritius, are some of the most prominent meridional pairs. The other trend, however, is followed by a magnificent line of eruptive lunavoes with bright ray systems: Tycho–Bullialdus–Euclides–Kepler–Aristarchus. These most probably represent a secondary activity along the great tectonic fracture which gave rise to the Sea of Rains and the Ocean of Storms and may have been initiated at the capture of the Moon by the Earth, or a close approach of the two bodies.

To sum up, there seems to be little doubt that the ring mountains of the Moon are lunavoes, due to a form of volcanic activity, mainly limited to the escape of gas, and related to the tidal stresses set up in the mass of our satellite by the gravitational attraction of the Earth at the time of capture or close approach. The great basins of the maria may have been produced substantially in the same way, by upheaval, deflation, and collapse at that critical selenological age. The transformation would seem to have been more or less catastrophic.[10] Yet the unequal age of the maria indicates that it was spread over a considerable period, and may otherwise have been associated with and followed by a change in the position of the polar axis.

For all this, some meteoritic craters must exist on the Moon and one would expect them to be rather more numerous and in a better state of preservation than on the Earth. If so, how can they be recognized? Whipple[11] has suggested that the impact of a large meteorite may act as a trigger mechanism and release a volcano, in which case there will be no definite way of distinguishing a purely volcanic ring from a meteoritic one. A somewhat similar variant of the meteoritic hypothesis has recently been put forward by Kuiper,[18] who assumes meteoritic origin of the ring mountains as such but recognizes the volcanic character of the cratered central peaks. Vulcanism would thus be a subsidiary development.

There are, however, a few dish-craters, which do not appear any older than a typical ring mountain of the post-mare period, yet differ conspicuously from the latter. They are comparatively shallow, have no central peaks, and the rim is lower in proportion. Would these be meteoritic craters pure and simple? This seems likely.

To sum up, while there is probably some truth in the meteoritic idea, it does not appear to be adequate by itself to explain the observed features and one is forced to fall back on the plutonic conception, which is the more natural of the two in any case and requires fewer unverified assumptions.

REFERENCES

1. BALDWIN, R. B. *The Face of the Moon.* University of Chicago Press, 1949.
2. BRITISH ASTRONOMICAL ASSOCIATION, THE. *The Journal*, Vol. 64, No. 6.
3. FIRSOFF, V. A. *Arran with Camera and Sketchbook.* Hale, London, 1951.
4. *Observatory, The*, Vol. 75, No. 889, 1955.
5. MOORE, PATRICK. *Guide to the Moon.* Eyre and Spottiswoode, London, 1953.
6.   *Lunar Summit Craters. J.B.A.A.*, Vol. 64, No. 1.
7. NASMYTH, J. and CARPENTER, J. *The Moon, Considered as a Planet, a World and a Satellite.* London, 1916.
8. PICKERING, W. H. *The Moon.* Doubleday, Page and Co., New York, 1903.
9. PROCTOR, R. A. *The Moon, Etc.* London, 1873.
10. SPURR, J. E. *Geology Applied to Selenology* (4 Vols.), 1944–9.
11. WHIPPLE, F. L. *Earth, Moon and the Planets.* Churchill, London, 1946.
12. WILKINS, H. P. *Our Moon.* Muller, London, 1954.
13. FIELDER, GILBERT. 'Some Aspects of Some Lunar Ray Systems. . . .' *J.B.A.A.*, Vol. 66, No. 6, 1956.
14. FIRSOFF, V. A. 'On the Structure and Origin of Lunar Surface Features.' *J.B.A.A.*, Vol. 66, No. 8, 1956.
15.   'Palaeography of the Nubian and Imbrian Plains.' *J.B.A.A.*, Vol. 67, No. 4, 1957.
16. GOLD, T. 'The Lunar Surface.' *Monthly Notices of the Royal Astronomical Society*, Vol. 115, No. 6, 1955.
17. JEFFREYS, SIR HAROLD. *The Earth.* 3rd Edn. Cambridge University Press, 1952.
18. KUIPER, G. P. 'On the Origin of the Lunar Surface Features.' *Proceedings of the National Academy of Sciences U.S.A., of the*, Vol. 40, No. 12, 1954.
19. MONOD, T. *Bulletin de la Direction des Mines*, No. 15, Dakar, 1952.
20. MOORE, PATRICK. A lecture delivered at the Manchester University, 1956.
21. RICHARD-MOLARD, J. *Bulletin de la Direction des Mines*, No. 15, Dakar, 1952.
22. UREY, H. C. *The Planets.* Oxford University Press, 1952.
23.   'The Cosmic Abundances of Potassium, Etc.' *P.N.A.S.*, Vol. 41, 1955.
24.   Some Criticisms of *On the Origin of the Lunar Surface Features* by G. P. Kuiper. *P.N.A.S.*, Vol. 41, 1955.
25. WILKINS, H. P. and MOORE, PATRICK. *The Moon.* Faber, London, 1956.

7

THE SUNLESS SEA

THE METEORITIC HYPOTHESIS has its points, but it fails to account adequately for the varied features of the lunar surface and vulcanism has constantly to be brought in by the back door, as it were, to supply the deficiencies of meteoritic interpretation. Yet the volcanic alternative, too, has some awkward hurdles to take and may require further modification.

Its supporters incline to talk of fire and smoke, ash and lava; and these are not very much in evidence on the Moon, while such evidence as there is may be questioned. The lunavoes would seem to have been more like our geysers, or perhaps mud volcanoes, than like Cotopaxi, Etna, or Krakatoa. Their activity consisted mainly in emission of gas, which was primarily steam and may occasionally have turned into liquid water.

True, the radial gullies of Aristillus and other similar craters have been alternatively explained by S. R. B. Cooke[4] as star systems of dykes, comparable to the radial dyke families emanating from the Tertiary volcanic centres in the Scottish islands of Mull and Arran. The difficulty of this interpretation lies in the point that the dykes owe their present appearance to erosion, which first removed great thicknesses of overlying rock and then attacked the weak traps in the dykes themselves. Sir Archibald Geikie[6] estimated that about 1,000, feet of rock had been removed from above, say, the Witch's Step dyke in Arran. On the Moon, however, the surface has not been eroded to any great extent since these radial channels originated and normally the surging lava would have flowed out in sheets. We have already encountered this problem on page 40, in Chapter 5, and it is possible that the lunar 'lava' is unable to reach the surface owing to the great lightness of the rocks that compose it. This point is germane to the subject of the present Chapter.

In any case radial splintering accompanied by emission of gas could perhaps have resulted in or contributed to the appearance of these radial groove systems, especially in the case of Tycho, where they seem to disregard pre-existent surface relief. Still the hypothesis of erosion of light volcanic deposits by running water appears plausible enough. And what reason is there, pray, for opposing so strenuously past water action on the Moon's surface?* These temporary watercourses would soon have been drained by evaporation and possibly by reabsorption in the porous surface rocks, so that they would be petering out into nothing precisely as observed.

* *See* Chapter 15.

Thus we may take it as one of the few cases of water erosion on the Moon. Pickering[11] draws attention to the peculiar meandering 'rill', which looks very much like the bed of an ordinary mountain stream, at the foot of Mount Hadley, in the Apennines. There is also Spurr's putative 'alluvial fan'* of light-coloured 'highland' matter spread over the dark lunabase of the Sea of Rains where three converging valleys of the Apennines debouch upon it, north-west of Eratosthenes.[12] I have already referred to his suggestion that this lunavo may have issued forth in a flow of mud, not lava.

Otherwise, however, water action is seldom invoked in explaining lunar formations. Only that those 'lavas' which formed the maria seem always to have behaved very much like water, and Spurr stands by no means alone in making this observation.[2] This is explained on the assumption that the flood was of hot highly liquid basic lava. In fact, assuming that the Moon has been captured by the Earth, as suggested in Chapter 3, the story of the maria will read something like this.

The Moon, once an independent planetary body, approached the Earth from the south, so that the present north-eastern portion of the Moon's surface where her original north pole lay came under the most direct action of the Earth's tidal pull. This pull lifted the crust bodily in blisters and liquid magma surged from below beneath the carapace of the uplift. For the great stresses set up in the Moon's largely solidified body by this tidal pull resulted not only in deep-seated fractures but raised by friction the temperature of the rocks to the melting point, so that large areas of the lunar surface 'broke out into universal pustullation'. Explosions of gas pierced and deflated the uplifted domes, and through the orifices opened up by these molten magma flowed out in a great flood. It was hot and 'mordant' and rolled down the inclines, breaking up, dissolving and submerging the older formations, some of which can still be seen as pale 'ghost rings' of light-coloured lunarite embedded in the lunabase of the maria. Other rings were broken up and floated on the surface like rocky icebergs, to be scattered over the plains and sometimes brought together in jumbled fragments by the currents, where they remained embedded as lonely peaks or 'scum mountains' when the lava had set and hardened.[12]

Thus arose the dark circular plains of the maria. The radial and concentric faulting, the central subsidence and the upheaval of the 'coastal' ranges, accompanied or followed these crustal movements. The rotation of the Moon was now slowing down rapidly. The upheaval had shifted her axis into more or less its present position and the tidal pull was tending to break up the Moon into meridional flakes, rather like a peeled orange. Thus the great meridional fractures and the 'Centrameridional Horst' arose, and along these gases bubbled up from inside the lunar globe, raising

* This is interpreted alternatively as a ray system emanating from a small crater.

63

STRANGE WORLD OF THE MOON

the smaller domes, which let off steam and rarely lava, eventually to subside and leave behind the ring scars distributed along the invisible lines of tectonic weakness, referred to in Chapter 6.

The differences in the age of these formations indicate that all this did not happen at once but in three stages, separated by long selenological periods of unknown duration. In other words, the Moon may have approached to and receded from the Earth more than once in her decipherable history, probably as a result of the perturbational evolution of her orbit, combined with the effect of shrinkage on the period of rotation and tidal interaction mentioned in Chapter 3.

The last of these great upheavals was marked by what Spurr calls 'the Imbrian revolution'. It was then that Mare Imbrium and the other northeastern 'seas' were formed, while the western sea complex belongs to an earlier age. Having put the temperature of the Moon at the time at between 1,000° C. and 2,000° C., Spurr[12] seeks in vain for a geological period corresponding to this stage in the life of our satellite. For he maintains that the heat radiated by the Moon would have been sufficient to destroy all life on the Earth. No such geological period is known and he concludes, accordingly, that this must have happened before the dawn of geologically recorded history of the Earth.

To me this conclusion appears to be totally unwarranted. Assuming even that the whole Sea of Rains and Ocean of Storms were simultaneously a blistering expanse of liquid magma, they would represent only a fraction of the Moon's disk and would, moreover, be swathed by thick mists and vapours. The heat received by a unit area from a surface at a given temperature is proportional to its apparent size, irrespective of the actual distance; and this size would on every reckoning have been a good deal less than the apparent area of the Sun, which is between 3 and 6 times hotter than the assumed temperature of liquid lunabase. Thus, discounting obscuration by mists and clouds on the Moon, which at the rate of gas emission revealed by the lunavoes must certainly be expected, the Moon could not have contributed more than a fraction of the normal heat of Sunrays. The moonlight would have been only tepid, so that no catastrophic alteration in the overall climate of the Earth need be anticipated. Still, even if her mean temperature went up by as much as a couple of degrees it would make a considerable difference, so that what we must look for is a comparatively warm geological age, characterized by volcanic activity corresponding to the happenings on the Moon as the Earth's response to the disturbance of her isostatic equilibrium by the coming of the Moon.

Such an age is well known to geology. It is the Tertiary. Sea became land. A girdle of mighty mountains arose out of the depths of the primordial 'geosyncline' of Tethys. The Atlantic continent foundered beneath the waves. Tropical beasts roamed and fought among the rich forests of

Britain, while the volcanoes of the west roared defiance to the skies. There were prodigious floods of basic magma, every bit comparable to the Imbrian revolution itself. A sheet of molten basalt spread from the British Isles to Greenland. Most of it now lies at the bottom of the shallow North Atlantic, but the Plateau of Antrim bears witness to this eruption.[3,6] In India and the north-western United States areas of about 150,000 square miles each were smothered under liquid basalt.[3,12]

And, as on the Moon, the upheavals would appear to have been followed by a shift in the position of the polar axis, or rather perhaps the slipping of the crust on the substratum of glassy basalt.[13] The North Pole wobbled, bringing ice and snow to the previously warm lands, then receded again until it came to rest in its present location, so far as is known for good.

The correspondence between the terrestrial developments in the Tertiary and the undated happenings on the Moon is too striking to be lightly dismissed. One may add the comparative depression at the North Pole of the Earth and the upraised nature of the South Pole, as well as the respective distribution of the seas and continents on the two bodies, which are precisely the opposite of one another, as a further indication that this interpretation may be correct, though other explanations are possible.

However, there exist some important differences between the lunar and the terrestrial upheavals, which must be rooted in the differences of structure between the two globes.

On the Earth the effusion of basic lava has not generally given rise to subsidence (apart perhaps from the foundering of the North Atlantic Continent), whereas on the Moon the maria lie on the average about 5,000 feet below the level of light-coloured 'land'. Thus it seems that, while on the Moon the tides pulled up the crust, as it were, bodily; on the Earth the reciprocal action of the Moon precipitated these developments by a distortion of the glassy basalt as a whole and no large domes were uplifted, though laccolithic intrusions undoubtedly occurred on a smaller scale. This may be the real explanation of the absence from the Earth of large ring structures, deriving directly from the great disparity in mass and density between the planet and the satellite.

Basic lava shrinks in cooling, so that a field of this lava becomes shrivelled and seamed with innumerable fractures. The lunabase of the maria, on the other hand, has not only set to a smooth finish but appears to have expanded in cooling, so that it had to wrinkle into ridges in order to fit the basin it had worn out for itself in the molten state. This may perhaps be accounted for by the general shrinkage of the lunar globe, due to the expulsion and dissipation of vast amounts of gas from the interior, so that the reduction in the size of the lunar surface as a whole may have counterbalanced the reduction in the volume of the cooling mass of lunabase. As we shall see further on, there is something in this. Yet a field

65

of lava, even 400,000 square miles in area, will cool comparatively quickly. Urey considers a pool 10 km. deep at a temperature of 1500° C. sheathed by a 100-metre layer of pumice floating upon it and finds that it would require 100,000 years for solidification; the time will increase with the depth of the pool and the thickness of the overlying pumice.[15] This is a very short period selenologically and it seems very doubtful if it could altogether catch up with the indubitably much slower process of decrease in the Moon's volume.

Hence the inference is that lunabase must be very different from basalt.

Most substances occupy less room when solidified than they do in liquid state at the same temperature (freezing point), while a drop through 1500° C. or more will involve a considerable shrinkage in volume, liquid or solid. Ice, sulphur, and a few other substances expand when solidifying.

There exist, however, quite different considerations against too close an analogy with terrestrial conditions. The mean density of the Moon is $3\frac{1}{3}$ that of water, which is comparable to the density of basalt. Even on the Earth, which is $1\frac{1}{2}$ times as dense as the Moon, the proper seat of basalt is some 30 miles below the surface, while the density of surface formations, not counting water, which is also 'rock' from the geological point of view, is just about $2\frac{1}{2}$ and a good deal less than $\frac{1}{4}$ of the density expected to be found at the centre, as well as less than $\frac{1}{2}$ the mean density.

Owing to the smaller mass, gravitational compression will be far less in the Moon's interior and the differences in density will be toned down. Even so the compressibility of solids and liquids is small, so that the materials composing the lunar sphere must be intrinsically, as well as structurally, lighter than those of the Earth. There will be very little nife and most of the inner portion of the lunar globe would consist of our sima or similar rocks, whilst the outer layers may be a rather thicker counterpart of sial.[19] Yet, if the internal structure of the Moon is anything like that of the Earth, the specific gravity of lunar surface materials, even if closely compacted, should be a good deal less than in our crust. This would be so even without pores and hollows—and we have seen that, having consolidated under very low gravitational and atmospheric compression, lunar surface rocks must be extremely porous. A density substantially less than unity appears, accordingly, to be highly probable, even if, as Urey maintains[14,15] and Kuiper[21] denies, the lunar globe has never been molten as a whole and fractional separation of materials of different densities is only partial or largely absent (the water processes would operate at low temperatures and some separation would take place on this count alone).

Wright, Lyot, and others who have studied the polarization of light by these formations, all agree that they resemble pumice or volcanic ash. Thermal behaviour of lunar rocks indicates comparable structure.[10] Even

66

Urey assumes that the Moon is covered with pumice to an unknown depth but does not develop this idea.[15]

Now terrestrial pumice is lighter than water, and so lunar pumice, even if of identical composition, would be lighter still—and I have just pointed out why the matter of which this rock froth is composed may be lighter *in specie*. The extreme fragility of lunarite has often been remarked upon by selenologists and selenographers alike, who have observed the apparent ease with which these rocks have been fractured and parted by crustal movements. Thus there seems to be little doubt that lunarite is lighter than water. Lunabase is equally certainly more massive than lunarite, but it, too, appears to be highly porous and there is no reason to believe that its density in compact state will be more than 50 per cent higher than that of lunarite in a similar condition (this is far in excess of the difference between our basic and acid rocks). In other words, lunabase, too, may be expected to be less dense than water.

When the Earth consolidated from her primitive state, whatever this may have been, her materials became stratified according to their specific gravity and the lighter rocks of the sial came to be buoyed up on the heavier sima, which was probably liquid to begin with and remains plastic to this day, forming the balancing medium of our isostasy. The same principle must apply to the Moon with some variation due to the smaller mass and relatively greater abundance of lighter chemical elements. The lunavoes have exhaled prodigious amounts of gas, that is to say, mainly steam, carbon dioxide, and nitrogen, great quantities of which must have been contained in the Moon's interior. The gases would be dissolved in either the hot molten rock of the interior or water, but if the water was heavier *in specie* than the surface rocks it would naturally accumulate not *on* but *below* the surface, where in 'caverns measureless to man' sprawled and may still be sprawling a 'sunless sea'.

The old craters of the Moon bear witness to changes in her shape and dimensions. The change in shape reflects the diminution of oblateness. As the rate of rotation decreased so did the centrifugal force at the equator and an hydrostatic adjustment ensued, the upraised girdle of land subsiding and the globe assuming a more nearly spherical shape. A further change in the surface area arose out of the formation of the tidal bulge. Yet quite apart from these readjustments, the lunar globe has shrunk, as is clearly shown by the old ring mountains which have been compressed to about three-fifths of their original diameter and given a polygonal, usually hexagonal, form. Such distortion may sometimes be due to crowding, where contemporaneous craters impinge upon one another like cells in a honeycomb, and assume hexagonal outlines.* But the comparison of widely scattered formations shows that the decrease in the original dia-

* This applies especially to the southern polar regions.

67

meter of old ring formations has been uniform and universal, although it is somewhat more marked at the equator, where the compression or 'appression', as Spurr[12] calls it, was mainly lateral. From these data Spurr concludes that since the Mesoselene, or the intermediate period of selenology corresponding to the 'Imbrian revolution', the equatorial diameter of the Moon has shrunk by between 250 and 300 miles, and the polar diameter by at least 200 miles. The Proteroselene diameter of the Moon may have been over 3,000 miles as against the present 2,160 miles.

'Part of the equatorial shrinkage, and all of the axial shrinkage', writes Spurr in Vol. IV, *The Shrunken Moon* of his selenological study (p. 8), 'was general, attendant on, and no doubt due to, the steady enormous gas-exhalation. This conception is startling, for it indicates evolution of the present moon from a more gaseous condition and larger bulk, by the loss of primitive gases.'

The existence of an underground hydrosphere and even an underground atmosphere overlying it make this situation understandable. Since none of the solid part of the lunar sphere could have escaped, except possibly for small quantities of volcanic ejecta shot out at speeds exceeding the velocity of escape, this reduction of volume must be wholly due to dissipation of gases from below the surface. If so, the original mean density of the Moon was a good deal less than 3 and possibly only about 2, which will further reduce our previous estimate of the specific gravity of the surface formations. She was not so much a cannon-ball as a balloon, which was slow-punctured by the stresses of the Earth's tidal attraction and developed multitudes of blisters, whose ring scars now mark her face.

Such must be the structure of the satellites of the giant planets, and more particularly of Callisto. The density of Mars is higher than the Moon's. Yet it is possible that also there an underground hydrosphere exists and his 'seas' may be in the nature of mudflats. Some people find the idea of all or nearly all the water being concentrated underground, while there is hardly a drop of moisture on the surface, difficult. But it will not in the least surprise those who dwell in limestone districts,[9] to take the Mendip farmers of Somerset for an example, and it is now known that vast lakes and rivers exist beneath the parched sands of the Sahara,[1] all this despite the fact that the overlying strata are considerably heavier than water.

However, to return to the Moon, it seems hardly questionable that vast amounts of water obtained and may still obtain at an unspecified depth beneath her surface. Most of this water may have lain twenty or more miles underground, ascending to and descending from higher levels through the vast systems of caverns and channels under the influence of the powerful terrestrial tides. Lunar isostasy may thus have been based on the buoyancy of the porous honeycomb surface layers resting like a rubber sponge on a cushion of gas and water. In any case, this structure readily explains the observed peculiarities of lunar vulcanism and must affect our estimate of the other associated phenomena. In particular, any outpourings of ordinary lava become improbable and an alternative interpretation of the apparent lava flows, few as these are, must be provided.

The substance of the Moon being generally lighter, many of the chemical elements of low atomic weight which are comparatively rare on the Earth will abound in the superficial rocks of the Moon. Compounds of these elements are often soluble in water, and in the absence, or great scarcity, of surface moisture mountains made up of, say, common salt could endure for millions of years. In other words, one is led to suspect that lunarite will largely, if not wholly, dissolve in water, especially hot acidulated or alkalized water. The rocks of the Apennines have been 'etched' by the gases ascending from the clefts of this area;[15] and, since the bulk of these gases is probably just steam, this lends further support to our assumption.

Thus, when the pull of the Earth raised those blister domes that were to become maria, it could not have drawn magma from the interior, for the simple reason that there was no magma to drawn on. It would have drawn water and the frictional heating would have seen to it that this was hot water. Ascending through the interstices of the lunar honeycomb of caverns, this hot water surged in beneath the domes, permeating, breaking up, and dissolving on the way the soluble surface formations, to transform them into a kind of fuming paste, very similar to ordinary lava but at a much lower temperature, which may not have been over 300° C.

It must be observed that the difference is only one of degree, for—to give an example—water-rich basaltic lava in the crater Kilauea, in Hawaii, remains liquid down to 600° C.[8] Dilute it still more with hot brine and silica gel and you will have a good approximation to the lunar lavas envisaged here.

However, such a hot paste or lava, call it what you will, would exhibit great 'mordancy', to use a geological term, and wreak havoc among the surface relief. At first, though, it would cake up immediately on reaching the sub-vacuum of lunar air-space and exude great amounts of gas until this had raised the barometric pressure sufficiently for the hot liquid to flow freely. The liquid being in the nature of mixture of hot brine and dilute silica jelly, no great pressure would be required for that (*see* Chapter 15).

When this had happened the maria became seas in more than figurative meaning, flowing and ebbing 'exactly like water', for, in fact, they were but a kind of thick, hot brine.

The upheaval subsided. The gases, held down only lightly by the Moon's feeble pull, spread out wide around her. The first fierce contest between the momentum of lunar rotation and the friction of the tides had repelled the Moon away from the Earth, and the tides slackened. No more water was coming up to the surface. Soon the seas of the Moon were transformed into

69

mere mudflats, which were beginning to harden on the surface into a kind of rock gel, again very much like the siliceous gel of volcanic rhyolite probably including crystals of salts and even some of the common terrestrial rock-building substances, such as quartz, which is soluble in hot briny water, as well as muddy particles of undigested rock. The 'lavas' which have been poured out by the few eruptive lunavoes would fall into the same category.

On this reading of the situation, apart from the water of hydration, there will be very little chemical difference between lunarite and lunabase. The latter has been produced simply by a degassing,* dissolving and recongealing of the former. Yet lunabase will be comparatively compact and probably largely glassy in appearance. This will make it absorb heat more readily, which is the case, though it is still a very poor conductor of heat, so that a little way below the surface of the maria lunar ground is in a condition of permafrost (*see* Chapter 11). One must, therefore, expect to find there large amounts of ice, black muddy ice, heavily permeated with mineral material. If so, the surface of the maria will have expanded on hardening, as indeed we know it has.

On this reckoning, too, the specific gravity of lunabase will be higher than that of lunarite. Even so it is probably below that of water.

Deposits of ice and lunabase will also have formed underneath the bowls of the lunavoes and pulled these down by their superior density. These vertical movements reacted on the underlying elastic cushion, so that the lunarite rims experienced upward pressure and where this was sufficiently strong rupture occurred on the boundary between the two types of rock, usually invisible, with concentric up- and down-faulting and the splintering of the fragile lunarite. These appearances, though, are absent from the craters below 10 miles in diameter, as one would expect: 10 miles is rather a low line of division, suggesting, on the one hand, that the mechanical strength of lunarite is exceedingly low and, on the other, that the 'cushion' lies fairly close to the surface.

Even a small quantity of liquid water emitted by lunavoes would act corrosively on lunar rocks, and lunarite in particular. We will recall here those peculiar pits round Tycho and the radial gullies of Aristillus and other similar craters, but the country round and especially to the south of Copernicus deserves notice in this connection. It bears the appearance of a terrain ravaged by tremendous floods, which have left great loop-shaped banks of rubble, partly submerging some old denuded rings. Glaciation would have resulted in a similar state of affairs and possibly this has intervened at some stage as well.

* That degassing has occurred is shown by the fact that rings submerged under lunarite are frequently outlined by crater chains. This also indicates the high porosity of the gas-imbued lunarite.

PLATE VII The much-discussed Mare Imbrium. *(Page 54)*

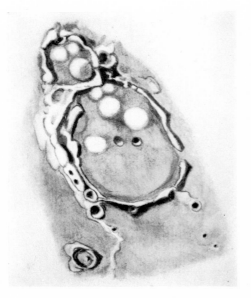

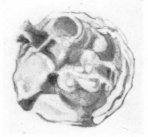

Above: Variable high-Sun markings in Copernicus

Left: Low domes in Posidonius and Chacornac
(Power: ×200; red filter)

Above: Variable high-Sun markings in Eratosthenes
(Power: ×200; red filter)

Right: The walled plain of Gassendi, which is devoid of bright markings under a low Sun but exhibits several later in the lunation (Power: ×240)

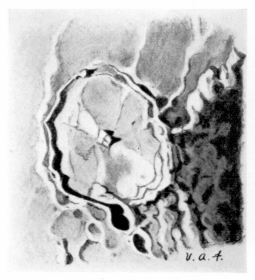

PLATE VIII Observational drawings made by the author with a 6½-inch reflector.
(Pages 56, 165)

Ice and snow would eat rapidly into the surface rocks, as they do to some extent even on the Earth, producing depressions that would remain after they had gone. This might account for the indications that the bright ray matter, even if now composed only of salt, which it often recalls when observed through colour filters, is distributed at the bottom of shallow hollows. In many cases, however, the rays behave more like snow, being comparatively dull in the red and violet.

Many minor craters put one in mind of the Pretoria Salt Pan, which Baldwin describes as a 'great hollow . . . almost perfectly circular, with diameters north to south of 3,460 feet and 3,300 feet measured at right angles. The circumscribed ridge rises an average of 100 feet above the level of the neighbouring country. . . . The floor of the crater lies 300 feet below the rim and presents a strange appearance. The outer portion is generally covered by a dazzling saline incrustation, while a dark pool of soda–salt brine fills the centre.'[2]

Baldwin believes that the Salt Pan is a meteoritic crater, but this is irrelevant here. Neither the salt nor the soda brine came from the meteorite, and it is in these that the real resemblance to a lunavo may lie; only that in the latter the brine would have congealed into a solid cake.

Thus our desert regions form a natural climatic approximation to lunar conditions. It is only a question of more or less. As stated, our magmas, too, contain water, some of which is retained after their consolidation. Terrestrial obsidians, to which lunabase has been compared (Landerer), may be up to 20 per cent water in composition. Silica gel was discovered in the igneous rocks of Mull.[8] On the other hand, not all lunar surface rock need be soluble. It is possible that such features as Pico, Piton, and other fragmentary mountains of Mare Imbrium owe their survival to insolubility. East of Aristarchus there stretches the so-called 'black desert', which behaves very much like ground permeated with sulphur fumes and appears jet-black in ultra-violet photographs, showing dark in the short wavelengths generally—though I cannot say that I have found it very conspicuous. If sulphur this is, however, and the effect may be due to something else, it does not appear to be very common on the Moon. (The ultra-violet part of the lunar spectrum shows some absorptions, which have been attributed to silicates.)

The assumed solubility of surface formations raises the issue of erosion from below. We have seen that many lunar clefts are formed by continuous concatenations of small craters, and may have originated from the gradual dissolution of surface compounds by the vapours ascending from the underground hydrosphere, or what remains of it, through minute tectonic fissures. Here and there lunar landscape displays an effect which can best be described as 'burrowing', as though a lot of moles had been at work. Strings of craters weave in and out of mountain intricacies, dive

F

under the rings of large walled enclosures and reappear on their other side. The issue of O'Neill's Bridge[20] and some tunnels recently reported on the Moon* remains undecided, but they appear to be definitely possible with this type of topography, which emerges as something intermediate between volcanic and Karst country, only that 'phreatic' water circulates upwards and the swallets may have a similar trend.

In Mare Foecunditatis lie the interesting rings of Messier and Messier A, or Pickering, the latter of which is the head of the so-called 'Comet Tail'. The 'Tail' consists of two slightly divergent white streamers trailing eastwards from the crater, between which Walter Goodacre[7] has identified five 'obscure' rings, 'reduced by erosion or other action almost to a state of obliteration'. Such a chain of substantial ring mountains may serve as a *coup de grâce* for the meteoritic hypothesis; but its present interest lies in the possibility of this being another instance of 'burrowing from below'. It looks as though Pickering had been, so to speak, creeping bodily to the west, abandoning on the way its previous incarnations. The size of the crater may indicate that the flow of steam from the interior was exceptionally copious and by gradually enlarging the vent succeeded in making the whole structure soggy and plastic until it collapsed, blocking the further supply of vapour, which was forced to seek another outlet farther along the hidden sublunar crevice.

Other interpretations are, of course, possible, and the very existence of these ghost rings has been questioned by some observers, including Patrick Moore. I have not seen them myself either, but this does not necessarily mean that the rings are not occasionally revealed under some special angle of illumination.

To wind up, however, let us revert to the conception of the underground hydrosphere, which forms the title theme of this Chapter.

Harold C. Urey,[14,15] a prominent American chemist, to whose work frequent reference has been made, is a follower of Baldwin's meteoritic hypothesis and regards it as a foregone conclusion that the features of the Moon's surface have been produced by impact, although he admits local volcanic activity, represented *inter alia* by the oft-referred-to chain of small craters between Copernicus and Eratosthenes. He calculates that if the Moon contained about the same amount of radioactive matter as does the Earth, she would still be molten through some 0·8 of her diameter. This he regards as incompatible with the preservation of the 'fossil' bulge and 'fossil' polar flattening discussed in Chapter 4, as the resulting pressure at the centre of the lunar globe would be 20 atmospheres or so, which would require the material there to have the rigidity of brick. Magma would have yielded to this pressure and the Moon would have assumed a shape consonant with her present moments of inertia taken round the three axes,

* Private communication from H. P. Wilkins.

72

towards the Earth, the polar axis, and that at right angles to both, He concludes that the Moon is cold and rigid throughout and could never have been molten, having been formed by the accumulation of cold meteoritic matter, as proposed by G. K. Gilbert in 1893. The issue is *sub judice* and in particular the moments of inertia along the three axes are subject to doubt.[19] But this would clearly wash out the idea that the Moon could ever have been part of the Earth, though we have seen that some readjustment in the Moon's shape has taken place and is revealed among others by the deformation of the ring forms.[5,12]

Urey also sees some difficulties about the interpretation of maria as simple outflows of lava, with which I see no reason to disagree. However, the rigidity of the lunar globe forms Urey's main argument against the volcanic or plutonic theory of the origin of crateriform features, though it is not apparent how the alleged absence of internal heating is to be reconciled with the admitted and curiously local manifestations of lunar vulcanism.

No satisfactory answer is given to this query and Urey's own reasoning would indicate that past volcanic activity on the Moon by itself gives sufficient reason to believe that plutonic forces are still at work there, a matter to be considered in more detail in the following chapter.

Nor is Urey's conclusion that the inner core of the Moon is rigid indispensable. Although a large mass acts at a distance as though it were all concentrated at its centre of gravity, gravity declines when this point is approached and becomes zero when it has been reached. If heating be due to radioactive matter, originally uniformly distributed throughout the meteoritic agglomerate on the Moon's mass, it will proceed from the centre outwards. In loose uncompacted matter conduction would be slow, so that a considerable excess of temperature could arise in the core leading to volatilization whilst the outside layers remained solid or plastic. With a small mass, such as the Moon's, the downward pressure of the overlying rocks would not be high and could be easily balanced by the molecular pressure of very hot gas combined with the centrifugal force of rotation. Thus a zone of low density could be produced at the core of the lunar globe (*see* Appendix, p. 189).

Since the large molecules of radioactive substances naturally become fitted into the silicate lattices and silicates, being lighter than other materials, would fractionate upwards, they would carry with them the radioactive materials and remove them from the lunar core, cutting off the further supply of heat and bringing down the temperature there. In certain conditions, however, the internal zone of low density would be maintained. Gravity within a hollow sphere is zero, and if some comparatively rarefied matter were present it would still be low, whilst the upwardly directed gravity on the bounding external surface would be comparatively high, so that the heavy material located there would have no tendency to fall towards the centre, provided that the shell were sufficiently rigid not to be crushed by the pressure of the overlying mass. Such 'hollow' structure appears possible for planetary bodies of small mass and would result in surface gravity exceeding the value calculated from mass alone, as well as in an excessive polar flattening, as observed in the case of the Moon.

This, however, is a side-issue. The point is that Urey's arguments favour the ideas advanced in this chapter, which offer a solution reconciling volcanic activity with comparatively low underground temperatures.

To return once more to the asymmetry of the Moon's shape, the entire discrepancy is a matter of a mile or so and the surface formations are extremely light, so that if this discrepancy were localized in these no great stress would result at the core. The 'fossil' distortion may thus be confined to the outside layers, buoyed up on a honeycomb of water- and gas-filled caverns, which, having once been pulled out of shape by tidal forces, set more or less rigidly in the form imparted to them at the time and have failed to keep pace with the readjustment of the interior when these forces ceased to act. Yet, as we have seen, some considerable recoil has occurred and the Moon has responded, though incompletely, to the altered state of affairs.

Even on the Earth there exist gravitationally anomalous areas[8] for which no wholly satisfactory explanation has been found. These may be due to similar gas and water basins accumulating somewhere beneath the rigid crustal formations, which they are unable to pierce. On the Moon they would have lain still closer to the surface, and when she approached the Earth and tidal action increased they actually broke out, convulsing the whole superficial area with gas-and-water vulcanism, domelike uplifts, and subsidences.

Passing reference has been made on several occasions to the rival cold genesis of the maria recently proposed by T. Gold.[18]

He holds forth, firstly, that there exist indubitable signs of a denuding action on the lunar surface; secondly, that this action is partly the result of slow erosion by short-wave radiation causing superficial disintegration of rock to fine dust and partly the similar effect of condensation and evaporation of atmospheric gases; thirdly, that the fine dust thus produced acquires a dark colouring through irradiation with the short ultra-violet; fourthly, is transported to low positions by thermal agitation similar to Brownian movement and by electrostatic repulsion, and, finally, becomes compacted there by its own weight into a kind of sedimentary rock covered with dust. The latter would be the real nature of lunabase, whilst the maria would be parts of the lunar surface submerged under this slow flood of fine dust.

Some of the processes suggested by him probably actually occur, but as a global explanation of the origin of the maria the hypothesis is signally unsatisfactory. The mare basins have to be there in the first place to receive the dust, so that the hypothesis still needs other forces to account for the existence of the maria—Gold accepts the meteoritic alternative. No explanation is given of the sharply contrasting areas of different intensity and hue within the maria, the areas which are often delimited by geometrical outlines, nor of the agency whereby submerged ring-forms, which have no vertical existence, can still manifest themselves on the surface of a mare by differences of shade. The existence of light-coloured matter at the bottom of clefts and hollows is difficult to understand on this interpretation, for they would have been the first to be submerged under the dust seeping in from above. Yet possibly the strongest argument against Gold's ideas is the appearance of the wrinkle ridges, which in some regions, such as Mare Tranquillitatis, look exactly like the skin on boiling milk agitated by the currents.[17] (See Plate IX.) There is here definite evidence of viscous flow, incompatible with gradual accumulation of dust.

REFERENCES

1. BAKER, ST. BARBE. A wireless talk (B.B.C.).
2. BALDWIN, R. B. *The Face of the Moon*. University of Chicago Press, 1949.
3. BARRELL, JOSEPH. *On Continental Fragmentation and the Geologic Bearing of the Moon's Surficial Features*. U.S. Government Printing Office, Washington, 1929.
4. COOKE, S. R. B. 'The Origin of Lunar Formations.' *10th Report of the Lunar Section, Memoirs of the British Astronomical Association*, Vol. 36, Part I, London, 1947.
5. FIRSOFF, V. A. 'On the Structure and Origin of Lunar Surface Features.' *J.B.A.A.*, Vol. 66, No. 8, 1956.
6. GEIKIE, SIR ARCHIBALD. 'The Building-up of the Island.' *The Book of Arran Archaeology*. Glasgow, 1910.
7. GOODACRE, WALTER. 'Messier A and the "Comet Tail".' *9th Report of the Lunar Section of the B.A.A.*, 1936.
8. JEFFREYS, SIR HAROLD. *Earthquakes and Mountains*. Methuen, London, 1935.
9. NORTH, F. J. *Limestones*. Murby, London, 1930.
10. PAWSEY, J. L. and BRACEWELL, R. N. *Radio Astronomy*. Oxford, 1955.
11. PICKERING, W. H. *The Moon*. Doubleday, Page and Co., New York, 1903.
12. SPURR, J. E. *The Shrunken Moon* (Vol. IV). Business Press, 1949.
13. STEERS, J. A. *The Unstable Earth*. London, 1932.
14. UREY, H. C. 'The Origin of the Moon's Surface Features.' *Sky and Telescope*, Vol. XV, Nos. 3 and 4. Harvard, 1956.
15. *The Planets*. Oxford University Press, 1952.
16. FIRSOFF, V. A. 'Palaeography of the Nubian and Imbrian Plains.' *J.B.A.A.*, Vol. 67, No. 4, 1957.
17. A letter to the Editors, *The Observatory*, Vol. 76, No. 894, p. 194–6, 1956.
18. GOLD, T. 'The Lunar Surface.' *Monthly Notices of the Royal Astronomical Society*, Vol. 115, No. 6, 1955.
19. JEFFREYS, SIR HAROLD. *The Earth*. 3rd Edn. Cambridge University Press, 1952.
20. WILKINS, H. P. 'O'Neill's Bridge.' *J.B.A.A.*, Vol. 65, No. 2, 1955.

8

REALITIES OR SHADOWS?

I N SPEAKING OF CHANGES on the Moon it is well to begin by clari-
fying our ideas about what we are to expect.

Our minds naturally turn to the march of seasons as we know them
from the Earth, the growth and decay of vegetation, the formation, movement, and dispersal of clouds, the precipitation and melting of the snow,
which would especially attract the attention of a telescopic observer of our
planet. Mars, though a smaller and sterner world than she, yet clearly
displays such seasonal alterations, beside some more enduring transformations, probably of a climatic nature, causing the contraction or expansion
of the vegetated areas.

The Moon, however, can know no seasons comparable to those of Mars
or the Earth. A slight fluctuation in the amount of sunshine received in the
higher latitudes will take place depending on the changing position of the
lunar poles relatively to the Sun, but the total wobble amounts to barely
3 degrees. Thus the cyclic drama of the Moon is ruled wholly by her night
and day, each about a fortnight long. This coincidence, as it were, of day
and year will tend to smooth out and mask any seasonal changes, which on,
say, Mars are clearly separable from the period of axial rotation. This has
hardly ever been given sufficient weight: the Moon is essentially weatherless
and seasonless in our accepted meaning of the term.

Add to this the extreme rarefaction of the atmosphere and we get at once
the conventional picture of a stark rocky desert, alternately scorched by a
merciless Sun and gripped by equally merciless frost, which is borne out
well enough by appearances. Hardly a suggestion of a livelier hue varies the
grey-brown monotone. There are no polar caps of gleaming snow, no
expanses of dark greenery, no obvious clouds, which make Mars so
fascinating an object to watch.

Yet, as our study progresses, as we begin to take score of minor features,
more delicate fluctuations of shape, size, colour, and tone, the validity of
this simple picture becomes more and more doubtful. Experienced observers systematically record changes of appearance in the intensity or
extent of this or that dark or bright marking depending on the time of
lunar day, or intervention of an eclipse. There are local fade-outs of
visibility by which the rest of the disk remains unaffected. Transitory
shades and bright patches, resembling mists and clouds, appear and
reappear in certain localities. There are glows and lights, which seem to
bear witness to some kind of activity.

All this cannot be due just to the changing effects of lighting or librational shift of the features on the Moon's surface relatively to the observer. Here theory must pause laying down the law and listen to the objective record of observations, which is the only way to the truth.

This is one type of change, which we will consider in more detail later on. There are, however, on our Earth more permanent changes, for the most part very slow: earthquakes resulting in crustal movements, volcanic eruptions with outpourings of lava, landslides, the rise and fall of the surface of the land, advances and recessions of coast-lines, and so on. There can be no reason in the nature of things why similar changes should not be in progress on the Moon. Barrell[1] assumes as much as a matter of course. As we shall recall, he dates the great mountain ring of Copernicus no farther back than mid-Tertiary on the evidence of heat erosion alone, a point of view which many students of the Moon may hesitate to endorse. Thus, for instance, the usual absence of screes at the foot of lunar peaks is often invoked against the effectiveness of heat erosion; and indeed the pumice-like structure of lunar rocks would make them far less susceptible to flaking-off, or exfoliation, (Whipple) than the compact terrestrial formations. Yet most lunar mountains are only moderately steep, despite the low force of gravity which should preserve precipices and here and there one does find unmistakable landslides and accumulations of detritus.

The conventional view of extreme geological antiquity of lunar features is, after all, a bare hypothesis, resting mainly on the manifestly untrue contention that the face of the Moon shows no signs of erosion, on the one hand, and the view that as a body of smaller mass she will long have lost her internal heat, which the more massive Earth has succeeded in preserving, on the other.

At first sight this may seem to be a reasonable enough assumption. Yet loss of internal heat by radiation into space depends on the effectiveness with which it is conducted outwards by the surface rocks, and it so happens that the porous, or dust-covered, rocks of the Moon are almost perfect insulators, whereas the thermal conductivity of the compact terrestrial formations is fairly good. On this reckoning alone the Moon would be losing her internal heat at a lower rate than the Earth, though it remains true that as a small mass she was probably never as hot as the Earth.

It is, however, generally held nowadays that the steep thermal gradient observed in our mines, as well as vulcanism and much of isostasy to boot, are all due primarily to the evolution of heat in the radioactive substances concentrated in the upper layer of 20 or 30 miles in thickness and becoming very scarce in the heavy dunite and peridotite rocks of the sima below.[5,9]

If so and the Moon and Earth are of similar age and composition, the same radioactive substances will be present in comparable quantity in her subsurface layers—possibly a little lower down but also through a comparatively greater thickness of rocks, for on the Moon the sial layer will be more strongly represented. The evolution of radioactive heat would thus be greater per unit volume, and, while the absence of seas and a shielding atmosphere may aid the dissipation of such heat as reaches the surface from the interior, this is more than offset by the very low thermal conductivity of lunarite, which is only slightly lower than that of lunabase. In sum total the argument against lunar vulcanism from the loss of internal heat is clearly threadbare.

It must also be borne in mind that permanent surface changes are seldom very noticeable, both by reason of their slowness and limited extent. Accurate observations of the Moon cover only a period of about 150 years, the earliest of them having been made with inadequate optical equipment, while the objective test of photography did not arrive till the end of the last century. We have seen in Chapter 4 that photography has many limitations and even visually the largest telescopes seldom permit to discern objects less than 500 feet in diameter. Further, these largest telescopes are pointed at the Moon but rarely, so that most of the watch on the face of our companion world is kept with much less powerful instruments.

This is a very crude measure to apply to transformations of surface detail, and any observer of the Moon will know how its aspect varies with the position of the Sun and libration, to say nothing of the unsteadiness and turbidity of our own atmosphere. This may and does create appearances of change where no change has taken place. Yet the same circumstance may equally disguise real changes and it is much abused to explain away any observation indicating one. It must, of course, be freely admitted that unreliable observers and observations exist; but on the whole I am inclined to put greater trust in the man at the eye-piece than his critic in the arm-chair who knows all the answers.

It is also salutary to reflect that even on the Earth no striking surface changes, especially if we abstract from de- and re-afforestation and a few other man-made features, have occurred during the last 150 years. The annihilation of St. Pierre on Martinique by the eruption of Montagne Pelée in 1902 may have been a great human tragedy but the observer on the Moon would hardly notice any difference in the appearance of the place. Even the shattering explosion of Krakatoa in 1883, apart from the scattered ash, would in its effect be but a pinprick on the face of the Moon. The absence of the mobile element of surface water will make land movements on the Moon especially difficult to detect.

But how, one may ask, about the actual volcanic eruptions? These would be visible. Only that, unlike our volcanoes, the lunavoes were comparatively quiescent even in the past selenological ages of great volcanic activity. They used to go off not so much 'with a bang' as 'with a whimper'. Indeed, lunar vulcanism comes very close to the class of change that

may be described as 'weather'. As geologically it was on the Earth, vulcanism on the Moon must be the main source of atmospheric gas, and for
this reason its manifestations are very closely linked up with other appearances of change, which on the Earth we would not dream of associating
with volcanic activity.

It is, therefore, truly remarkable that there exists at least one well
authenticated case of considerable volcanic upheaval on the Moon. I am
referring to the oft-repeated story of the crater Linné. Here is the account
given of it by Pickering in *The Moon*[8] (p. 39):

'. . . Our earliest evidence depends on a map constructed by Riccioli in
1651, where Liné [*sic*] is represented as a deep crater of moderate size. It is
next noted by Schroeter in 1788, who described it as "a very small, round,
brilliant spot, containing a somewhat uncertain depression". It is certain
that if the crater Liné had been no larger than it is now it could not have
been detected by either of these astronomers with the imperfect telescopes
of their times.

'With more modern instruments, however, the testimony becomes much
more precise. Thus, early in the last century Lohrmann described Liné as
being very deep and as more than 4 miles in diameter. Maedler observed it
seven times, and described it as very distinct under the oblique illumination
of the Sun . . . , measuring 6 miles in diameter. Schmidt drew it eight times,
and represented it as being 7 miles in diameter and 1,000 feet deep.
Schmidt, in 1843, was the last astronomer, apparently, to see it with any
such dimensions, and in 1866 he announced that it had disappeared. A few
months later, however, he found in its place a small 'craterlet' about $\frac{1}{4}$ of a
mile in diameter, which, in the course of a couple of years, gradually
increased to a mile and a half. Although still visible, its diameter has now
(1903) sunk to $\frac{3}{4}$ miles.'

No transformation of this nature could possibly be simulated by mere
periodical changes of illumination, so that the case for real change seems
to be foolproof. But in the case of minor alterations no comparable
certainty exists, especially as the vagaries of individual draughtsmanship
must also be taken into account. This does apply to some other 'lost'
craters. However, near the western edge of Mare Crisium Schroeter
recorded 'a large distinct crater, with bright walls and a dusky floor' which
he christened Alhazen and measured as being 23 miles in diameter. He
often referred to it the positions of other features, which shows clearly that
the crater was a conspicuous object. Today no such crater exists. There is
only an ill-defined depression between two peaks at the point indicated by
Schroeter. The old Alhazen would seem to have been destroyed and largely
filled up, so that the name has been transferred to another formation.[6]

There are also persistent reports of new features. The most puzzling of
these is the newly discovered abundance of small domelike upswellings of

the surface with summit vents and the dusky bands on the inner walls of many craters. Both are plainly visible even with medium-sized instruments, and yet, for some reason or other, they were overlooked in the past by adequately equipped and painstaking observers. Wilkins[11] asks whether they could have been formed in recent years and prudently refrains from giving an answer to this query. Unless, however, we are to assume that the domes and dark bands are due to the 'industrial activities of the Selenites', once invoked by Schroeter, or represent the efforts of, say, Martian colonists on the Moon, the wholesale appearance of a new type of marking all over her surface is difficult to contemplate. The psychological approach provides a simpler answer.

Such features may appear perfectly obvious to someone conditioned to expect them but an unprejudiced eye might skip them in the search for, say, craterlets or crevices. Canal-like markings had existed on Mars before 1877, when they became 'news' in the hands of Schiaparelli. Though noticed by some observers, including Schroeter in the eighteenth century, they had generally escaped attention. But as from the fatal date astronomical spiders got very busy on the Red Planet.

This does not, of course, necessarily exclude the possibility that a few of the lunar domes and dark radial bands in particular are really new, and we seem to have at least one case in reverse. Mädler described and depicted four dark bands on the floor of Plato which, according to Wilkins, are no longer there.[11*] Similarly a very dark area in Petavius shown by the old observers has disappeared.[6] This suggests that the bands and some other dark markings come and go, being subject to periodical fluctuations, not unlike certain dark areas of Mars, although the scale is very much larger in the latter.

However, Plato is one of the lunar localities where some kind of volcanic activity appears to be in progress. The 60-mile-wide steel-grey 'lake' of its level floor is scattered with a number of small craters which have a way of fading out, springing into prominence, to disappear altogether and reappear again in an unpredictable fashion.[6,8] Sometimes nothing at all can be made out of the floor detail even with the largest instruments, though the seeing is good and illumination favourable. There exist numerous records of such observations by painstaking and experienced men. The great walled plain of Schickard in the south-east quadrant is likewise subject to mistiness obliterating interior detail, as, for instance, in Moore's observation of 2 August, 1939. On this occasion two bright points showed clearly among the mist; and on 31 August, 1944, Wilkins saw the craterlets inside Schickard as white spots, although under the low Sun they should have shown clear shadows, as they did on other occasions.[6,10]

---

* I have seen, using a red filter, a suggestion of four dark bands on the floor of Plato, but may have been mistaken.

Taken in conjunction, these observations indicate that the craterlets were the source of the obscuring veil, whatever its nature may be.

For a record of an actual eruption in progress, however, we have to go to the Cobra-Head, that pearlike hollow from which issues Schroeter's Valley, one of Pickering's 'river-beds', below the ring mountain of Herodotus in the 'Ocean of Storms'.*

Observing at Arequipa in the Andes, in 1893, Pickering[8] was struck by the peculiar appearance of this feature which suggested to him an active volcano, or I would rather say geyser, in the state of eruption. He writes (p. 40–1):

'So striking, indeed, was the appearance, that . . . I determined to make a series of careful drawings of the apparent vapour column, in order to determine whether any variations in its outline might be detected from time to time, or whether, like a stain, it was immovably attached to the lunar surface. . . . A casual examination of the sketches shows the great changes that are from time to time undergone by the vapour column . . . changes that are readily detected by a six-inch telescope under ordinary atmospheric conditions.

'The most marked of these changes depend for their existence upon the altitude of the Sun, for apparently no volcanic activity whatever is exhibited until one or two days after sunrise.'

This last remark is interesting, though it does cast some doubt on the volcanic nature of the phenomenon. However, F. H. Thornton, using an 18-inch reflector, on 10 February, 1949, saw here 'a puff of whitish vapour obscuring details for some miles'.[6]

Mists and obscurations have been noticed in many other craters as well, and a complete register of these observations would make a substantial catalogue.[2,3,4,6,8,10] Mistiness and diffuse cloud-like objects have been seen in Sinus Iridum, that remnant of a gigantic mountain ring which forms a conspicuous 'bay' in the north-eastern 'coast' of Mare Imbrium. There is an area of variable brightness in the Alps, some peaks of which occasionally appear ill-defined, although the remaining country is sharply outlined. However, probably the most remarkable region in this respect is the south-eastern portion of Mare Crisium, in the vicinity of the small crater Picard. Some of the obscurations observed there, an account of which will be found in Patrick Moore's *Guide to the Moon*,[6] would appear to have persisted literally for years, completely screening surface detail.

In a few cases the mists seen in the craters seemed to be self-luminous, or else a glow was observed. On 27 March, 1882, A. S. Williams saw the floor of Plato at sunrise 'glowing with a curious milky kind of light'. In 1892 the keen-sighted American observer Barnard at the Lick Observatory could see the bowl of Thales, near the north pole, filled with a pale luminous

* Kozyrev's observation is referred to in a footnote to p. 56.

haze. An interesting observation was made by Wilkins on 29 March, 1939, when the interior of Copernicus was faintly visible as though 'in a luminous mist' four hours before the ring was touched by the first rays of the rising Sun.[10] The same observer reports that Aristarchus, which can usually be made out on the unlit portion of the disk as a bright patch, on one occasion suddenly increased in brilliance showing its inner structure in clear relief for about two minutes, then faded out again. Sir William Herschel is said to have mistaken Aristarchus for an erupting volcano, which might refer to a comparable temporary brightening-up, as the starlike point observed by him in 1783 'became fainter and finally vanished'. There is, however, no definite reason for identifying this with Aristarchus. Haas suggests that he may have observed the 'impact flare' of a large meteorite on the lunar surface. In 1787, on the two consecutive nights of 19 and 20 April, he again saw three bright spots on the earthlit part of the Moon, which he described as 'volcanoes', the brightest of which appeared like 'a small piece of burning charcoal covered by a very thin coat of white ashes seen in faint daylight' and lay 3' 57" from the 'northern limb'. The latter statement would seem to exclude the possibility of its having been Aristarchus.

Similar observations were made by Schroeter in the same year of grace. His bright white spot was located close to Plato and would appear to have been in the same position as the one seen by Grover in 1865. Schroeter's spot fluctuated in intensity, whereas in Grover's record it remained steady for about half an hour and answered well to the description given by Herschel. There is a comparable observation by G. S. Jones.[4]

Aristarchus and some other brilliant areas of the Moon often show quite clearly in the earthshine, but these records, with one possible exception, do not appear to correspond to any known objects of this character. The meteoritic interpretation appears rather doubtful in view of the long periods for which these lights endured, but volcanic or possibly electrical phenomena may have caused these unusual appearances.

However, on 14 July, 1940, Walter H. Haas observed a 'milky luminosity' on the outside east wall of Tycho. Harold Hill's observation when, on 30 January, 1947, he found that the central peak of Eratosthenes cast no shadow, must be classed in the same category.[6,10]

Sometimes the glow is red. Thus, on 20 May, 1948, R. M. Baum saw the surface of the Moon to the north-west of Philolaus, near the north pole, glow red for 15 minutes, then return to normal. The same astronomer observed a red glow west of Lichtenberg on 21 January, 1951. Timocharis in the 'Sea of Rains' is one of the craters that have often been seen filled with mist, and to me its brilliance appears to vary considerably at the same phase in different lunations. In my colour work I have been struck by its occasional brilliance in red, notably on 10 October, 1954, while its 'big brother' Copernicus appeared bright with blue and violet filters that nearly extinguished Timocharis. On other nights, however, the behaviour of the two craters was exactly the same, which would appear to indicate a red glow in Timocharis, though none could be seen directly.

In blue and violet many craters seemed to flash now and again, which, though, was probably an illusion due to the fact that in these colours detail shows more clearly when one looks sideways into the eye-piece, while the opposite is true of the longer wavelengths of light. Thus, as one moves the centre of the eye from one feature to another, the relative brightness of the peripheral image changes, which might produce the impression of spurious flashes. This effect, however, cannot account for my observation of 8 September, 1954, when, at about 8 p.m., Proclus seen through a blue monochromatic filter seemed to brighten up, sometimes to dazzling brilliance, for periods of several seconds and even minutes at a time and again drop to the usual level. Two hours later on the same night it no longer showed any fluctuations of brightness in blue or any other colour. Gas, as is well known from the colour of our sky, scatters the light of short wavelengths more effectively than that of the longer (Rayleigh's Law), and it seems that great waves of gas, possibly charged with small particles, were welling up from the crater's interior. These were invisible to the unaided eye, but the blue filter brought them clearly out.

There are several localities of the Moon which show a kind of misty radiance in the blue and violet monochrome. One is centred on the Haemus Mountains and the crater Menelaus, between Mare Serenitatis and Mare Vaporum, in the first quadrant, which contains a number of similar areas along the north-west limb. In the second quadrant, Aristarchus and Copernicus, as well as Kepler, Bessarion, and a few minor craters are very bright in blue, but I have not observed any extended brilliant area, apart from the north pole. In the third there is a region of greenish-blue misty sheen east of the Percy Mountains, and on the border between the third and the fourth quadrants a misty blue glow develops towards the full phase to the north-west of Tycho, round about the old ring of Walter.* There would seem to be some fluctuation in its intensity, but this is not definitely established, as the altitude of the Moon and the transparency of the air greatly affect the amount of the blue and violet in her light. Another blue mist appears to hover about the Petavius–Furnerius area, and the south polar lands are bright in the blue, though nothing to compare with the north polar 'cap'. However, this subject properly belongs to the next chapter.

These features are prominent with low powers but when a higher power is used the misty effect disappears, which is probably due to the general reduction in brightness.

* This glow appears to be centred on a small bright crater in the five short rays lying within the great ring of Regiomontanus.

Blue mists have also been observed without filters, and in particular by Goodacre and Molesworth, who in the years 1895 and 1896 several times noticed a faint bluish mist on the inner east wall of Aristarchus, also seen by Barcroft on 27 December, 1939.[4] It appeared soon after sunrise and remained visible only for a short time. On 25 June, 1955, I observed a similar effect in Theophilus.

What is perhaps more puzzling is Arthur Mee's conclusion[2] that the 'wonderful fan-shaped light rays emanating from Proclus appear to shift their position and alter their form in a manner incapable of explanation on the basis of varying libration or angle of illumination'. On this H. P. Wilkins, when he was the Director of the Lunar Section of the British Astronomical Association, commented that 'the intensity of the rays varies, the appearance at minimum being of a translucent veil through which the dark surface of the mare (Crisium) can be faintly seen'. Next comes the surprising statement by Pickering that the great white streaks of Tycho are believed to be 'analogous to our cirrus clouds, save that they lie close to the surface'.[7] We shall see later on what interpretation it is possible to put on it.

Such effects are delicate and often ephemeral; they come as something of a surprise, so that one tends to doubt the evidence of one's own eyes. And yet on what other evidence does the view of the Moon as a changeless world rest—except for its greater superficiality? Thus while mistakes are possible and now and again are undoubtedly being made, one must also take into account the opposite bias not only with the critics who tend to discount the reality of such reports but even with the observers themselves who make them.

I will return to these matters in considering the problem of lunar atmosphere. There are, however, other changes—on the ground, which are recurrent and thus predictable and measurable, and at least some of which must be regarded as definitely established. These are closely linked up with the somewhat controversial issue of lunar colourings and form the subject matter of the next two chapters.

REFERENCES

1. BARRELL, JOSEPH. *On Continental Fragmentation and the Geologic Bearing of the Moon's Surficial Features.* U.S. Government Printing Office, Washington, 1929.
2. BRITISH ASTRONOMICAL ASSOCIATION. *Tenth Report of the Lunar Section.* Vol. 36, Part 1, London, October 1947.
3. *Eleventh Report of the Lunar Section.* Vol. 36, Part 3, London, July 1950.
4. HAAS, W. H. 'Does Anything Ever Happen on the Moon?.' *The Journal of the Royal Astronomical Society of Canada,* July to November 1942.
5. JEFFREYS, HAROLD. *Earthquakes and Mountains.* Methuen, London, 1935.
6. MOORE, PATRICK. *Guide to the Moon.* Eyre and Spottiswoode, London, 1953.
7. PICKERING, W. H. 'Lunar Changes.' *7th Report of the Section for the Observation of of the Moon.* British Astronomical Association. London, 1916.
8. *The Moon.* Doubleday, Page and Co., New York, 1903.

9. STEERS, J. A. *The Unstable Earth.* London, 1932.
10. WILKINS, H. P. *Our Moon.* Muller, London, 1954.
11.   'Recent Research on the Moon.' *Journal of the British Interplanetary Society*, Vol. 14, No. 3, London, 1955.

SEASONAL CHANGES

IN CHAPTER 8 we have considered observations, which, errors excepted, relate to volcanic or atmospheric effects on the Moon, but there are other changes, on the ground, of seasonal or irregular nature, which still demand attention. It will be understood that no rigid boundary can be fixed between the two types of change, partly because of the possibility of correlation between them, and partly for the simple reason that in some instances it may be impossible to decide with certainty whether the change is on or above the ground, volcanic or climatic. On the average, though, the distinction is clear enough and does not require elaboration.

It is salutary to bear it in mind that an alteration in the intensity or hue of a surface marking does not necessarily imply a parallel change in its physical or chemical constitution, let alone a manifestation of biological activity, such as growth and decay of vegetation. Rock can be green without anything growing upon it, and the same rock may appear brown, red, black, or yellow depending on the angle of illumination and reflection. A variation in the tint or shade (these terms define the result of adding white or black respectively to an otherwise unaltered colour) is even less conclusive. Most commonly it is due to shadow or increased illumination, and here the possible effect of combined shadows or reflections produced by objects too small to be discerned must always be considered. This may be illustrated by comparing a darkish sheet of smooth brown paper with another of light-coloured sand-paper under different angles of lighting and presentation. In oblique light the sand-paper, seen sideways, will appear much the darker of the two.

On the other hand, it is clear that an explanation based on this assumption may itself be untrue and a real change may be taken for a mere play of light and shade, for there is no intrinsic reason, other than the prejudice arising from an unproved hypothesis, why no change should take place on the Moon. And this is not a very good reason.

However, effects due to the presence of sub-telescopic detail undoubtedly play a part in the changing appearance of the Moon. From a mathematical analysis of the variation in tint (brightness) of selected lunar areas it has been deduced that lunar rocks must be pitted with small cup-like depressions, as one might otherwise expect from their 'bubbly' (scoriaceous) texture. This general roughness of the Moon's surface, both in large-scale and invisibly small relief, is well illustrated by the rapid drop in the intensity of moonlight with decreasing phase; or, conversely, by the dazzling brightness of the Moon's full face in the telescope by comparison with the

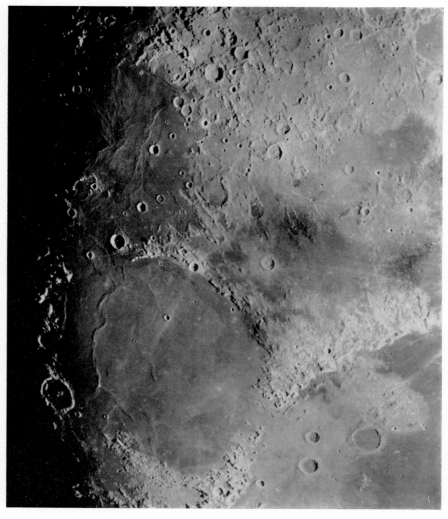

PLATE IX Wrinkle ridges in Mare Tranquillitatis suggest the skin on boiling milk. (*Page 75*)

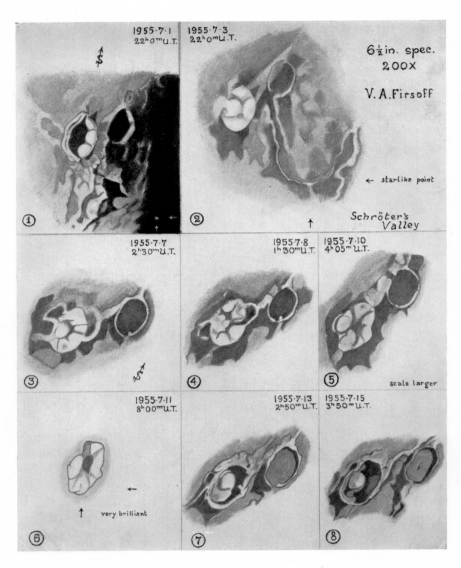

PLATE X Observational drawings of the Aristarchus area by the author, giving consecutive views through a lunation. The drawings are unretouched and reproduced as made at the eye-piece. *(Page 92)*

same part of it, seen with the same instrument and eye-piece only at a quarter phase.

This is the global effect. But the Moon is a mountainous place and outside the maria there is not much level ground there, while even the maria are not perfectly level. When the Sun is low even a slight slope will greatly affect the amount of light received and reflected by the ground, and the effect will increase with the inclination. Take a 45 degrees incline facing the Sun. It will be under vertical illumination not when the Sun stands overhead but when he is 45 degrees above the horizon. Similarly, a vertical rock face will be under maximum illumination with the Sun on the horizon. If, however, it is viewed from above at a small angle, its surface will yet appear very dark, even black if the face be smooth, as most of the light will be reflected back towards the Sun. In view of the general roughness of lunar rocks the reflection will in reality be a diffuse one, which will reduce the extremes. Indeed, the steep scarp of the Straight Wall, though seen in the telescope very nearly from above, does not appear under a low Sun as a dark but as a bright line, which leads one to suspect that it may in reality be white or of a very light colour, for something of the effect described above would otherwise be noticeable.

Curiously, though, if a surface consisted entirely of hemispherical hollows the total amount of light received and reflected by it would not differ much with the changing angle of illumination, once this has exceeded about 25 degrees, for the incident light would always fall vertically down on some part of the hollow and the increase of illumination in any one part of it would be largely balanced up by a decrease in another. A spherical surface of this kind, viewed from the direction, or close to the direction, from which the light comes, would appear to be of a nearly uniform brilliance, except for the extreme edges, where the decrease of lighting on the inter-spaces may begin to tell. This is very nearly true of the full Moon, which, moreover, displays a brilliant limb (edge), largely owing to the crowding in perspective of the brightly sunlit mountain-sides. A smoother sphere would not behave in this way and would look noticeably brighter towards the centre, while, on the other hand, it would be less affected by the phase, which causes long shadows to be cast by the unevennesses of the ground.

However this may be, the investigation carried out by W. H. Haas[3] of a representative selection of various lunar features in relation to phase shows that the variation in their tint is consistent with the assumption that the reflecting surfaces are sparsely pitted with hollows whose axes are perpendicular to the surface. Yet *no* surface of such constitution could attain its darkest shade under vertical lighting as is typical of many lunar markings. This effect might be produced by a carpet of vertical crystals, a point which does not appear to have been considered. The side facets of the crystal pyramids would reflect the light away from the line of sight, thus making the surface appear dark even though the Sun was at the zenith. This explanation, however, requires that the marking in question should suddenly be transformed from a dark into a bright one under a certain angle of illumination, where the light thrown off by the crystal facets would fall in with the line of sight, and darken equally suddenly a short while after. From the position of the Sun at the time of brightening-up and the inclination of the slope one could then compute the angle of the facets and thus determine the nature of the crystals responsible for the effect. No comparable behaviour has been observed in the dark markings under review, though some bright areas on the crater-sides which vary in outline as the lunation progresses could be due to the presence of crystalline matter.

Under a low Sun some lunar mountains often exhibit a short-lived dimming or increase in brilliance that is not easy to account for by the simple chiaroscuro. I once watched a sunrise on one of the Leibnitz peaks. To begin with, the mountain formed a brilliant isolated star-point on the dark side of the terminator, but as the light crept closer to it it became duller, again to regain its pristine brightness about 10 minutes later. In the virtual absence of an atmosphere it would have been fully sunlit from the start. The decrease of contrast with the surroundings could have caused a slight apparent dimming, though hardly to the extent observed, but it could not explain the subsequent return to the original brilliance. Possibly a crystalline mantle caused this fluctuation in brightness, or else an atmospheric obscuration, say, a cloud of evaporating gas, carrying small crystals in suspension, intervened.

Haas records frequent transient darkenings or brightenings-up of lunar features under a low Sun, and his table of 'typical intensity-variations'[3] contains a few examples of fluctuation in tint which might be due to the presence of crystalline material. On the whole, though, the effect is only slight and clearly superimposed on the more general trends, four of which were distinguished: progressive darkening or, conversely, brightening-up from sunrise to sunset, which is really the same sequence in reverse and is clearly related to, though not necessarily explained by, the slope; and progressive increase in brightness or darkening with a maximum close to the noon point. The last-named is of especial interest, for, as already indicated, it cannot be explained in simple geometrical terms. Slipher has suggested that it may be due simply to the increased brightness of the surroundings, but it is not very clear why the surroundings only should be affected. True, there may be some reason to believe that lunarite surfaces are intrinsically rougher than the darker lunabase, so that they would gain in brilliance more rapidly with the Sun's ascent, but this would affect chiefly the morning and evening intensities which have been expressly excluded from consideration. Indeed, Haas points out that the tendency is brought out more clearly if the data relative to the first and last sixth of the Sun's path in the sky are suppressed.

Thus we have here a clear indication of real physical or chemical change brought about by the heat of sunrays.

But the low-Sun behaviour of lunar landscape is likewise instructive. In the light of our previous deliberations it will be clear that steep mountain slopes will attain their maximum brilliance at sunrise or sunset, or close to either, depending on the quarter of the sky they face. Let us now survey the features in the neighbourhood of the terminator.

Even a cursory glance will suffice to show that not all heights near the dividing line are equally bright and that there is no clear relationship between their tint on the one hand and height or steepness on the other, except inasmuch as the lower elevations will not be reached by the rising, or abandoned by the setting, Sun simultaneously with the higher, an allowance for which can easily be made. The highest summits of such mountains as the Apennines may be brighter than their lower peaks, but this brightness is not a simple result of more intense illumination, as their inspection at full Moon will show, especially if monochromatic colour filters are used. They remain relatively brighter, recalling, in fact, our own snow-clad summits. Pickering[7,8] believed that this brightness was really due to snow, but, whatever it may be due to, it certainly indicates a physical difference in the nature of the reflecting surface. Possibly the summit rocks are more frothy in texture, or else they are coated with something.

However, features of equal height also differ greatly in their reflecting power (or albedo), as can readily be sampled by observing the sunlit crater rims at the terminator. A few of these, to take those of Proclus, Theophilus Copernicus, Eudoxus, and Manilius, for example, recall to a mountaineering eye snow-clad mountains under 'mirror-crust'—they appear glazed. But this apparent 'glazing' does not endure long, as though it were but a thin film that was soon thawed up or transformed by the heat of sunrays.

Here it may not be out of context to mention the mother-of-pearl coating of the crater Atlas observed by Wilkins.[9]

What is true of the fully sunlit portions of peaks and craters applies also to their shadows. Not all of these are equally intense. The best known instance is that of the morning shadow in Eudoxus[2,3] which is much lighter than the shadow inside its southern twin, Aristoteles. The effect is sufficiently marked to be shown on photographs. This could be due to the presence of gas, but no mistiness has ever been observed here, so that this explanation does not appear to apply. In both cases the shadowed side of the crater will be illuminated to some extent by the light reflected from its sunlit eastern walls. The slopes are comparable, so that either the sunlit slopes of Eudoxus' bowl or its dark side, or possibly both, are better reflectors of light than the corresponding portions of Aristoteles. I have just alluded to the peculiar sheen on the morning-lit rim of the former, and the interesting point is that this early greyness of the inner shadow of Eudoxus does not last; under a somewhat higher angle of illumination both craters appear equally dark inside. They are also equally dark under an evening Sun.

This would seem to corroborate my surmise that the interior of Eudoxus may be coated with a thin reflecting film, which later disappears—as a matter of fact, simple hoar-frost would suffice! It could be a dry-ice (carbon dioxide) hoar-frost, but there is no sufficient reason why it should not be just ordinary water rime. There exists no cosmic ban on the homely H_2O (or D_2O).

Another pair of craters, Stevinus and Snellius, in the fourth quadrant, behave in a similar way to the Eudoxus–Aristoteles pair, but some time after sunrise the relationship is reversed.[2] the shadow of Snellius being the lighter of the two. Would this be due to the higher latitude of Snellius, or is the reflecting matter in the two craters of different nature, say, a carbon-dioxide frosting in Stevinus and common hoar-frost in Snellius? The latter would not volatilize equally readily and, though thinner, might endure after the other coating had gone.

Pythagoras and Phocydides, on the other hand, are said to have sunrise shadows darker than those of the neighbouring ring mountains,[2,3] which might be due to the roughness of their texture, or perhaps the absence of hoar-frost, occurring to some extent in all the other formations. In 1896 Goodacre made the following observation of Macrobius: 'Interior nearly filled with shadow at sunset; inner side of west wall very bright; there was seen a distinct penumbral fringe to the black shadow cast on it by the east wall: best seen using high powers.'* This may properly belong to Chapter 8 except for that great brightness of the sunlit west wall, which leads me to suspect a reflecting film formed by the partial precipitation of the gas that caused the penumbral effect. Sometimes chocolate shadows (Goodacre, Haas) were also seen, indicating both an obscuration and a reddening of light.

In the case of Eudoxus and Aristoteles we had a lack of symmetry in behaviour at sunrise and sunset, the sunrise effect not reappearing when the Sun was at the same altitude in the evening. On our interpretation this is perhaps not very surprising, as the rocks and the gas forming the deposit would be both somewhat warmer at sunset; the latter might be even largely absent, having dispersed in the course of the day.

This diurnal asymmetry is quite common. There are craters which appear equally bright, morning and evening; but many do not. Aristarchus

* Quoted from Patrick Moore's private note-book.

is very much a case in point; of dazzling brilliance at sunrise, it becomes dull and grey with the approach of the evening, only the central peak gleaming bright inside the bowl. It may, however, be contended that, whilst the inner slopes receiving the morning light are in full sight of the observer, those illumined by an evening Sun can only be seen in extreme foreshortening owing to the crater's proximity to the eastern limb. I do not believe this explanation is adequate, but it is *possible*. If so, however, a bright crater similarly located with regard to the western limb should behave in the opposite way. There exists such a crater—Proclus—but quite like Aristarchus it appears duller at sunset than at sunrise. Craters at the centre of the disk should show no preference either way, but some of them do.

Thus, once more, we have evidence of physical or physico-chemical change of seasonal nature.

Another curious phenomenon has been noted by Haas:[3] often an area, recently in the shade, remains darkened after the Sun has reached it, and that for days on end, without any definite relation to the inclination of the ground. It would appear that in this case the darker colour is due to the lower temperature, though, lunar rocks heating up very rapidly on the surface, the difference in the temperature would have to be seated at a certain depth below it. This may have physical significance.

In a general way the bright ray systems and haloes, so conspicuous round some craters at full Moon, do not appear until the Sun has reached an altitude of about 30 degrees at the latitude where his path passes through the zenith (this is not necessarily coincident with the equator), progressively becoming more prominent and again fading out with the declining Sun. This may be accounted for by the distribution of the light-coloured matter at the bottom of those small hollows that have been inferred from the study of the 'light-curves' of lunar features, and, indeed, the fact that the floor of the clefts, such as Schroeter's Valley, Ariadaeus, Triesnecker Clefts, etc., appear bright under a high Sun supports this interpretation. It is fairly clear that by and large the haloes of the smaller craters represent a similar, perhaps thicker, distribution of the same colouring material; and on the whole these haloes behave very much like the rays. But this is far from a universal rule.

According to Pickering,[6] the small crater Hell (near Tycho) brightens up with the progress of the lunation, whereas an opposite change is conspicuous on Piton, an isolated mountain in Palus Nebularum, at the western extremity of Mare Imbrium. Like its neighbour, Pico, Piton is snow-white at sunrise, but, while Pico is equally bright at sunset, the other peak is grey and dull at that time, and, to boot, not always to the same extent. This is especially apparent with monochromatic filters, which strengthens the suspicion that a real change is involved.

The small crater pair, Pickering and Messier, have been much observed in the hope of elucidating the apparent changes of their outline in the course of the lunation. Sometimes the one, sometimes the other of the two appears larger than its companion, while the shape alters from a circle to an oval or an inflated triangle.[7] Pickering explained these transformations by the evaporation and redeposition of hoar-frost round the rims of the snow-white craters, depending on whether this or that slope received more heat from the Sun. The high temperature of the lunar surface at midday is usually held to exclude this possibility, whether rightly or not is another question; but the changes themselves are fully authenticated. A coating of crystalline material might possibly simulate such changes. Yet, if so, with the slopes being generally symmetrical on all sides, one would expect dark areas to appear within the bright halo at certain angles of illumination as they do on folded silk, which is not the case, so that this explanation would seem to be largely washed out and the only convincing alternative is the formation and variation in the distribution of a deposit of some kind or other.

Another crater with a variable white halo is the famous Linné. Micrometric measurements of the halo have been made by several astronomers (Pickering, Barnard, Wirtz, Haas),[3] who all agree that the diameter of the halo is smallest at the local noon and most find it somewhat larger at sunrise than it is at sunset in conformity with the tendency noted before. Barnard made a number of measurements of the diameter of Linné before and after an eclipse (lunar), using the two largest refractors in the world, the 40-inch one at Yerkes and the 36-inch Lick instrument, and found a definite increase in the diameter at the end of the eclipse.[7] His result has been confirmed since, in this and other cases.

This shows clearly that this type of white halo contracts with a rise of temperature and *vice versa.*

Less is heard about Aristarchus, the Moon's most brilliant feature, and yet the white areas in and near this crater display changes of shape, distribution, and diameter fully as remarkable and much more conspicuous than those of Messier, Pickering, or Linné, the only difficulty of seeing these to advantage residing in the circumstance that they develop fully towards the end of the lunation, visible in the early hours of the morning when most observers at most times prefer the comforts of their beds to the splendours of heaven.

I have made a number of drawings of Aristarchus, some of which are given in Plate IX, where these changes are shown. The apparent shape of the crater may, no doubt, be affected by librations which will tilt it variously to the observer's line of sight, but the deformations of the outline are rather in excess of reasonable expectation and there can be no doubt whatever that the total area of the white material is considerably reduced, both inside and outside the cauldron of Aristarchus by the last quarter. It is however, the movement and transformation of the external white appendages of the crater that are perhaps the most remarkable. That weak ridges are in existence which do to some extent correspond with the apparent distribution of these white areas is not in doubt, but at a time when none of these cast visible shadows there seems to be no apparent reason why a part now of one, now of another of them should suddenly become or cease to be white-washed, unless a precipitation and/or disappearance, through evaporation or otherwise, of a white deposit of some kind had intervened. Furthermore, there is a movement of the shaded areas, both inside and outside the crater, which seems to keep pace with some of the changes in the distribution of white features, occurring precisely in the positions where one would expect the shadows cast by the latter if they were in suspension above the ground to fall.

Thus a suspicion is aroused that at least some of these white features are atmospheric veils or jets of finely divided white matter emitted by the crater, or some parts of it, such as the little white craterlet near the east rim where the peculiar handle-shaped white extension originates. However, this is a matter of interpretation.

The general course of these changes is reproduced every lunation, but there is considerable variation of detail which deserves further study.

Many dark features undergo comparable alterations each lunation. The shaded areas around Aristarchus have received little attention, but on the inner walls of the crater, and partly overrunning these, there are dusky radial bands, which develop, broaden, and darken as the Sun approaches the local meridian and a little after, to be wiped out at the approach of the evening. It is true that A. P. Lenham[1] denies the reality of these changes, but, while I highly respect him as an excellent observer, I feel that this is due to a kind of super-caution that arises out of looking too much at one and the same thing: in fact, the process is quite obvious to any unprejudiced student.

The basic distribution of the bands is repeated at the same phase, but their width, intensity, and minor features vary a good deal from case to case. The quality of seeing undoubtedly intervenes here to some extent, but the bands are not necessarily the darkest and clearest when the seeing is at its best, so that other factors must be present. These may be changeability of the markings themselves or partial obscuration, and my personal impression is that obscuration plays here an important part.

Moore[4] lists 33 craters with similar radial bands, but Abineri, Lenham, and Whitaker[1] have since brought their number up to 188, including several distinct types. There is some evidence for an association between radial bands and bright crater walls and rays, though banded craters appear to be absent from the heavily whitened region of Tycho. There are further dark markings which are really in the same category and which I have described as of the 'Maltese cross type'; one of the craters thus marked is Bullialdus (not listed by the cited authors). Copernicus, too, shows vestigial bands. In any event, these bands are very common on the Moon.

Radial bands are conspicuous by reason of their shape and position, but hosts of other dark markings, some of which have been covered by Haas's survey, behave in a similar way.

Near the centre of the Moon there is a cluster of very dark irregular blotches, comprised within a circle of about a thousand miles in diameter centred at the east end of Mare Vaporum. They resemble the radial bands in attaining maximum intensity near full Moon, though I have no evidence of any change in either their area or outline in the course of the lunation.

Pickering thus summarizes the results of sustained observation by him of the variable dark markings of the Moon:

'The general phenomena exhibited by a variable spot are a rapid darkening beginning shortly after sunrise followed by an equally rapid fading towards sunset. The darkening is sometimes accompanied by a diminution in size [this might be due to the simple optical illusion whereby a darker area of the same size as a brighter one appears smaller to the eye.—V. A. F.] and the fading by an increase. Near sunrise and sunset the spots are almost invisible. At their maximum some of the spots are intensely dark, some are a dark gray, and others a light gray. Near the equator the changes in density occur frequently in the course of a few hours after sunrise; in higher latitudes several days pass before the changes begin, but they are usually very rapid. No spots are known north of latitude $+55°$ and south of latitude $-60°$'. (*The Moon*, p. 56.)[7]

These findings are largely confirmed by Haas,[3] who also remarks that dark features seem to avoid smooth maria, except for the edges. The latter is very much the case in Mare Serenitatis and Mare Humorum. It would also appear that the dark areas are generally situated somewhat lower than lighter land, which might indicate specifically denser rock.

The radial bands follow the course of change described by Pickering, as also do a number of irregularly shaped markings, mainly inside craters, such as Atlas, Alphonsus, Hercules, Riccioli, Bullialdus, and Kepler.[3,4,6,7,9] A somewhat similar process is in progress in the maria as a whole. These are comparatively bright when they first emerge from the night, although the sunward hillsides are at this time at the apex of their brilliance, which should make the maria seem darker to the eye. To some extent this is true in their portions nearest to the terminator, where the lighting declines rapidly in any case. Nevertheless, this sunrise and sunset pallor of the maria is intriguing, for they are pock-marked with small hollows, traversed by wrinkle ridges and in places resemble in structure the pocketed surfaces of névées or summer snows in the mountains. All these unevennesses cast small shadows, which one would expect to cause a general darkening. Yet a mare does not begin to darken till it is well away from the terminator, and sometimes days after sunrise, achieving the maximum intensity of shade at or close to the lunar noon. Mare Frigoris, the most polar of the larger maria, is especially tardy in darkening and remains pale long after Mare Serenitatis and Mare Imbrium have assumed a deeper tint. The effect may be related to libration, though hardly to the slight variation of the altitude of the Sun due to lunar seasons, but Mare Frigoris differs in shade from lunation to lunation and sometimes is barely distinguishable from the lunarite highlands.

This is paralleled by the marked brilliance of the polar regions, especially the northern, though I have known the south polar lands to be brighter than the north, possibly owing to the same factors which cause a similar fluctuation in the tint of Mare Frigoris. Anyway, these bright 'polar caps' likewise appear to contract towards full phase, as though they, too, were governed by thermal effects, which would tally well with the apparent absence of variable dark markings in high latitudes, though, most of these being situated on crater floors, this may be due, at least in part, simply to perspective.

At the centre of the disk, and thus beautifully placed for observation, the ring mountain of Eratosthenes displays a most striking constellation of variable markings. These develop rapidly with increasing phase into a conspicuous cluster of smudgy pseudo-shadows, non-coincident with the outlines of the crater and largely disregarding its steep ridges and terraces, particularly on the west side. Neither hollows nor crystals could produce this effect, as they would be required to give identical reflections despite most diverse inclination of the slope within a single clearly bounded area.

Pickering, observing in the excellent atmospheric conditions of the hills of Jamaica, devoted years of his life to the study of these ever-changing features, among which he mapped a veritable maze of lines and streamers intersecting in dark spots in the manner of Martian 'canals'.[5,7] Indeed he used the term 'canal' quite freely, although this appears to be rather unfortunate when applied to the Moon in view of the overtones it has acquired. He found that, whilst the general pattern of changes followed a recognizable course every lunation, some of the markings shifted about in an unpredictable fashion, advancing up the inner slopes of the crater and spilling over the ridges as though they were composed of swarms of small animals, small because of the comparative slowness of their movements. Thus originated the famous story of 'lunar insects' which has brought undeserved discredit on his otherwise excellent observations. For there can be no doubt that Pickering was an excellent and painstaking observer, much more successful in depicting what he saw than many of his critics.

In the British conditions and with a less powerful instrument I have been unable to trace the minor 'canals' drawn by Pickering and am generally inclined to suspect that he fell into the common error of exaggerating the linearity of lunar markings, which often appear to me as irregular curves. Yet it has been noted by Haas[3] and others that the variable dark markings are associated, in common with the bright ones, with small craterlets and crevices, so that a good case can be made for the rectilinear appearance of at least some of them, as witness the radial bands on the crater walls. Though, once more, Patrick Moore saw some of these resolve into irregular chains of minor detail when observing with the 32-inch refractor at Meudon.[4]

However this may be, the main 'plats' and 'runs' represented and described by Pickering are undoubtedly there and they do change in outline and position with the progress of the lunar day, first darkening, then creeping away from the centre of the crater, while thickening round the periphery, and eventually fading out with the approach of evening shadows. The pseudo-shadows of Bullialdus, a crater of similar age and character, would likewise appear to follow a comparable course of development.[3]

The non-seasonal movements of Pickering's 'runs' have not definitely been confirmed by other observers; but neither have they been disproved and nobody else has brought so much care to their study as did Pickering, so that there is probably something in his contention, even though his observations could easily be explained by, say, heavy vapours issuing from vents or cracks within the volcanic complex of Eratosthenes which need not be all active simultaneously, or follow any set pattern.

Haas[3] observes that both the dark and the bright markings have a tendency to occur opposite the Sun and at least the latter have been seen both by Pickering[8] and himself to rotate inside the crater bowls so as to keep facing the Sun. I have noticed this, too, but in the case of bright areas this may be partly due simply to the fact that any slope facing the Sun will be most intensely lit. This explanation, though, cannot apply to *dark* features, so that generally speaking the heat of sunrays appears to be essential for either type of marking to develop. It will be recalled that in Pickering's view vulcanism on the Moon remains dormant until the Sun has reached a certain height above the horizon.

Thus all these lunar phenomena appear to be closely connected with the main season cycle of the lunar day and fall into one easily recognizable scheme.

The variation of the tint (intensity) and shade (density) of lunar markings is often associated with colour effects to be considered in the next Chapter.

REFERENCES

1. ABINERI, K. W. and LENHAM, A. P. 'Lunar Banded Craters.' *J.B.A.A.*, Vol. 65 No. 4, London, 1955.

SEASONAL CHANGES

2. AVIGLIANO, D. P. 'Unusual Lunar Shadows.' *The Strolling Astronomer*, Vol. 7. Las Cruces, New Mexico, 1952.
3. HAAS, W. H. 'Does Anything Ever Happen on the Moon?' *The Journal of the Royal Astronomical Society of Canada*, Vol. 36, No. 7, 1942.
4. MOORE, PATRICK. *Guide to the Moon.* Eyre and Spottiswoode, London, 1953.
5. PICKERING, W. H. 'Eratosthenes, 1–6.' *Popular Astronomy*, Nos. 269, 287, 295, 312, 317; 1919–25.
6.   'Lunar Changes.' *7th Report of the Section for the Observation of the Moon, British Astronomical Association.* London, 1916.
7.   *The Moon.* Doubleday, Page and Co., New York, 1903.
8.   'The Snow Peaks of Theophilus.' *Popular Astronomy*, Vol. 25, 1917.
9. WILKINS, P. H. *Our Moon.* Muller, London, 1954.

10

COLOURS AND HUES

IMPRESSIONS OF COLOUR are proverbially subjective.
De gustibus—et coloribus—non est disputandum. One should not argue about tastes and colours. Yet, if colour is a sensation, the wavelength of light to which it corresponds is a physical entity and can be precisely described. Discrepancies in judgment arise from the fact that different people do not necessarily associate the same hues with light of the same wavelengths, and this is especially true when faint colourings are assessed. Colour blindness apart, the intensity of reaction of individual eyes to particular wavelengths appears to vary, especially towards the two ends of the 'optical window'. Younger people would seem to see a little more of the spectrum at the violet end, where the normal eye is more sensitive in dim light. In the yellow, which is at the centre of the sensitivity range of the eye in full lighting, there does not seem to be any great difference between individuals. But within the red and green, where much of the colour blindness occurs, not all eyes are alike in dim lighting or when faint traces of the colour only are present.[14,15]

I will always remember how in the blackout during the war a match struck at a distance or a lit cigarette used to seem grass-green, though at close quarters they looked red. Thus with a neutral colouring when the light is faint the eye has a green bias, and when it is strong a red bias. Otherwise, in dim lighting blues and violets appear intensified (Purkinje effect).

On the Moon most colourings are faint. In fact, at first sight she is a very colourless place. Possibly this impression is partly due to the habit of looking at black-and-white lunar photographs and drawings. Personally I can see hardly any colour on the Moon unless and until I ask myself the question of how I would paint a certain feature of the surface; then I begin to try in my mind, and even better on paper, to match what I see with paints from a paint-box. Suddenly colour appears where only light and shade were before, and, having come, it stays.

One of the most definitely coloured areas of the Moon is the diamond-shaped stretch of ground to the north-east of Aristarchus. It is of a mustard-yellow hue, which can easily be made out if the Moon is high and clear. The greenish-khaki tone of the south-western foothills of the Apennines, where these mountains touch the Haemus range, is almost equally strong.

However this may be, even with a moderate aperture and magnification of between 100 and 200 diameters a full Moon makes a dazzling sight, for here a brilliantly sunlit landscape is presented suddenly to an eye adjusted to the delicate gradations of night lighting. Small wonder it appears as a grey-and-white expanse. One way of dealing with it is to stop the telescope to a smaller aperture. Yet the American student of lunar colour D. P. Avigliano[1] recommends using a reflector (a reflecting telescope is free from chromatic aberration and therefore preferable to a refractor in colour work) of 8–10 inches in diameter and a focal ratio of $\frac{1}{8}$ to intensify the colours and maintains that these are more difficult to see when the brilliance of the image is reduced. There may be something in that— theoretically—but I doubt if many observers will support this point of view. A possible way of reconciling the contradictory requirements is to use a large aperture with moderate magnification and block off most of the disk, so that only a small area is presented to the eye at a time. The simplest method is to withdraw the eye from the eye-piece: the 'pupil' of the eye-piece contracts quickly but the apparent size of the image is not affected, so that any particular feature can easily be isolated.

Colours seen at small phase are usually more distinct, though often different from those observed when the Moon is full. The reduction in the glare may have something to do with this, though the angle of illumination and reflection is certainly a very important factor. It is essential, however, for direct colour determination that the Moon should be high up in the sky and the air as clear as possible. When colour filters are used this condition may not be equally important, though still highly desirable.

When low down the Moon appears golden, which is, of course, due to the intervention of our own atmosphere and the scattering by it of the light of short wavelengths, so that the transmitted light is 'reddened' as a result ('reddening' means a shift of greatest intensity towards the red end of the spectrum). In fact, in thinking of lunar colours we must always take the Earth's atmosphere into account. It is there even if the Moon is directly overhead. If all of our air could be compressed to sea-level density it would form a uniform layer $5\frac{1}{2}$ miles deep. This is the so-called equivalent atmosphere, sometimes referred to as 'air mass'. Its transparency will vary from case to case, but unless we are on a high mountain there will always be at least 5 miles of air at sea-level density between our eye and any celestial object directly overhead and a good deal more than that in most cases, for the zenith is merely a point that is seldom reached by a celestial object, which, moreover, will never remain anywhere near it for long.

Thus in comparing lunar and planetary colourings with those of familiar terrestrial objects we must think not in terms of our immediate surroundings but of horizon views, 7 to 10 miles distant and preferably seen through a telescope. Mountains are particularly suitable for comparison, both because the Moon is a mountainous world and because our mountains rise above the ground haze or mist and are thus reasonably free from the coarser effects of atmospheric obscuration. As a rule distant views of mountains show very little colour. I observed Scottish hills through the same telescope as I was using for lunar observation and found that by and large the variety of hue was not much greater than on the Moon, although grass, heather, peat, scree, bare rock, water, and snow were present.

This is instructive and there can be no doubt whatever that if we could see the Moon without the interference of our air she would appear far more colourful than she does now, which, though, does not mean to deny that most lunar colourings are slight as compared with those of Mars or Jupiter. They are, in fact, best revealed by indirect methods, foremost of which is the use of monochromatic filters.

A monochromatic filter transmits only a narrow band of wavelengths, for instance, within the red part of the spectrum. If red is present in the observed lunar markings these will appear brighter through a red filter than they do to the unaided eye; but a green or blue filter will suppress the red component in the reflected light, so that these markings will look darker by comparison with their surroundings. A yellowish surface may be comparatively bright with both a green and a red filter, and, of course, brightest of all with a yellow one. A blue or violet filter, on the other hand, may show it as coal-black and vice versa. Monochromatic filters not only reveal slight hues that the eye would be able to perceive directly in favourable conditions; they also allow a distinction to be made between different whites, blacks, and greys which seem all alike without filters. The white of snow is not quite the same as the seemingly identical white of quartz or magnesia, and so on. By the use of infra-red and ultra-violet filters together with either the photographic plate or the electronic image-converter 'colour' study can be extended beyond the visible range of the 'optical window' and also yield valuable information.

Polarimetry is in many ways similar to colour study; only here the differences in the studied light reside not in the wavelength but in the direction of those electro-magnetic oscillations which are responsible for the sensation of light. In a ray of ordinary unpolarized light the oscillations are always normal to the direction of the ray but they may and do occur along any of the innumerable normal lines that can be drawn to this direction at any point. To make it clearer, let us stick a pin vertically into a sheet of paper and let this pin stand for the direction of the ray. Any straight line drawn on the paper and passing through the centre of the pin-hole will be normal to the pin, and in unpolarized light oscillations along all possible normal lines are jumbled together. In polarized light, however, oscillations along one or another of these lines predominate; and in fully polarized light all other oscillations will be completely excluded. Thus unpolarized light resembles white light, produced by jumbling the spectrum, whereas polarized light is analogous to monochromatic colour.

All reflected light is polarized to some extent and this polarization differs depending on the nature of the reflecting surface.

The angle and degree of polarization can be determined by means of a polarimeter, consisting usually of a pair of nicol prisms, each of which transmits oscillations only in a single line (or plane). These prisms can be rotated and with crossed nicols no light will pass. Polarizing filters can likewise be used.

However, to revert to colour filters, filters used in photography are not usually fully monochromatic; they give preference to one colour without eliminating the others. Such filters are not much use for our purpose, but the tricolour separation filters used in the manufacture of colour films and for some other purposes are very nearly monochromatic, or, to be more precise, they separate out as nearly as possible the three distinctive colour responses of the colour-sensitives cones in the retina.[14,15] In most lunar work imperfectly monochromatic filters were used in the past, which led to somewhat disappointing results. Further, in order to be able to trace faint gradations of intensity comparison must be made quickly, so that if we are to fiddle with filters, exchanging them by hand, the freshness of the impressions will be lost and our judgment correspondingly impaired.

In my device I had a set of filters, monochromatic and dichromatic (transmitting two colours), mounted on a swivel beyond the eye-piece, so that any of them could be brought to bear on the Moon in a fraction of a second. The results referred to below have been obtained in this way and cover several hundred determinations made in different lunations over a period of about three years.

This work, taken together with the data amassed by other observers, collectively and individually, clearly shows that various colours exist on the Moon and that many of these are subject to variation in the course of the lunar day, and possibly to some unperiodic, or long-period, changes as well. There exists a wide area of agreement between individual investigators, but, perhaps not surprisingly, considerable marginal differences persist, especially with regard to the brown and green hues, the same features being described by some as brown, while others at the same time profess to see them green.[1,2]

Before considering my own results, which refer to some extent to aspects of the situation not covered in the other observations, we must review in brief the work of earlier investigators.

Between 1910 and 1930 photographs of the Moon were taken through colour filters at several observatories. The first of these attempts would appear to have been made by R. W. Wood in the U.S.A., but some work on the same lines was initiated soon after in Germany and Russia. In particular Miethe and Seegert used an interesting method of projecting their photographs obtained by ultra-violet and orange light on to a screen through filters of complementary colour, which reversed the effect, showing a negative as a positive in correct colour (within the chosen range). By this means they have been able to identify numerous chromatic differences on the surface of the Moon, most of which have been subsequently verified in the survey made at Lick by W. H. Wright and Miss Dorothy Applegate in 1926.

These investigators used ultra-violet, violet, green, orange, red, and extreme red, between the wavelengths of 3,600 Å and 7,600 Å, and secured some very fine negatives with the Crossley Reflector. Six of these are reproduced as actual photographic prints with Wright's paper appearing in *Publications of the Astronomical Society of the Pacific*,[12] where they can be studied with a magnifying glass. The photographs have been taken in pairs with ultra-violet and extreme red light at waxing gibbous, full and waning gibbous Moon. (See Plate XI.)

The comparison is highly instructive and will be referred to in the course of this and following chapters. Yet it will be seen that with images chromatically thus spaced any markings of intermediate colour, including the light greens in particular, will come out about equal in intensity in both impressions. Moreover, the photographic processes used in the two cases have been different, so that some difficult allowances have to be made to bring the effect down to a common denominator. Wright tried to overcome this by establishing intensity scales for each colour and such devices as printing all negatives in the same grade of hardness; but any photographer will realize that such methods are very crude and Wright admits their limitations. In this respect direct visual comparison is unquestionably superior, though it does not result in an objective record, such as a photograph.

Wright observes that there is not much overall difference between the images of the Moon in different colours (though again if the photographs are scaled down to the same level it is not easy to see how such differences could be brought to light), but that local inequalities exist. However, his photographs seem to indicate plainly, which he does not mention, that the maria are generally more uniform in ultra-violet, whilst light of longer wavelengths appears to be prevalent among the highlands and some special regions of the maria as well. Thus he does remark on the pallor of Mare Frigoris in extreme red (I have found this area distinctly yellowish in tinge). Apart from the Aristarchus 'diamond', the most conspicuous colour areas, showing dark in extreme red and so presumably green or blue, are in the north-east of Mare Imbrium, just south of Sinus Iridum, and in Mare Tranquillitatis, whence this colour appears to spill over round the edges of the neighbouring plains. Otherwise there is a good deal of red and yellow in Oceanus Procellarum, parts of Mare Imbrium and Mare Serenitatis.

Miethe and Seegert have found Grimaldi very dark in longer wave-

PLATE XI The Moon photographed by (*left*) ultra-violet and (*right*) extreme red light. (Taken with the 36-inch Crossley reflector at Lick by W. H. Wright and D. Applegate, 1926.) (*Page 102*)

PLATE XII The country south of Copernicus has a washed appearance, as if it had been swept by tremendous floods. *(Pages 44, 158)*

lengths, which Wright's photographs do not show, though violet has been seen there visually by some observers. The differences they have observed in Mare Crisium have not been definitely confirmed at Lick.[12]

In recent years and more or less simultaneously with myself D. P. Avigliano, in the U.S.A., carried out a systematic colour survey of the Moon, visually, with and without filters, and photographically.[1] Since black, grey, and white, which he lists among the colours observed by him, represent the absence of colouring, while brown may be regarded as only a shade of yellow, Avigliano has found on the Moon two colours and two colours only: yellow and a little red. He could see none of the greens, blues, and purples reported by other observers, and claims that this result is fully confirmed by the colour photographs taken by him, although another American observer, Latimer Wilson, is said to have obtained colour photographs showing green in the maria.

Colour photography, however, is far from the impartial test one might expect it to be. If any one colour is present to excess it tends to smother all other hues. Over-exposure gives a red bias and, conversely, under-exposed films exaggerate the shorter wavelengths of light, which is an analogue of the Purkinje effect. Suppose now that Avigliano tended to over-expose his films, as his addiction to great brightness of the image leads one to suspect, while Wilson under-exposed his, we shall have the results as quoted without anything being proved thereby.

It is *a priori* improbable that no colours other than red and yellow exist on the Moon, and green, blue, and violet hues have been recorded by nearly all the other observers. These colours are also clearly indicated by Wright's photographs. Avigliano himself admits as much and suggests differences in individual vision as a possible explanation. Indeed, in many cases the colour observed seems to have been olive or khaki, as it were on the margin between the green and the brown, so that a slight colour bias would be quite sufficient to tilt the scale. Similarly, the purple is usually described as brownish, and in this context blue and grey fall very close together.

Yet there is no denying that yellows and browns are present in many parts of the Moon. The intensity curve of the lunar spectrum shows a pronounced reddening of light as compared with direct sunlight,[9] which would confirm the prevalence of these hues and usually indicates the presence of an atmosphere, for the light is reddened in passing through a layer of gas, a striking example of which is provided by our sunsets and sunrises. From the study of polarization of moonlight B. Lyot concluded that the average behaviour of lunar rocks is best reproduced by that of a mixture of grey and brown volcanic ash. He also found that the Moon, Mercury, and Mars are all covered by a layer of dust of either meteoritic or volcanic origin.[6] On the other hand, we may recall that Landerer found the polarization of

H

light reflected from the maria to correspond to that of obsidian, a volcanic glass which often affects a greenish hue, though it may simultaneously appear brownish or reddish in transmitted light, and vice versa.

Avigliano notes a rusty-brown hue along the terminator, which he ascribes to a lunar atmosphere.[1] It has already been mentioned that Goodacre, Haas, and some other observers attributed a chocolate tone to some of the lighter shadows inside lunar craters, which might constitute a comparable effect. I have seen the shadow in Plato appear darkest in blue, which would indicate a brownish colouring.

Colours have been seen on the Moon by most of the distinguished selenographers, such as Gruithuisen, Mädler, Klein, Schmidt, Birt, Pickering, Wilkins, Haas, to mention but a few.[2,3,4,6,10] In the years 1934–7 colour observations were made in Germany by the *Arbeitsgruppe für Mondbeobachtungen* (Working Group for Lunar Observations) headed by Kaiser. Among others green colour was recorded in Mare Serenitatis, occasional brown in Plato, as well as a cycle of colour variation in Ptolemaeus from grey to olive green in the lunar morning and thence to a yellowish tone towards the evening. Similar group observations were carried on in the U.S.A. in the years 1936–8 under the direction of Walter H. Haas, who has presented their results in a paper published in *The Journal of the Royal Astronomical Society of Canada*.[2] Finally, Rudaux and de Vaucouleures's work *Astronomie* contains a colour chart of the Moon compiled by the former,[6] which is in fairly good agreement with the results obtained in America and Germany. At first sight the colours in it appear somewhat exaggerated. This, however, is partly due to the fact that the disk of the Moon is not properly shaded, and partly to the fact that not all colours can be observed at the same time. Indeed, from my own study I can confirm that most of them are undoubtedly there in undiminished intensity, once these two points are allowed for.

It is almost impossible to produce a wholly satisfactory colour chart of the Moon, as many of the colourings are transient and can be seen only at a certain phase, while different and differently distributed colours may be seen at one and the same place under different illuminations, whether by reason of real physico-chemical change, or merely because the colour depends on the angle of incidence and reflection of light as it often does with semi-transparent materials, it is difficult to decide.

Rudaux and de Vaucouleurs note that coloured areas are often sharply delimited and of geometrical outline, being bordered by those light-tinted lines and streamers which are so characteristic of many portions of the lunar surface, especially in the maria.[6]

If now the Moon is covered by volcanic or meteoritic dust, as polarimetric data appear to show, one would expect all colour, nay, difference of tint, to have been entirely effaced beneath a uniform grey pall, as it would be 'in a long neglected household', to use Rudaux's simile. One might even go further and invoke Öpik's argument for Mars.[11] He pointed out that the green areas of that planet must have regenerative powers, for else they would long have been smothered by a red deposit brought by the frequent dust-storms and become indistinguishable from the rest of the surface. Vegetation alone is capable of overgrowing the dust brought by the winds. On the Moon there are no dust-storms, nor ordinary winds for that matter. Even so a slow obliterating action of meteoritic dust must be present and in a geologically short period would produce much the same result.

The existence of areas differing in shade and colour may not by itself be sufficient to establish organic processes on the Moon, but it does constitute indubitable evidence of change on a considerable scale within recent and present time, which it is simply impossible to brush aside.

Haas thus sums up the results of his and his group's colour observations:

'2. Low-sun colours are relatively striking but very transient, seldom being distinguishable between relative colongitudes 30° and 150° [that is to say, within the middle $\frac{2}{3}$ of the lunation.—V. A. F.] The hues are usually greens, sometimes browns, and perhaps occasionally purples (or blues). Though infrequent even along the terminator, these colours affect chiefly very dark crater floors near that line.

'3. High-sun colours are very inconspicuous but very stable. . . . The colours are blues (or purples) in the high-sun dark areas, especially the darkest ones; browns in delicate darker shadings on dark floors, the use of different filters having confirmed these browns to the extent of showing that some marks are redder than others; and greens over large dark areas, although greens more than 2 days from the terminator are very rare. Blue and brown are probably sometimes both present in the same area.' (p. 43).[2]

Wilkins in *Our Moon*[10] (pp. 130–2) writes:

'The greenish tint is generally seen either on the plains, especially the Sea of Conflicts (Mare Crisium), and the Sea of Peace (M. Tranquillitatis) and the smaller Sea of Humours, or within such craters as Grimaldi and Ptolemy. . . . Sea of Conflicts shows the greenish hue best near sunrise and sunset. . . . The Sea of Humours is often a fine light green, especially close to sunrise and sunset; while the Sea of Peace is a clear greenish tint near full moon. . . .

'When the sky is very clear and the lighting favourable the Sea of Peace looks very green. . . .'

I have never seen the brilliant greens in Mare Crisium and am inclined to suspect that the faint-light green bias operates here, but without filters I have noticed an olive tone in Maria Tranquillitatis and Serenitatis, a bottle green in the dark spots of Sinus Medii and Mare Vaporum, and on 11 September, 1954, I made the following entry in my note-book: *Western maria, also Humorum and Vaporum, noticeably darker than the eastern in all*

105

colours, but especially in dichromatic purple (red and blue), *which throws them into bold relief. This would indicate a green tinge. Oceanus Procellarum and Mare Frigoris very pale in green and yellow. A yellowish-green hue can be made out even without filters.* (My results are in this case beautifully confirmed by Wright's photographs.)[12] Indeed, this yellowish green tone appears to me to be most widespread on the Moon, varying from brimstone to khaki in shade. On that occasion it was a full Harvest Moon, high up in the sky and very clear, though the telescopic image was somewhat unsteady, which, however, is of little importance in global colour estimates.

Filters make it abundantly clear that the green component is very strong in the light of a young Moon, even when it appears reddish to the eye against the blue twilight sky (the green bias does not affect the filter view), and, once more asymmetrically, not quite so strong in that of a waning crescent. Thus, for instance, on 24 April, 1955, despite haze and a low position in the sky, which would normally enhance the red at the expense of other colours, the crescent Moon appeared brightest with a green filter. This greenness does not affect the maria or the crater floors only but is spread over the totality of lunar features and is also very prominent in the earthlit portion. The earthshine is usually described as bluish, but my colour tests always put it first in green. Most of the bright crater rims, floors, and rays are likewise brightest in green. Occasionally terminator heights also show a strong green reaction, though as a rule they are brightest in *red*. I have verified this time and again and regard it as significant.

As the Sun climbs higher into the lunar sky and warms up the ground this greenness fades away rapidly.

What hides behind these appearances?

It is pretty obvious that this green tinge cannot be due to vegetation even if conditions are otherwise suitable for it to exist, for it coincides with very low temperatures. Yet, surprisingly enough, the snow reflects most strongly in the green part of the solar spectrum and comparatively poorly in the red and violet, in which respect it differs conspicuously from, say, white quartz which seems to glow in red and blue, as well as is a good reflector of violet rays. I have never had an opportunity to examine dry ice (carbon dioxide snow) through filters and have no data regarding its reflectivity; it may behave similarly to water snow. I have, on the other hand, observed through a telescope distant hill-sides lightly powdered with hoar-frost and their filter reaction was not dissimilar to that of a crescent Moon. It is, therefore, not impossible that the effect is due also here to a fine precipitation of ice and perhaps dry ice, which quickly evaporates in the heat of the Sun.

This interpretation is also corroborated by the fact that while the green element in the maria declines they become paler in the violet, appearing at the same time darker in all the other wavelengths. This result could be explained by assuming some special properties of the reflecting medium, but such an explanation is rather strained; while it is well known that gas scatters primarily the shorter wavelengths of the spectrum (Rayleigh's Law), to which among others the blue colouring of the sky is due, so that its presence manifests itself first of all in the ultra-violet and violet, as in the famous photographs of Mars taken by Wright. The evaporating hoar-frost might thus form a thin layer of gas over the low-lying ground, such as the maria, the floor of Grimaldi, where this effect is strongly marked, and a few other localities.

When the disk of the Moon is viewed through a set of monochromatic filters it will be noticed that in the red the maria are dark, the general relief is clear, the terminator detail being particularly well defined. The differences in brilliance due to the angle of illumination appear to be fairly smoothed out, whilst the brightening-up at the limb, which is very noticeable direct, is present but not striking. With a yellow filter the maria are generally paler, the contrasts of light-and-shade are somewhat flattened, as it were, except for a few minor markings which appear very dark (e.g. the dark spots in Eratosthenes). The green brings out very distinctly all the bright features and Tycho's rays in particular, but there is a perceptible fading of light along the terminator, the brilliance of the limb being enhanced simultaneously. In the blue the terminator is distinctly dull; some of its highlights can be barely made out; but the limb is much brighter than the rest of the disk and this brightness spreads out at the poles into a kind of caps.* There are also several minor bright areas referred to in Chapter 9. In the violet the whole is duller still, the terminator detail being barely visible unless the Moon be very high up and the sky clear, and the limb brilliance narrower than in the blue, though still strong. So too are the polar 'caps', often appearing slightly hazy, as though seen through a luminous veil.

The violet is very sensitive to the state of the atmosphere and when the Moon is low it is but poorly represented. This, however, only serves to underline the comparative intensities of different parts of the disk; for instance, the terminator will be almost invisible but the polar 'caps' very bright nevertheless.

On 22 July, 1954, I observed the sunset on the Apennines. The Moon was low, which depleted the violet component, thus intensifying the usual effect. In the red the summits of the range shone like a string of lamps spaced along the dark pool of the advancing night; they were easily the most striking feature of the half-Moon. A flick of the finger brought the violet filter forward and, suddenly, all this glory was gone: the mountains

---

* The brilliance of these in the blue was remarked upon by Pickering, who observed visually, but Wright failed to see any of the listed effects in his photographs.

were a dull grey, though the limb and the 'caps' continued to glow as usual. I repeated the observation again and again. This was thrilling, for it meant that the sunset on the Lunar Apennines was *really* red, perhaps not quite so red as it appeared but red all the same.

Just as the brilliance of the limb in the violet, this reddening of light at sunset indicated the presence of gas, probably filled with minute crystals of water or carbon dioxide, analogous to the Violet Layer of the atmosphere of Mars.[8] This redness of the terminator has also been commented upon by Avigliano, who could see it without filters,[1] which I do not. Somewhat similar terminator effects have also been seen by others *without filters*; but with a red and a violet monochromatic filter they are within anybody's reach at any time, though the intensity of the contrast seems to vary not only by reason of the changing transparency of our own atmosphere and the altitude of the Moon.

On the east limb of the Moon there is a marginal Mare Orientale, occasionally brought into view by a favourable libration, and just in front of it runs a conspicuous beaded line of dark lunabase named *Mare Veris* by Franz. This is a very clear feature, at any rate when viewed directly or with red, green, and yellow filters (See Fig. 1). Yet in blue and violet it is often strikingly pale and sometimes almost invisible. One might perhaps expect something of the kind from the general brightness of the limb in these colours, but this does not by itself explain it, and also I have just said that this effect is not always present. It might be said that a violet-blue colouring occasionally appears on the floor of the Valley, but this explanation does not ring true and obscuration by gas, or rather a 'blue cloud', similar to the concentrations of crystalline matter in the Violet Layer of Mars, suggests itself at once as a more likely alternative. The behaviour of stars at occultation in blue light observed by me serves further to corroborate this view.[13]

There are several other regions where such 'blue clouds' or 'mists' seem to occur (*see* Chapter 8). One of these is north-east of Aristarchus. It is a conspicuously yellow area, which should normally make it very dark in violet and ultra-violet, as indeed it has been found to be by some observers. Wright's ultra-violet exposures show the area very dark at the northern edge.[12] And yet I have often seen it pale through a violet filter, while A. G. Smith, who observed the Moon with an electronic image-converter in the infra-red and ultra-violet, has also failed to see the darkening expected here in the latter.[7] He saw Grimaldi pale in the ultra-violet, which agrees well with my own violet observations. In addition he notes a bright ultra-violet area between Copernicus and the southern Apennines, which may indicate gas exhalation, possibly from the longitudinal chain of small craterlets passing about midway between Copernicus and Eratosthenes. Further, Smith draws attention to the peculiar behaviour of some of the bright rays, which sometimes showed strongly in the infra-red and sometimes in the ultra-violet.

Such are the general features. As for minor instances of colour, most changeable dark markings show some colouring, usually green, brown, or blue, which are often interchangeable, passing into one another. The shaded areas of Eratosthenes, however, have a distinct violet tone. This has been noted by Pickering[5] and is startlingly confirmed by monochromatic filters when comparison is made with the near-by greenish markings of Sinus Medii and Mare Vaporum. The effect is clearly shown if one compares Wright's extreme red and ultra-violet pictures of the full Moon.[12]

The French astronomer G. Delmotte in a private letter to Patrick Moore mentions a 'rough band' in Atlas which 'took on a dark violet-tinted colour which disappeared during lunar eclipses'. The Haas group records here a 'slight brownish hue, perhaps very slightly tinted with purple'.[2] Violet colour has also been seen near Mount Hadley in the Apennines[4] and Haas notes a persistent purple hue in Hercules. In a private letter to me the late H. MacEwen wrote of an 'occasional' purple colour 'resembling heather in bloom' in some craters. 'Deep purple' was seen by Haas in Riccioli on 28 September, 1937, though otherwise this area appeared to him to be brown.[2] The same observer records 'bluish grey or purplish grey' in the dark part of Schickard.

Green appears in many craters at sunrise and sunset, but a large number, perhaps the majority, of the dark markings, including radial bands, look very dark in both red and violet, which denotes a green tone, also under a high Sun. Reddish colourings are rarer, but a shortlived orange to rose-red tone has been seen around the small crater Lichtenberg by Mädler, Barcroft, and Baum.

Some markings, among which I would class the dark area of Riccioli, are of an indefinite blue-brown hue which Rudaux describes as *enfumé*— smoked.[6]

It would exceed the scope of the present work to go into full details of the various, in part discordant, colour observations made on individual formations. The general picture is that the Moon appears greener at sunrise than at sunset, and greener at a small phase or near the terminator than when near full and close to the subsolar point. This may in part be due to a greenish colouring of sub-transparent volcanic glasses, or their lunar counterparts, occurring especially in the maria, and in part to the latent colour of thin hoar-frost, be it H_2O or CO_2, precipitated in the night's cold and to a less extent at the approach of the evening. The diminution of the green component in the moonlight is paralleled by an intensification of the violet hue in the maria, certain craters and other localized areas. This may be due to evolution of gas.

Formation of 'blue clouds', particularly in the polar regions where the hoar-frost is thicker and largely endures throughout the lunar day, is indicated. These clouds would seem to lie very close to the ground.

Sunlight at the terminator is appreciably redder than under a high Sun and occasionally the effect is striking. It is difficult to account for this in any other way than on the assumption of scattering by gas, probably laden with minute crystals. Part of the reddening of the sunlight reflected by the Moon may be due to the same cause, and so too would be the short-wave brilliance of the limb, where a blue tone has been observed on mountains and other features (Baum, Firsoff).

Some green, brown, blue, and violet hues persist in the maria and inside the crater enclosures. These may in part represent the intrinsic colouring of the rocks or superficial deposits; yet some of these coloured areas display regular alterations in intensity, position, and extent in the course of the lunation, which implies physical or chemical change, including possibly biological activity, depending on the heat of sunrays.

We have thus approached the problem of lunar atmosphere, but in order to be able to tackle this with any hope of success we must first make acquaintance with the climatic conditions obtaining on the Moon. These form the subject of the next chapter.

REFERENCES

1. AVIGLIANO, D. P. 'Lunar Colors.' *The Strolling Astronomer*, Vol. 8, Nos. 5 and 6.
2. HAAS, W. H. 'Does Anything Ever Happen on the Moon?' *The Journal of the Royal Astronomical Society of Canada*, Vol. 36, No. 7, 1942.
3.   'Color Changes on the Moon.' *Popular Astronomy*, No. 446.
4. PICKERING, W. H. 'The Double Canal of the Lunar Crater Aristillus.' *Popular Astronomy*, Vol. 22.
5.   'Eratosthenes, 1–6.' *Popular Astronomy*, Vols. 29, 30, 32.
6. RUDAUX, L. and DE VAUCOULEURS, G. *Astronomie*. Larousse, Paris, 1948.
7. SMITH, A. G. 'Lunar and Planetary Observations with an Electronic Image Converter.' *The Strolling Astronomer*, Vol. 7.
8. VAUCOULEURS, G. DE. *Physics of Planet Mars*. Faber, London, 1954.
9. WHIPPLE, F. L. *Earth, Moon and the Planets*. Churchill, London 1946.
10. WILKINS, H. P. *Our Moon*. Muller, London, 1954.
11. ÖPIK, E. J. *The Irish Astronomical Journal*, Vol. 45, No. 1, 1950.
12. WRIGHT, W. H. 'The Moon as Photographed by Light of Different Colors.' *Publications of the Astronomical Society of the Pacific*, Vol. XLI, No. 241, June 1929.
13. FIRSOFF, V. A. 'Lunar Occultations Observed in Blue Light and the Problem of the Moon's Atmosphere.' *J.B.A.A.*, Vol. 66, No. 7, 1956.
14. PIRENNE, M. H. *Vision and the Eye*. Pilot Press, London, 1948.
15. WRIGHT, W. D. *The Perception of Light*. Blackie, Glasgow, 1938.

11

BETWEEN THE HEAT AND THE COLD

As COMPARED with the complicated climatic zones and seasons of the Earth, the regime on the Moon is simplicity itself. The year and the day are one; and although the Moon undergoes a whole medley of movements affecting her orbit, orbital velocity and orientation relatively to the Earth, her axial spin and the axis about which she spins remain substantially unchanged. We will recall that while her orbital velocity varies with the distance from the Earth her axial rotation is uniform, the discrepancies between the two causing librations in longitude.

Her polar axis, however, pays no respect to either the Earth or her own orbit; it is related directly to the Sun and preserves a constant inclination of about 1° 35' to the axis of the ecliptic, or the Earth's orbit round the Sun. Owing to this peculiar arrangement, the inclination of the lunar equator to the ecliptic follows the same rule with regard to the plane of the ecliptic and the Sun can never depart in the lunar sky either south or north by more than that $1\frac{1}{2}$ degrees or so from the lunar celestial equator, which is, of course, only a projection of the lunar equator on to the apparent sphere of heaven. Compare this with 23° 30' for the Earth, 25° 10' for Mars, and 32° for Venus![9]

Thus, while the Moon, too, has a kind of seasons, these are a mere geometrical refinement with hardly any climatic significance, except possibly in the immediate neighbourhood of the poles.

The climatic cycle of the Moon is wholly governed by her day, in which the only important irregularity is provided by the comparatively frequent eclipses, which may engulf the whole of the visible hemisphere and from which the averted half of the Moon is entirely free.

The Moon describes her elliptical path round the Earth in 27 days 7 hours 43 minutes and 11·47 seconds and turns once round herself in the same time. Her orbital motion, however, is considerably affected by the varying pull of the Sun and the neighbouring planets, which may give rise to deviations from the mean amounting to 7 hours in time and 10 minutes in the angle between the orbit of the Moon and the ecliptic, whose mean value is 5° 8'. These perturbations express the insecurity of the Earth's grip on her satellite discussed in Chapter 3.

The lunar day does not coincide with the period in which the Moon turns round herself, or the time between two successive crossings of any given lunar meridian by the same star, any more than it does on the Earth. For clearly it is the return of the Sun to the meridian, marking the sun-dial noon, that makes the real day, and the Sun is moving among the stars

111

both by reason of the common motion of the Moon and Earth round him and of the Moon's own travels with regard to the latter. In effect the Sun gains two days on the ground and the period between, say, two full Moons or two new Moons, which is called lunation, equals 29 days 12 hours 44 minutes and 2·8 seconds on the *average*—as it, too, is affected by perturbations and the varying speed of the Earth–Moon system with regard to the Sun. The lunation and the lunar day are approximately one and the same thing—approximately only because the position of the terminator on the lunar disk at the same phase may vary as a result of librations by as much as 15½ degrees.

However, it is accurate enough to say that the lunar day is 29½ of our days long. Along the line where the Sun passes through the zenith (this can never be farther than 1½ degrees of latitude from the equator) night and day are of the same length. In higher latitudes there will be a slight differ-ence, but it is quite insignificant. This is an important point to bear in mind, for even if the Moon had a considerable atmosphere she could have no real weather in the usual meaning of the term, as weather is mainly the outcome of rapid rotation on an inclined axis.

The distance of the Moon from the Earth is such a small fraction of their common distance from the Sun that the Solar Constant (*see* Chapter 2) is the same for both bodies, both on the average and at any given time. Only on the Earth the intervention of the atmosphere, with its mists and clouds, cuts the theoretical allowance of two gram-calories per each square centi-metre under vertical illumination per minute down to about one calorie as an average for the whole globe[1] and down to a good deal less in our latitudes. On the Moon, the tenuous atmosphere can offer no serious obstacle to radiation, except possibly in the ultra-violet if, say, any ozone is present, so that the two calories get down to the ground all right. Thus the surface is exposed for over a fortnight at a time to an insolation comparable to that encountered in our deserts with not a puff of wind to temper the effect and for over a fortnight at a time it is entirely withheld, once more without an atmospheric shelter. It stands to reason that this must lead to great excesses of heat and cold.

Even so the situation is usually badly overpainted. It has been an almost universal practice to treat the Moon as though she were a flat pancake facing the Sun from dawn to dusk and simply quote the maximum midday temperature observed at the subsolar point, referring with a vague flourish to the extreme cold of the lunar night, when the thermometer *must* sink close to the Absolute Zero. Yet a moment's reflection will show that a subsolar point can occur only within a narrow belt, 3 degrees of latitude in width. Moreover, the Sun can never be directly overhead in more than one place at a time. And how about all the rest of the lunar globe?

Nor is it all. It has been found that the subsolar temperature measured at full Moon, when the radiations coming from the vertically illuminated portions of the ground contribute most to the effect, comes out about 50°C. higher than when the same temperature is taken at a quarter phase, with the subsolar point on the horizon and only the inclined slopes in view. The latter is probably the true explanation of most of the difference, but it is within the bounds of possibility that the lunar atmosphere is also responsible for it in part. A minute amount of carbon dioxide, water vapour or some other gas (and we shall see later on that this is not impossible) could cause appreciable absorption of the Moon's 'obscure heat'.

By and large, however, the climatic effects of such selective absorption can be safely disregarded. Conduction of heat in gases is an extremely slow process anyway and any convection, i.e. carrying of heat by the wind, cannot amount to much in view of the extreme rarefaction of the lunar air. It cannot be expected either to chill or warm up the ground to a noticeable extent. Generally the air above the surface should be a good deal colder than the surface itself.

If we further add that the materials which make up the ground are almost perfect insulators it will become clear that virtually all traffic in heat on the surface and above the surface of the Moon will be by absorption, reflection, and reradiation. This will make for great differences in the temperature of such portions of the surface as may differ in albedo and/or specific heat. The mean albedo of the Moon is very low. She absorbs 93 per cent of the incident radiations, but areas of any shade from snow-white to soot-black can be found on the surface of the Moon and, say, the inside slopes of Aristarchus will reflect something like 80 per cent of the sunshine they receive. This will make them very much colder than, say, the dark portions of Mare Nubium at the same distance from the equator.

All this is true irrespective of the angle at which the light strikes the ground. But the Moon is a rough mountainous world and even with the same albedo the local distribution of heat will differ greatly in any given locality at the same hour of the lunar day, some slopes facing the Sun, others being turned away from him at all manner of angles. With negligible conduction and no tempering effect of the air, this will lead to differences of temperature unimaginable on the Earth. The ground will be many degrees below freezing point in the shade a few inches away from a sunlit area which is scorching hot. Even the so-called subsolar temperature represents only the mean of various temperatures within a fairly wide compass. Locally one must expect temperatures far in excess of this mean—as well as far below it. It is almost certain that some portions will attain +200°C. Terrestrial botanists are well aware of the so-called microclimates, one side of a tree-bole having quite different moss and lichen growth from the other. The Moon is a world where microclimates run riot.

In these conditions one must expect physical and chemical action, which

113

STRANGE WORLD OF THE MOON

may either temper or further enhance the differences. There are also indications of considerable differences in the conductivity of lunar rocks, for instance the darker maria are not warmer than the light-coloured lunarite highlands, though they must certainly absorb more heat. This means that part of this heat is here more readily led away into the interior. And this is a large-scale effect.

To sum up, while the climate of the Moon as a whole is extremely simple and stable, the situation in detail is one of extreme complexity, the complexity which has not yet been even superficially sampled.

The temperatures of small portions of the disk of Mars have been measured, although the telescopic image of this disk will fit into many a lunar crater; but to date no comparable radiometric study of a lunar locality has been made. Our knowledge of the thermal conditions on the surface of the Moon is far too general and unsatisfactory, which precludes accurate treatment of many a fascinating problem of lunar physics.

What we know about the temperature of the lunar surface derives almost wholly from the series of observations made by Edison Pettit and S. B. Nicholson and Edison Pettit alone with a zinc–bismuth vacuum thermocouple at the focus of the 100-inch Hooker Telescope, at Mount Wilson.[3,4,5]

These investigators found that the temperature at the centre of the night hemisphere was about 120° K., or −153° C., and thus, although certainly very low, a good deal above the Absolute Zero. Again, however, this is only the mean temperature, so that locally much lower temperatures must be expected. Furthermore, their result is not very reliable, for at such temperatures the infra-red radiation which they measured becomes very feeble. For the subsolar point at full Moon they obtained 407° K., which was 17 degrees more than the theoretical blackbody temperature (the temperature which would be attained in the same conditions by a perfectly black body absorbing all of the incident radiation).[3] This appeared improbable to them and they reduced their estimate, accordingly, to 390° K., although a small amount of carbon dioxide could produce at least part of the observed effect.

However, their results, rendered in degrees Fahrenheit, are summarized in a diagram appearing in Whipple's *Earth, Moon and the Planets,*[8] p. 140, which is reproduced here. See Fig. 2.

Nicholson and Pettit let the image of the full Moon drift across the thermocouple and found that the indicated temperature fell off symmetrically in both directions, east and west, from the central meridian, though rather more rapidly than the simple spherical geometry would require, but at the limb, where the heat came from the slopes facing the Sun, the thermocouple reading went up by about 60 per cent above the figure for the adjacent maria. Both effects are due to the roughness of the lunar surface and the diagram is the result of 'smoothing out' the actual readings.

It will, however, be observed that such drifts will have taken the thermocouple substantially along the lunar equator and the distribution of temperatures north and south need not correspond to that east and west. For, although in higher latitudes the angular distance from the subsolar point may be the same as along the drift belt and the sunrays will, consequently, be reaching the ground at the same angle, the past thermal history will have been different, the total amount of heat received since sunrise being a good deal less than at the equator. It is possible, however, that the inaccuracy arising from this is of no account for the surface to which the readings refer. In any event the symmetry of the temperature curve between its

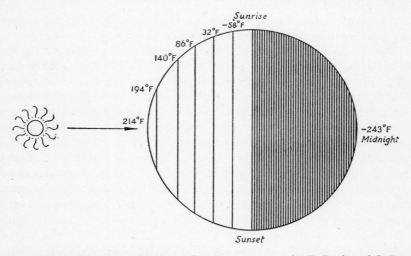

Fig. 2. Temperatures on the Moon, from measurements by E. Pettit and S. B. Nicholson. (*After* F. L. Whipple.)

morning and evening halves shows that the lunar surface gains and loses heat so quickly that so long as the angle of illumination has been the same for a few hours its past thermal history does not affect the thermocouple reading. This may sound a little bit involved, but it means that if, for instance, two slopes have both been inclined to the sunrays at, say, 30 degrees, one near the equator, the other near the pole, for five hours their superficial temperature will be the same, assuming identical structure and composition.

This, though, does not necessarily mean that their condition will be identical in all respects. If, for instance, they both contained a pocket of snow or similar substance to begin with, this might have entirely evaporated on the equator but remained substantially intact on the polar slope.

115

However this may be, the diagram shows that the mean temperatures within 30 degrees from the poles never exceed the ice point of water, and within caps 10 degrees from the poles will not rise above 28° F. of frost. Many portions of the ground will, of course, be very much colder, and if we take, for instance, the inner portions of the bowl of Newton, where the Sun never shines, their temperature will not be much above the Absolute Zero, so that they may act as a kind of gas trap, all gases penetrating there being frozen out and deposited as a solid glacier, the temperature of which would be kept very low by superficial evaporation. This may be one of the mechanisms of depletion of the lunar atmosphere. In any case, the low circumpolar temperatures may have a bearing on the apparent brilliance, especially in the blue, of these parts and strengthen the suspicion that this is due to hoar-frost of some kind.

No less important than the general measurements of lunar temperatures are Pettit's observations of temperature changes during a lunar eclipse.

He followed the variation of temperature in a small area near the centre of the lunar disk through the total eclipse of the Moon on 28 October, 1939.[5] At 4 hours 10 minutes, Greenwich Mean Time, the reading was 370° K.: 15 minutes later, as the area entered the penumbra, the temperature fell by 10 degrees. Then the rate of decrease accelerated and within one hour, from 4·31 to 5·30, the drop was from 357° K. to 198° K. At this moment the full shadow of the Earth covered up the observed area. The total eclipse lasted till 7·45, but during this time the temperature decreased only gradually, reaching the lowest point at 177° K., and remained over 50 degrees above the new Moon temperature. This indicates conduction of heat from below. Even more spectacular was the rise of temperature upon re-entry into the penumbra. By 9·14 the reading was back to and, in fact, slightly above the original 370° K.

Such rapid changes are possible only if the superficial layer of the Moon's surface consists of extremely poor heat conductors. Even pumice, which is very effective as a thermal insulator, falls short of the lunar requirements, which it is almost impossible to meet by any combination of substances occurring in a natural way on the surface of the Earth.[2,3,7] I will return to this point further on.

In one respect our knowledge of the temperatures encountered on the Moon is superior to the similar information available for Mars. We know something about the temperatures and their variation also below the ground. Nicholson and Pettit measured the radiations from the Moon in the lower infra-red, to which the ground is opaque, so that the temperatures thus obtained refer only to its uppermost 'skin'—and the word 'skin' may have here an almost literal meaning. Yet a body at a low temperature emits also short radio waves, to which the ground is largely transparent. These can be studied with a radio telescope, and in 1948 J. H. Piddington and H. C. Minnett in Australia[6] explored the radiations from the Moon in the wavelength of 1·25 centimetres. The studied radiations came from various depths, averaging 40 centimetres (1¼ feet) below the ground.

Translated into temperatures, these microwave results differ considerably from the infra-red measurements by Nicholson and Pettit.

As one would expect, the amplitude of daily variation is smaller. Only a proportion of the heat available on the surface will penetrate underground. In fact, a considerable part of this surface heat, amounting to about one-third of a gram-calorie per square centimetre per minute, is reradiated into space and so lost, except for such proportion of it as may be intercepted by appropriately situated features of the ground relief. And, of course, the greater the volume of the material heated the more thinly the heat will be spread and the lower its temperature will be as a result. For this reason the temperature of the rocks will fall with every inch of descent and fall very rapidly, for, as has often been stressed, lunar surface materials are almost perfect insulators and the flow of heat in them is extremely slow. By the same token, however, any heat, once trapped under the surface, will take a long time to escape, so that the subsurface temperatures will never reach the extreme cold of lunar midnight.

Indeed, a depth must exist where the loss and gain of heat exactly balance up and the temperature remains unchanged throughout the climatic cycle. This depth will vary from place to place, as the rocks will often be hollowed or cracked and may also contain pockets of gas or liquid; but it will not be very great. Still farther down the temperature must be expected to increase once more owing to the evolution of heat in the decay of radioactive substances, as it does on the Earth; and, since the materials of the lunar surface are such good insulators, this internal heat of the Moon will be sealed off more effectively. On the Earth, we will recall from Chapter 8, it is precisely the lighter acid rocks that contain most of the radioactive materials to which the increase of temperature with descent below the ground (thermal gradient) is attributed. The total thickness of these rocks does not exceed 20 miles on the average, but, with a lower density, this Sial layer should be much thicker on the Moon. The conclusion is that the subsurface sources of heat will be much more abundant on the Moon; the thermal gradient will be correspondingly steeper both for this reason and on account of the low conductivity.

Reference has already been made to one consequence of this situation. On the Earth the great ages of intense volcanic activity and surface movement, when mountains are formed, continents founder and sea floors are raised above the waters, are held to be associated with a temporary excess of this radioactive heat. If so, there is every reason to believe that on the Moon such crises will be the more frequent and in proportion to the smaller dimensions of the lunar globe all the more powerful.

117

In any case we may expect to find pockets of underground heat in many of the volcanic regions of the Moon.

To return, however, to the upper few feet of the lunar crust, owing to the slow circulation of heat, the maximum temperature will not be attained here at lunar noon but some time after. We are quite familiar with this situation on our planet, for the hottest time of our short day is not when the sundial shadow points at 12, but two or three hours later. The air takes time to be heated and our surface materials are by no means perfect insulators. Their thermal capacity will also be a good deal higher. In other words, their temperature cannot and will not vary as rapidly as that of their lunar counterparts. Yet, with the slow march of the Sun in the lunar sky two hours would make a negligible fraction of the day, and even if conditions were otherwise exactly similar to those of the Earth the peak of light and heat would coincide quite closely. As it is the coincidence is almost perfect.

If, on the other hand, we could sink our thermometer only half an inch below the surface we would find a very different situation, whilst at the mean depth of 40 cm. where the maximum of Piddington and Minnett's radiations lay the heat maximum and minimum are 45 degrees out of step with the phase. This means that this layer of lunar subsoil is at its warmest one-eighth of a revolution, or approximately $3\frac{1}{2}$ days, after the noon, and conversely at its coldest a similar time-lapse after midnight. If the studied area lies at the centre of the disk noon and midnight will correspond to full and new Moon respectively.

This time-lag in the heating of the subsoil as contrasted with the almost instantaneous temperature changes of the outer 'skin' of the Moon, is of considerable interest. For the changes in the colour and intensity of lunar markings are also, as we have seen in Chapters 9 and 10, out of step with the phase. Since these changes must primarily be due to thermal factors, it means that their seat is below the visible surface of the Moon, as though something were oozing out to the lunar top-soil and were reabsorbed when the temperature of the subsoil fell. Alternatively or coincidently, the melting or sublimation (vaporization without melting) of some deposits which become gaseous at higher temperatures may contribute to the effect.

We shall see later what interpretation it is possible to put on this finding.

Numerically the mean temperature obtained by the Australian investigators for the layer under review in the equatorial belt of the Moon is 249°K., with a maximum of 301°K. (only 24°C. above freezing point) and a minimum similarly 52°K. (or °C.) below the mean, i.e. 197°K. The mean for the whole disk is 10 degrees less and the amplitude of the fluctuation is also less, only 40·3 degrees either way. They further estimate that in what they call the 'deep interior', defined as a layer where the temperature does not change, which need be no deeper than a few feet below the surface, this stable temperature will be 234°K., provided that there is no accretion of heat from below. The latter is almost certainly untrue as a general proposition, but, being given the extremely low conductivity of lunar rocks, this accretion need not be very marked at moderate depths.

In any case, there can be no doubt that the temperature of a layer not less than several feet deep at a comparable depth below the surface never rises above the ice-point of water; the subsoil of the Moon will exist in the condition of 'permafrost', like the subsoil of Alaska or Siberia. This may have important implications.

For the mean *surface* temperature of the new Moon Piddington and Minnett give 145°K., which compares satisfactorily with 120°k. obtained by Nicholson and Pettit and is probably the more reliable, as at such low temperature the thermocouple is less sensitive than the radio-telescope (the intensity of infra-red emission declines with falling temperature). Piddington and Minnett have also reduced the mean temperature of the subsolar point to 374°K., or just a degree above the terrestrial boiling point of water. This is stated to be the theoretical blackbody temperature (*see* Appendix) and the actual thermocouple reading was 407°K. The difficulty here lies in correctly estimating the loss of lunar (or planetary) heat in passage through our atmosphere, which varies a great deal depending on humidity. No obscuration or any other effect of the lunar atmosphere is considered by them and they give good grounds for believing that this would be negligible. Nevertheless, I am not quite certain that their inference is wholly justified, for they consider only the conventional model of an atmosphere that would be spread upwards to an effective height of about 30 miles. However, their results would not be seriously affected by any possible correction arising from this source.

The temperatures as quoted will not be in error by more than 20°C., which is quite a lot for particular cases, but does not affect the overall picture very much.

However, all these thermal investigations of the Moon concur in assigning special properties to her surface materials. An early calculation, based on Petitt and Nicholson's results, was made by Epstein, who thought the behaviour of lunar rocks could be matched by that of pumice. In 1947, however, A. J. Wesselink[7] submitted the then available data to a more rigorous analysis and concluded that pumice was still too good a conductor to duplicate lunar conditions, which, however, were well reproduced by the conductivity and specific heat of fine powders studied *in vacuo* by the Polish physicist Smoluchowski.

From this he inferred that the surface of the Moon was overlaid by a thick layer of dust or powder, of meteoritic or volcanic origin, as had otherwise been suggested by Lyot for polarimetric considerations, and that this layer was entirely free from any trace of gas, which would have caused

I

an increase in conductivity. He regarded this as an independent proof that the Moon was entirely devoid of an atmosphere.

There are, however, two points which he has overlooked.

In the first place, the conductivity of granular or powdery substances depends on the area of contact and the pressure at the points of contact between the grains. Both are affected by gravity. Smoluchowski's experiments had been made on the Earth with gravity six times the lunar. Consequently, his results cannot be applied to lunar conditions without an appropriate correction, which should be susceptible of at least approximate evaluation but had not been considered by Wesselink.

In the second, the critical term of comparison is a product of three quantities: conductivity, specific heat, and density. The result of multiplication is required to be somewhat below 1,000, which can be obtained by varying the three quantities *ad libidem* within the limits of physical possibility. Wesselink took the specific gravity of lunar dust as 2, but if this dust is of meteoric origin it may be very much denser *in specie*, containing as it would be a high proportion of iron and nickel. On the other hand, if of lunar volcanic provenance, it could have even lower specific gravity, which would affect the two remaining terms. Finally, there is no compelling reason why this material should be homogeneous.

These remarks are intended not so much as criticism as to indicate the intrinsic limitations and inconclusiveness of such mathematical methods, impressive as they may look on paper.

However, since that time Wesselink's analysis has been repeated by Harper and Jaeger (1950) with a fuller knowledge of the movement of heat and distribution of temperatures below the 'thermal skin' of the Moon.[2,6] They find that the best fit is obtained by a rock having the properties of terrestrial pumice *in air*—and that under atmospheric pressure—overlaid by an extremely thin deposit of airless dust, about one millimetre deep. A still better agreement with the lunar data is secured by assuming a dust coating of variable thickness (Pawsey and Bracewell).[2]

Once again, however, though highly likely, this solution suffers from the same oversight as Wesselink's. The consequences of the lower gravity are left out of account. Not only will this reduce the conductivity of the dusty layer, the existence of which is largely negatived by the optical data (fine dust is a good reflector of light),[8] but the pumice rock formed in lunar conditions will be far more bubbly than its terrestrial counterpart and thus prove an even better insulator. It looks, therefore, as though the lunar surface rocks conduct heat better than one might expect, so that there may be room for dispensing with at least part of the dust-covering altogether and certainly for a thin atmosphere filling the interstices between the dust or gravel and the cavities in the porous rocks.

This point will be considered in greater detail in the next chapter. To wind up, it may be added that from Pettit and Nicholson's data it follows that lunabase conducts heat better than lunarite, for, although darker and thus a more efficient absorber of sunrays, it was often found to be colder than the latter. This fits in well with the assumption that lunabase is more compact than lunarite and may have largely the structure of a glassy gel.

REFERENCES

1. COWLING, T. G. *Quarterly Journal of Royal Meteorological Society*, Vol. LXVIII, No. 296.
2. PAWSEY, J. L. and BRACEWELL, R. N. *Radio Astronomy*. Oxford, 1955.
3. PETTIT, EDISON and NICHOLSON, S. B. 'Lunar Radiations and Temperatures.' *Astrophysical Journal*, Vol. LXXI, 1930.
4. PETTIT, EDISON. *Astrophysical Journal*, Vol. LXXXI, 1935.
5.   *Astrophysical Journal*, Vol. XCI, 1940.
6. PIDDINGTON, J. H. and MINNETT, H. C. 'Microwave Radiation from the Moon.' *Australian Journal of Scientific Research*, Series A, Vol. 2, No. 1, 1949.
7. WESSELINK, A. J. 'Heat Conductivity and Nature of the Lunar Surface Material.' *Bulletin of the Astronomical Institutes of the Netherlands*, Vol. X, No. 390, 1949.
8. WHIPPLE, F. L. *Earth, Moon and the Planets*. Churchill, London, 1946.
9. KUIPER, G. P. 'Determination of the Pole of Rotation of Venus.' *Astrophysical Journal*, No. 120, 1954.

12

THE VEXED QUESTION OF LUNAR ATMOSPHERE

IN THE STRICT MEANING of physical science the question whether the Moon possesses an atmosphere does not exist. For even the heaviest and hardest solid substances evaporate, their vapour pressures rising with temperature, so that when exposed to the vacuum of space they would at once form a kind of atmosphere. It has even been suggested (Gold) that thermally agitated fine dust would simulate an atmosphere in the absence of gas. This point is often overlooked and it may be true enough that an atmosphere of this kind would be low and thin and not amount to much on our reckoning. Still, in lunar conditions it may be of some importance for the economy of the surface and it is a matter for surprise that this aspect of the situation appears never to have received attention.

I will return to it in the next chapter and here we will confine ourselves to the conventional problem of the atmosphere comparable to our air in extent and composition. On its existence, in however tenuous a form, many issues are hinged. In particular changes of the type discussed in Chapters 8 to 10 are *hardly* possible without an atmosphere, though, say, the colouring of surface rocks might alter under the influence of sunshine without any evolution or absorption of gas or moisture. On the whole, however, this is unlikely and any change, especially of periodical nature, in the colour or appearance of surface features that is not due to illumination alone constitutes strong evidence for the presence of a gaseous envelope. So far as mists or obscurations are concerned, these form direct proof of at least temporary existence of gas by which they are supported. Volcanic activity implies *ipso facto* emission of gas and would, therefore, result in establishing an atmosphere.

Indeed, the failure which has so far attended attempts at definite determination of the density, composition, and other properties of the lunar atmosphere forms the main obstacle to the general acceptance of the cumulative evidence of change on the surface of the Moon. The reality of these observations is hotly disputed, often with more heat than is good for dispassionate enquiry—but this is human nature. Whether the obstacle is really unsurmountable, whether even certain forms of life would not be sustained in the absence of the kind of air we are used to, is another matter.

A conventional atmosphere of light gases round a dark celestial body manifests itself to a distant observer in a number of ways.

Veiling of surface features and shifting clouds definitely show that an atmosphere is there. Mars, Jupiter and Venus display these convincingly even to an unsophisticated eye, but already in the case of Mercury, which is known to possess a thin atmosphere, their reality is questioned, and when it comes to the Moon the observed effects are on a small scale, evanescent or delicate, which leaves room for errors of judgment and opens the flood-gates of scepticism.

A high albedo is another indication of an atmospheric cover, and the albedo of the Moon is ruefully low: she reflects only 7 per cent of the incident sunlight.

It will be recalled that gas scatters light the more effectively the shorter is its wavelength: in fact, the scattering is inversely proportional to the fourth power of the wavelength (Rayleigh's Law), which is due to the fact that gas molecules are smaller than light waves and ineffective as wave-breakers—gases are transparent. But as the wavelength decreases the molecules break up the light waves to greater effect and the gas becomes more opaque in consequence. This causes any large body of gas, such as our atmosphere, to appear blue, the astronomical counterpart of which is the so-called Wright effect, whereby the diameter of, say, Mars appears larger when observed or photographed in the light of shorter wavelengths than when a red or infra-red filter is used. The less-refrangible light penetrates to the ground, showing hardly any of the atmospheric detail, except for thick clouds, whereas through a blue or violet filter we get primarily a view of the atmosphere of Mars with little and sometimes none of the surface.

Kuiper,[5] who has observed Mars visually through monochromatic filters and measured the apparent diameter of the planet in different colours, expresses doubts about the widening of the diameter in Wright's shorter-wave photographs. It is possible that some of it represented the peculiarities of the photographic emulsion rather than those of the Martian atmosphere. Besides, Mars is exceptional inasmuch as it is enveloped in the Violet Layer, at a height of 15–20 miles above the ground,[3,5] this layer strongly reflecting blue and violet light, which serves to exaggerate the otherwise natural result. Nevertheless, the principle itself is not in doubt; it is only a question of more or less.

For the same reason light passing through a layer of gas of sufficient mass becomes reddened, as it is conspicuously in a rising or setting Sun.

Here the Moon shows a positive reaction. It is an established fact that moonlight is redder than direct sunlight. This may represent the colouring of the lunar surface, but the reddening of the light at the terminator, observed by many, including myself, and my own colour observations showing a prevalence of blue and violet at the illuminated limb cannot be explained in this way. Wright[13] himself failed to find any indication of an atmosphere in his filter photographs of the Moon, although the first ultra-violet exposure illustrating his paper clearly shows the brightening at the limb. There are, however, several possible reasons for his lack of success. Firstly, comparison being made with Mars, his expectations were exaggerated. Secondly, in photographic study the brightness of the image or any part of it is a matter of exposure. Thus if the plate is exposed for long enough one can always get an equally clear picture of the terminator detail in blue or violet as one does in red or infra-red, but this does not mean that this detail appears equally clear in all colours. Wright has also failed to notice any blue in the lunar shadows, which is strange, for these are blue by reason of our own atmosphere alone—which, of course, proves nothing. It is difficult to say to what extent the apparent softening of the limb detail in his ultra-violet photograph of the full Moon is due to this cause or to the differences between the emulsions used here and in the extreme-red photograph, but it is certainly there. Moreover, the ground in the region of Endymion and Mare Humboldtianum appears slightly blurred in the ultra-violet exposure. The first two photographs also show something of the blue sheen in Regiomontanus.

Gas not only scatters the light falling upon it, but, if unevenly distributed, it will bend, or refract, the rays passing through it, the amount of refraction being again inversely proportional to the wavelength (but not to the fourth power thereof). Thus, since the atmosphere of the Moon forms a spherical shell and its density is falling off away from the surface, any star close to the limb will not only be dimmed and reddened but it will also appear displaced relatively to other stars. When the Moon passes in front of the star this should, as a result, remain visible for a little while after its position has actually been covered by the disk of the Moon; the star similarly reappearing on the other side of the Moon somewhat earlier than the simple geometrical relationship would warrant. In other words, the diameter of the Moon obtained from such an occultation, as the 'eclipse' of a star by the Moon or planet is called, should come out smaller than when directly measured.

In view of the small total mass of the lunar atmosphere and the low value of lunar gravity, which will cause this atmosphere to be spread out upwards some 6 times more uniformly than on the Earth, these effects cannot be expected to be very marked.

Barnard, Douglass, and Pickering have observed visually and the last-named has recorded photographically a dark band crossing the disks of Jupiter and Saturn[4,8,9] at the line of contact with the limb of the Moon when the planets were partly covered by her. This obscuring band was strongly inclined to the natural belts of these planets, so as to preclude any possibility of confusion. It was clear and unmistakable. As measured on Pickering's negatives it was about 3 seconds of arc wide, but would not print satisfactorily.[8] It appeared, however, only at contact with the sunlit limb of the Moon and was entirely absent on the dark side. This was taken by the critics as damning evidence against its reality. For if we have two unequally brilliant areas in contact the more brilliant of them will make the less brilliant appear even darker where the two touch.

It is not clear how this could manifest itself in a photograph, as the seat of the illusion is in the eye. But a fair test would be provided by an occultation of Venus or Mercury, which are brighter than the Moon, whilst Jupiter and Saturn appear duller owing to their great distance from the Sun and consequently reduced illumination. Thus, if the explanation by irradiation is correct, the dark band would appear not on the disk of Venus but on the Moon. I have, however, been unable to find any record of such observations, though Rudaux and de Vaucouleurs give in their popular *Astronomie*[9] a drawing of an occultation of Venus at the *dark* limb of the Moon showing no band.

This is inconclusive, for, as Pickering was quick to see, whatever causes the obscuration along the sunlit limb may simply not be there during the lunar night, having been precipitated by the intense cold. As against this it is pointed out that lunar peaks are silhouetted sharply against the Sun during a solar eclipse. Nor has an obscuring band ever been seen on the latter, where the photospheric grains show quite clearly at contact with the Moon. However, the brilliance of the Sun may be far too great for the feeble obscuration to be noticeable. At partial eclipse points of light cutting through the darker limb of the Sun at contact with the lunar limb have been seen by some observers, including myself in 1954, but have been accounted for as symmetrically spaced solar flares.

This effect, too, may be explained by irradiation, but in my case the solar image was projected onto a movable screen, which I withdrew so far from the eye-piece as completely to kill its brilliance; yet the lights remained, magnified in proportion, so that this explanation does not appear to be applicable.

Pickering also claimed to have found a flattening of Jupiter amounting to 0·5″, which was parallel to the Moon's limb and non-coincident with the poles of the planet, in his occultation photographs.[4,8]

Comstock and Pickering have observed widely spaced double stars close to the Moon and found a shift in their positions relatively to one another of between 0·2″ and 0·4″. From this Pickering inferred an atmosphere of the ground density one eight-thousandth or so of ours. Such measurements, however, are very difficult and cannot be relied upon. They show, nevertheless, that whatever atmosphere the Moon does possess is very rarefied and, apart from some local and temporary gas pockets, it cannot be expected to exceed the density obtained by Pickering, which corresponds to that of our air at the height of 40 miles.

The shift in the positions of a pair of stars seen close to the Moon is due to unequal refraction, the light coming from them being bent through a different angle because it passes through unequal amounts (masses) of gas. As we have seen, though, the density of the lunar air will fall off very slowly, so that this difference can never be large and the method is intrinsically unfruitful.

125

In observing an occultation we are free from this handicap and such measurements are susceptible of great precision. Unfortunately we meet another lion in our path in the shape of the rugged character of the lunar surface, which makes it almost impossible accurately to predict the length of the star's path behind the Moon, now a valley, now a mountain being on the limb. Yet, when long series of such observations are considered there should be a residual atmospheric effect, as the unevennesses of the limb would be smoothed out statistically with a large number of random situations.

Indeed, the diameter of the Moon as determined from occultations at Greenwich in 1864 was 4″ less than when measured directly. The *American Ephemeris* for 1925 gave a smaller difference of 1·5″.[8] True, a bright object if measured on a dark background always appears to encroach upon it through irradiation; but 1″ corresponds to about a mile and thus would make a considerable error, rather more than one would expect from this source alone. A refractive difference of 1″ between the diameter obtained directly and from occultations would give a ground density of the lunar atmosphere equal to 0·001 of ours at sea-level. From lunar occultations observed in different observatories an atmosphere of the ground density between 1/2,000 and 1/750 of our air at sea-level could be inferred.[9] These figures appear to be far too high, unless some unsuspected factor should supervene. This is not impossible.

In order to overcome the difficulties attendant on the determinations of the occultation diameter as a means of obtaining the density of the lunar air, I have suggested using a special binocular eye-piece, one ocular of which would be equipped with a red or infra-red monochromatic filter and the other with a similar violet or ultra-violet filter. The observation would be carried out either visually or photo-electrically. Practically all the difference in the behaviour of the star as seen through the two oculars would be due to the intervention of the lunar atmosphere, and in particular the irregularities of the limb would no longer matter. E. A. Whitaker of the Royal Greenwich Observatory has undertaken to try out this method, but no data are available as yet.

However this may be, even the highest figure attributed to the lunar atmosphere would probably be insufficient to cause a noticeable refraction halo round the Moon during a solar eclipse and it need occasion no surprise that this has never been seen. On the other hand, even with a greatly rarefied atmosphere one would expect a measurable twilight effect. The sunlight scattered by the high atmosphere of the Moon, however feebly this may be, would illumine portions of the disk beyond the terminator, forming the so-called twilight arc, whence the scattering power and at one remove the density of the atmosphere could be deduced. Russell, Dugan, and Stewart calculate that the effect should be traceable even with a ground density of 0·0001 of our air at sea-level.[10] Several observers from Schroeter's time onwards have claimed to have seen a twilight extension of the cusps of a crescent Moon beyond its geometrical boundary. In recent years this effect has been reported by Haas, Wilkins,[11] Barcroft, and others. Haas[4] writes:

'On the occasion of the clearest view (December 25, 1940, at colongitude 224°) each horn appeared prolonged by about 10 degrees. Vaughan saw definite prolongations on October 29, 1940, at 251°, the north horn being extended by about 15 degrees. Barcroft suspected similar prolongations near first quarter of March 6, 1941.'

In fact, with my filters I could see a kind of brilliance extending beyond the cusps, especially in red and green, I am, nevertheless, sceptical and this for two reasons. As already pointed out in Chapter 5, high mountains, too, would produce a twilight effect, and there are some stupendous peaks close to the south pole of the Moon, as well as lower but still impressive heights about the north pole. The cardinal point, however, is that the dark part of the Moon is quite powerfully illuminated by the gibbous Earth and near both poles there exist brilliant 'caps', so that the earthshine reflected from these could readily simulate twilight. On the other hand, in December 1955, I looked at the exceptionally narrow sickle of the new Moon, which at this time of the year rises comparatively high above the horizon, and noticed with some surprise something like a thin line of light rimming the 'old Moon' opposite to the crescent. The effect was strong enough to be plainly visible with the naked eye and resembled the 'silk thread' of Venus observed in similar configurations with the difference that the latter is in full light, whilst on the Moon it appeared only as an intensification of the earthshine. This observation requires confirmation, but it looks promising and is free from the objections just levelled at the would-be prolongations of the cusps,* the more so as no comparable appearance has been seen by me when the crescent was wider.

Apart from the earthshine, the observation of the lunar twilight arc is hampered by the brilliancy of our own sky diffusing the moonlight which is difficult to eliminate. Such attempts have, nevertheless, been made in Russia and in France.

The Russians relied on polarization to sort out the genuine twilight. In 1943 Fessenkoff observed an area close to the terminator near the centre of the half-lit lunar disk, but found no observable effect. He claimed that this would have been detectable by his method even if the Moon had an atmosphere of one-millionth of the terrestrial ground density. In 1949, however, his colleague Y. N. Lipski announced the discovery of a lunar atmosphere equal in ground density to 0·0001 of ours at sea-level. This

---

* It must, however, be borne in mind that the limb of the Moon appears bright in sunlight and so will presumably be bright in earthshine as well.

127

sounds reasonable and in good agreement with other estimates. But the precision of the methods employed in both cases has been questioned, and, it appears, rightly, by B. Lyot and A. Dollfus in France.[2,6]

They jointly, and later Dollfus alone, have investigated the suspected twilight with the help of the 8-inch (20 cm.) coronograph at Pic du Midi (the highest permanent observatory in the world) above the cusps of the Moon at first quarter and found no detectable effect. According to Dollfus's latest estimate an atmosphere one thousand-millionth of the terrestrial in ground density would still have been revealed.[2]

There can be no doubt that these observations were painstakingly made by highly skilled men with excellent equipment in first-class conditions, and, having neither the sufficient practical nor theoretical experience of the methods in question, I am unable properly to assess the accuracy of the results. Yet, despite the success of these methods in determining the densities of the atmospheres of Mercury and Mars, I am somewhat doubtful about the fundamental assumptions.

In the first place, the area of the sky under examination was some 100 miles above the dark side of the Moon beyond the morning terminator. The suspected gas was carbon dioxide at 0°C. The actual temperature of the underlying lunar ground would in these conditions have been not higher than −150°C. and probably lower, as this was a polar region. This means that practically all of the atmospheric carbon dioxide would have been precipitated as hoar-frost, with only a thin vapour present at lower altitudes. At the examined height there would have been none of this gas at all, although what the report actually said is that the 'observed distribution of light could be accounted for' by other factors, which, after all, is a matter of opinion and not of fact.

This criticism, however, does not impugn the accuracy of the method as such, and A. Dollfus when I wrote him about it agreed that there might be something in my point of view and that it would be desirable to repeat the observation at the last quarter, when the carbon dioxide volatilized during the day should still be present at high atmospheric levels. Even so the polar regions seem to be a fundamentally bad choice for this attempt. (The coronograph, which is essentially a telescope provided with an obscuring disk to cover up the image of the Moon, Sun, or planet and a carefully devised system of baffles to eliminate the scattering of light inside the tube, could not be used anywhere else with comparable effect.) Thus it may yet be possible to reconcile the French results with Lipski's determination of lunar atmospheric density for the equatorial regions.

There exists, though, another doubtful point.

The observations in question were made photographically and Wratten filters K3 (9) and 12 were used. Both these filters produce what is known in the photographic jargon as 'overcorrection' of the sky, that is to say, the blue of the sky is suppressed. Both K3 and 12 cut off the violet part of the spectrum altogether. K3 also suppresses part of the blue, whilst Wratten 12 suppresses it all.

This is, no doubt, excellent for eliminating the foreground brilliance of our own atmosphere, but it will be at least equally effective in eliminating the feeble radiance of the lunar air! Indeed, Dollfus justly remarks that greater precision could be attained if violet light were used instead. If it were only a matter of parallel and proportionally equal reduction in the brilliance of the terrestrial and lunar atmospheres this would not perhaps affect the result *much*. But, alas, on every reckoning this is not so!

The studied lunar atmosphere will be composed of pure gas scattering strictly in accordance with the Rayleigh formula; but our own air, even at the altitude of Pic du Midi (9,351 feet), contains a high proportion of larger particles, such as dust, ice crystals, and water droplets, which scatter the light of longer wavelength much more powerfully than the formula would warrant. Nor is it all. There are grounds for believing that the high atmosphere of the Moon consists predominantly of argon (Shapley). This is a monatomic gas, whilst the gases of our air are di- or tri-atomic. Any other gases that may be present at high altitudes above the lunar surface must likewise be expected to have been largely reduced to the monatomic state by ionization. Thus the scattering particles of the lunar air at the 100-mile level which was studied will be very much smaller than their opposite numbers in the terrestrial atmosphere even when this is entirely free from the impurities alluded to above. In other words, the lunar air will be much the bluer of the two and, in fact, it must be expected to be exceptionally transparent to all visual wavelengths.

Consequently, what Dollfus and Lyot have inadvertently succeeded in doing is first suppressing the image of the lunar atmosphere and then concluding that it does not exist. Until this point has been cleared their results cannot inspire much confidence and it is possible that Dollfus's estimate of the density of the atmosphere of Mercury will likewise require to be revised upwards.

The present desideratum is, therefore, that he should repeat his excellent measurements in violet light, as suggested by himself, and at the third quarter. The result may contrast sharply with the earlier determinations. Yet even if it does not this will not exclude the possibility of local gas clouds and of a generally higher air density at lower levels and in the regions closer to the equator more particularly.

Indeed, there is a strong indication that this is so.

Acting on E. A. Whitaker's suggestion that stars at occultation may show a 'blue flash', analogous to the green flash seen sometimes immediately after sunset in the denser atmosphere of the Earth, I observed the occultations of two stars (ι Tauri, $4^{m\cdot}7$, and 150 Tauri, $8^{m\cdot}5$) on 14 March, 1957,

129

with a $6\frac{1}{2}$-inch reflector, using a blue filter. Neither star 'snapped out' instantly at contact with the earth-lit limb of the Moon, which was a narrow crescent $2\frac{1}{2}$ days after new Moon, but dimmed rapidly, then flashed out in what seemed undiminished brilliance, to dim once more and disappear. No comparable effect was found by me at a fuller phase, which, however, may be due simply to the background glare of the moonlit sky.

So far these observations remain unconfirmed, but the effect itself was clear and unmistakable and would indicate the existence soon after sunset of an obscuring layer, resembling the Violet Layer of Mars, as well as of some gas, low over the surface of the Moon.[15]

There is yet another test for the existence of a gaseous envelope round the Moon. As on the Earth, meteors will be entering this at high inter-planetary velocities and, provided that the ground density of this gas is not substantially less than one hundred-thousandth (10^{-5}) of our sea-level figure, friction will cause them to incandesce more or less brightly and the more brilliant ones should be within easy reach of our telescopes. Such lunar meteors would be distinguishable from their terrestrial counterparts by their faintness and comparative slowness (only apparent and due to great distance). In fact a simple computation shows that only very bright meteors, such as attain in our skies magnitudes of -6 to -8, can be seen with a medium-sized telescope if off the limb or against the dark part of the disk.[4] Such objects are not very frequent on the Earth, and owing to the smaller attracting mass of the Moon they will be even less frequent there per equal area of the sky. On the other hand, since meteors in our atmosphere can become luminous at a height of about 120 miles and the conventional lunar atmosphere is spread out upwards much more uniformly, lunar meteors may be expected to show up at even greater altitudes above the surface. In any case, a ground observer on the Earth can cover only a comparatively small volume of the high atmosphere where meteors appear, as against which he has a whole half of the lunar globe, and a little more round the edges, within his sight, which should greatly improve his chances of spotting a bright lunar shooting star or fireball.

A systematic search for these has now been carried on for some years by the American Association of Lunar and Planetary Observers and well over a score of suspected lunar meteors have been reported, notably by Haas, who is an experienced astronomer. Thus once again there is evidence for a tenuous lunar atmosphere of the order of 0·0001 of ours in ground density, perhaps locally more and locally less, especially by night and in the polar regions.

This conclusion is not negatived by spectral analysis. For, although no lunar absorptions have so far been traced, these could not be discerned with the present methods for any of the gases occurring on the Earth in appreciable quantities. Such gases as nitrogen and argon absorb only in the far ultra-violet which is entirely blocked off by our ozonosphere; while in the case of the other atmospheric gases lunar absorptions would be entirely smothered by the stronger telluric lines. Nor can one have recourse to the Doppler shift arising out of the radial movement of the studied body relatively to the observer for separating the two sets of absorptions. Even with the planets the method is not very successful, but the Moon circles the Earth and the mutual velocity of their approach or recession never exceeds one-third mile/second. The resulting shift is too small to be detected.

Still, if the gas in question is rare in our atmosphere the telluric lines produced by it might be noticeably strengthened by the superimposition of the lunar absorptions. Kuiper has searched in vain for sulphur dioxide and ozone. Carbon dioxide, occurring on the Earth only as an admixture of 0·03 per cent and that mainly close to the ground, could perhaps be detected in this way. So far, however, none has been found.

On the other hand, Kuiper gives infra-red comparison spectra of Mars and the Moon (the latter as the standard airless body) between 2·4 and 0·8 μ, with principal absorptions identified, on page 358 of *The Atmospheres of the Earth and Planets* (2nd Edition).[5] Page 355 provides the following legend:

'Figure 85 gives a comparison of Mars with the Moon when these objects were close together in the sky and near the zenith. The moon was close to last quarter, and the spectrum refers to the region close to the subsolar point (near the bright limb). Mars was observed as one source, but the north polar cap, centered 14° from the limb, was not prominent even in visible light.'

The spectrum of the Moon appears to show a slight excess of water absorptions over that of Mars. Since, however, according to Jeans's formula applied in the raw the Moon *can* have no water absorptions, *ergo* Mars, having less—possibly because of the unfavourable position of the north polar cap—will have none. Yet there is no special reason why a certain amount of water vapour could not have been produced on the Moon quite recently by volcanic action, so that this attitude is highly questionable. Indeed, the reference to the Moon as the airless standard may vitiate the scale from the start for such gases as are not very abundant on other worlds.

One should, finally, consider here electrical phenomena, such as aurorae, which, too, may bring proof of the existence of gas, though allowing of extreme rarefaction. Baldwin[1] states that an aurora has never been observed on the Moon. Yet some of the lunar glows suggest electrical discharge in rarefied gas. Wilkins says that Piton occasionally appears to 'glitter and emit rays like a searchlight'.[12] On 24 May, 1955, at 9.40 p.m. (G.M.T.) I observed a very similar phenomenon close to the Moon's south pole.

The air was slightly hazy but the seeing was of exceptional stability and clearness. Beyond the south cusp of the narrow crescent there were two

131

bright points where the Sun touched the peaks of the Leibnitz range. Such 'lights' often dance and sparkle if the image is 'boiling', but this is general and cannot affect one point only. Yet the middle 'light', which was the weaker of the two, alone was dancing and sparkling and eventually a faint beam of light detached itself from it and shot up vertically into the sky above the Moon, becoming more intense as it ascended, simultaneously fading out at the base, then disappeared. The total length of the beam, assuming no foreshortening, would have been about 100 miles and it endured for 2 seconds, perhaps a little longer. It vividly recalled auroral streamers I had seen in the north of Scotland, which occasionally showed swift movement of the same kind, though usually more enduring. However, if observed from a great distance, the fainter ones would probably have been invisible.

I tried to manipulate the image in the telescope's field of view to see if a similar effect could be produced by purely instrumental optical factors, but without success, so that the phenomenon would seem to have been real, the more so as I have on occasion observed unaccountable fluctuations in the brightness of the terminator heights in the same region at small phase. The fading-out of the beam at the base, too, would be hard to account for on the instrumental basis. On another occasion, once again with exceptionally steady seeing and light haze, I saw a whole swarm of minute flashes over the south pole of a gibbous Moon. These flashes were distributed up to some 200 miles above the surface and appeared to be animated by a whirling motion. They lasted for several seconds. (Terrestrial origin is, of course, not out of the question.)

I know that astronomers who have never seen anything of the kind themselves will tend to deny the reality of these observations, but knowing the conditions under which they were made I have to treat them seriously.

An atmospheric density of the order of 10^{-9} of our sea-level figure should suffice (Herzberg and Kahn) for an auroral display of this kind.[2]

Finally, in the experiments made with bouncing radar signals from the Moon, both the U.S. Army Signal Corps in 1946 and 1949 and the Australian investigators Kerr and Shain in 1951, who used a different wavelength (20 Mc/s as against 111·5 Mc/s), found unexpected fadings in the echoes, which only occasionally came up to the computed intensity.[7] This must have been due to absorptive attenuation in passage through ionized gas. The whole question is where this gas was encountered. Kerr and Shain thought they could locate the obstacle in the F_2 layer of the terrestrial ionosphere, which would thus depart from the assumed structure. This may, of course, very well be so, but neither does it necessarily follow that the whole of the effect came from this source, nor can one altogether dismiss the suspicion that the usual bias against the lunar atmosphere had influenced their conclusion.

There exists another Australian radio observation showing an unexplained surplus effect, which may be partly due to a lunar atmosphere. On 12 September, 1956, Rishbeth and Little observed the occultation by the Moon of the radio source in Ophiucus associated with Kepler's Nova.[16] The source was within 3' of the limb of the Moon and should have been wholly covered by it, but a substantial excess was found, which could be attributable in part to refraction of the radio waves in the atmosphere of the Moon.

As against this in a Cambridge radio observation by Costain, Elsmore, and Whitfield of an occultation of the Crab Nebula on 24 January, 1956, slight refraction by the lunar atmosphere was found. This corresponded to an electron density of 10^4 per cubic centimetre, whence a ground density in the sunlit portion equal to some 10^{-13} (one ten-billionth) of the sea-level density of our air is inferred.[14] The assumptions made and other particulars of the method have not been published to date, so that no critical assessment of this result can be made, but it is a fair guess that it refers to a conventionally distributed high-level atmosphere. Moreover, if the high-level atmosphere of the Moon consists mainly of argon it could not be detected by this method, because, being an inert gas, argon has a very high excitation potential and will not be ionized to any extent in ordinary sunlight.

REFERENCES

1. BALDWIN, R. B. *The Face of the Moon.* University of Chicago Press, 1949.
2. DOLLFUS, A. 'Nouvelle Recherche d'une Atmosphère au Voisinage de la Lune.' *Comptes Rendus de l'Académie des Sciences,* 234, 1952.
3. FIRSOFF, V. A. 'Does Water Vapour Escape from Mars?' *J.B.A.A.,* Vol. 66, No. 2, 1956.
4. HAAS, W. H. 'Does Anything Ever Happen on the Moon? *The Journal of the Royal Astronomical Society of Canada,* Vol. 36, No. 7, 1942.
5. KUIPER, G. P. (Ed.). *The Atmospheres of the Earth and Planets.* 2nd Ed., University of Chicago Press, 1952.
6. LYOT, B. and DOLLFUS, A. 'Recherche d'une Atmosphère au Voisinage de la Lune.' *C.R.,* 229, 1949.
7. PAWSEY, J. L. and BRACEWELL, R. N. *Radio Astronomy.* Oxford, 1955.
8. PICKERING, W. H. 'The Lunar Atmosphere.' *Popular Astronomy,* 33, 1925.
9. RUDAUX, L. and DE VAUCOULEURS, G. *Astronomie.* Larousse, Paris, 1948.
10. RUSSELL, H. N., DUGAN, R. S. and STEWART, J. Q. *Astronomy.* Boston, 1945.
11. WILKINS, H. P. *Our Moon.* Muller, London, 1954.
12.   'The Moon.' Part of *Astronomy for Everyman* (ed. by M. Davidson). Dent, London, 1953.
13. WRIGHT, W. H. 'The Moon as Photographed by Light of Different Colors.' *Publications of the Astronomical Society of the Pacific,* Vol. XLI, No. 241, June 1929.
14. COSTAIN, C. H., ELSMORE, B. and WHITFIELD, G. R. 'Radio observations of a lunar occultation of the Crab Nebula.' *Monthly Notices of the Royal Astronomical Society,* Vol. 116, No. 4, 1956.
15. FIRSOFF, V. A. 'Lunar Occultations Observed in Blue Light and the Problem of the Moon's Atmosphere.' *J.B.A.A.,* Vol. 66, No. 7, 1956.
16. *The Observatory,* Vol. 77, No. 897 (p. 71), 1957.

13

STRUCTURE OF THE LUNAR AIR

IN CHAPTER 2 we have met with Jeans's theory of dissipation of planetary atmospheres,[5] which is called in to account for the tenuity of the gaseous envelopes round the bodies of small mass, such as satellites. In fact, only one moon, Titan, the largest member of Saturn's family, is definitely known to possess a considerable atmosphere, registering clear spectral absorption bands of methane. Had it been some other gas better represented in our own air this atmosphere might not have been discovered with equal ease, but this is another story. Moonlight has so far yielded no independent absorptions.

Jeans's theory in its original form requires two corrections.[6] His calculations include an error in the rate of dissipation and his formula gives only the time in which the mass of an atmosphere will drop to $1/e$ of its initial value. As a result all his figures for the 'life' of an atmosphere of a given gas must be multiplied by about 2·72 (e or base of natural logarithms). This, however, does not affect the order of magnitude and for most purposes 10,000 years gives one just as good an idea of how long an atmosphere will be able to maintain itself as 27,500 years, the figures being approximate anyway.

More important than this correction due to Jones is the one introduced by Lyman Spitzer, Jr., which arises out of the differences of temperature between the higher and the lower atmosphere, a difference that was not fully appreciated in Jeans's lifetime. In consequence of this Jeans's results have to be multiplied, depending on the ratio of these temperatures and corresponding densities, by a further factor which may be anything between 10,000 and 1,000,000. This alters drastically the order of magnitude and may considerably improve the theoretical chances of the Moon to retain the lighter gases. The correction, however, is rather difficult to apply, for whilst the high atmosphere may have a density and a temperature closely comparable to the terrestrial (owing to the slow rate at which density will decrease with height in the lunar atmosphere there will always be a level at which lunar air is denser than the terrestrial at the same level, however low the figure we start from), no definite estimate can be made of the density at ground-level, which may indeed bear no relation to the conventional model based on the terrestrial example—a point to be considered further on.

Another important limitation to the applicability of Jeans's mathematical conception to actual planetary conditions lies in the fact, long recognized in principle but hardly ever explicitly acknowledged, that this rests on the assumption that the atmospheric gases are ideal gases, that is to say such gases as wholly satisfy Boyle's Law and show no internal cohesion.[3] This is more or less true when the pressure is low and the temperature sufficiently high above the so-called critical temperature of the gas in question. Below this temperature the gas can be liquefied by pressure alone, above it no compression will turn it into a liquid. In other words, above the critical temperature the molecules will not stick to one another, though they will still exert a certain force of mutual attraction, but below it they become really sticky and tend to lump up together.

Such gas is called vapour, and in a vapour, even when no visible condensation occurs, larger molecular aggregates will form, so that it no longer satisfies the simple mathematical relationships postulated in the theory.

Now the critical temperature of water vapour is 374°C. For carbon dioxide it is 31°C. Thus both these gases will exist on the Moon substantially as vapours and escape the presuppositions made by Jeans, a point which he himself and all those who have followed in his footsteps have entirely overlooked. In the severe cold of the lunar night even oxygen and nitrogen will be only vapours, while ozone might liquefy. This will considerably affect the distribution and movement of these gases also during the day, but the mathematical treatment of the problem is extremely difficult. As for water, its molecules already at 60°C. are combined in threesomes (trihydrol),[7*] which raises its molecular weight from the postulated 18 to 54, and even according to Jeans's uncorrected estimate the Moon will be able indefinitely to retain any gas of this molecular weight.[5] This does not exhaust the problem but it goes to show on what slender foundations the usual assurance that there *can* be no water vapour or ice on the surface of the Moon rests.

Jones's and Spitzer's corrections and the considerations given above, all serve to improve the chances of a body of small mass, such as the Moon, to retain a substantial and varied atmosphere for cosmic periods. Jeans himself thought that the Moon should have been able to hang on to gases of a molecular weight 25 times that of the lightest gas, i.e. hydrogen (mol. wt. 2), found in our atmosphere, assuming that the conditions of temperature have been the same on both worlds.[5]

Generally speaking, the Earth as a larger mass should have been the hotter of the two in the remote geological past; but this is of little account if, as is now thought, the original atmosphere of the Earth has been completely lost and our present air is of secondary volcanic derivation. If so, there is no longer need to think in terms of thousands of millions of years, and with some volcanic action still in progress a few hundred million years ago—and I have shown that there is no sufficient reason why this should have ceased—losses through molecular dissipation could easily have been

---

* This applies to terrestrial atmospheric pressure. Under lower pressures the degree of 'association' will be less, but will rise as the temperature drops.

K

STRANGE WORLD OF THE MOON

compensated, or at least minimized. This reduces somewhat the threat to the existence of tenuous atmospheres represented by photodissociation, or break-up of compound molecules into light atoms under the action of short-wave radiation and their subsequent escape into space.[6]

Besides, when Kuiper emphasized this threat he would not seem to have fully considered the implications of the situation to which he was referring. The escape level in our own atmosphere is in the exosphere, where density will be falling off much more rapidly than in the corresponding outer gas shell of the Moon or any other body of comparable mass. Thus in this layer, which is the only relevant one, the atmosphere of the Moon will be the more massive of the two; it will also provide a better screen against the short-wave attack to the immediately underlying layers than does ours. The processes of photodissociation are reversible, the parted atoms tending to recombine as soon as the irritant of the ultra-violet rays is removed, as it would be by night. The sum total of this traffic has never been mathematically examined with anything approximating accuracy and such data as are now available do not warrant if only a tentative conclusion. All we have is the dissociation-recombination ratio in full sunlight, but the rate of diffusion of the liberated light atoms to the escape level in relation to the recurrent periods of darkness must also be drawn into account.

Kuiper,[6] who follows Jeans without modification, lists carbon dioxide (CO_2), carbonyl sulphide (COS), ozone (O_3), and sulphur dioxide (SO_2) as possible constituents of the lunar atmosphere. He has searched the spectrum of the Moon for the last two of these gases and found that if any of either is present the amount taken under normal conditions of temperature and pressure (0° C, and 760 mm. Hg) should not exceed 0·005 mm. Hg and 0·0003 mm. Hg respectively. Taking, however, into consideration the extremely low pressures expected to obtain on the Moon, these results do not appear to be particularly significant, except possibly for sulphur dioxide. Indeed, this leaves room for a relatively considerable ozonosphere.

All these gases, apart from ozone, as well as nitrogen, ammonia, and large amounts of water vapour, are given out in volcanic eruptions, whilst at least SO_2 is formed also by meteoritic impact. Radioactive decay is another source of gas. Thus there is evidence to show that the whole of our atmospheric argon has been produced by the decay of the radioactive isotope of potassium.[6,10] This should also be present on the Moon in comparable, perhaps, larger quantity. Argon is a neutral gas which does not combine even with itself to form diatomic molecules, but its atomic weight-equal in this case to its molecular weight is 40, so that the Moon ought to have been able to retain most of it. Harold Shapley has shown that if she had retained all of her argon liberated in the geologic time she would have an argon atmosphere with a ground density of about a thousandth of our sea-level figure.

Thus, even on the most unfavourable theoretical assumptions there can be no obstacle to the existence round the Moon of an atmosphere far in excess of anything at present admitted, or warranted by observation. It is, indeed, quite clear that the Moon does not possess an atmosphere of the conventional type with a ground density over a thousandth of ours, except perhaps in local gas pockets, or 'atmodomes', to use the expression coined by Spurr. It also appears highly unlikely that all the gas produced by lunar volcanoes—and these lunavoes (*vide* Chapter 6), would seem to have emitted enormous quantities of gas—and other sources has been simply dissipated into space. Some other mechanism must have supervened to deprive the Moon of the comparatively dense atmosphere she might otherwise have acquired. Such a mechanism exists. It is even obvious, but before considering this it will be useful to examine the theoretical structure of the conventional atmosphere of the Moon.

Our knowledge of planetary atmospheres is very meagre.[4] We have only two examples to draw on: the Earth and Mars, of which the latter is important mainly as a foil for the former. Yet even on the Earth our information is limited almost wholly to the lower half of the atmosphere and becomes very uncertain when the outer atmosphere is reached. This is of some importance for the vital problem of molecular dissipation.

However, the lowermost part of our air ocean, containing some three-quarters of its total mass, is known as the troposphere. Within it the atmospheric gases are more or less uniformly mixed by vertical air currents, whence its other name of convective atmosphere. The troposphere is approximately in the condition of adiabatic equilibrium, that is to say, it behaves very nearly as though it lost none of the heat received at the ground level, nor gained any from other sources. Fluctuations of temperature in an ideal atmosphere of this kind are due solely to the expansion or compression of gases as these are moved from one level to another by the winds. In a theoretical adiabatic atmosphere the drop in temperature is always the same for, say, each 100 yards of the ascent. There exists a comparatively simple formula giving the maximum possible height which such a theoretical atmosphere can attain and where its density becomes zero.[5] In the case of the Earth this is about 18 miles (29 km.).

In reality, however, flow in gases encounters resistance, which is a function of their viscosity, or stickiness. Moreover, curiously enough, this resistance is almost independent of the density (Maxwell's Law). As a result the ascending air currents can make no headway beyond a certain point above which the atmosphere tends to assume the state of isothermal equilibrium, that is to say, be of a uniform temperature throughout and become stratified according to the molecular weight of its constituents, the heavier gases petering out gradually as height increases.

We thus have another theoretical model, the isothermal atmosphere, conditions in which are once more governed by a fairly simple equation. This atmosphere goes on and on until a point is reached where the centrifugal force of rotation becomes equal to the force of gravity.[5] In actual fact, however, the molecules are moving of their own accord and will be flying away in overwhelming numbers long before this ideal boundary has been reached, so that it is entirely fictitious.

Our stratosphere represents a somewhat unconvincing approach to an isothermal atmosphere, and the boundary between it and the troposphere below is called tropopause. Jeans has failed to provide any clear connection between the two atmospheres; but the tropopause may be said to occur where the two, regarded independently as though the isothermal atmosphere extended all the way down to the ground, attain the same density.[3] On the Earth this is definitely known to happen where the density of the air drops to a quarter of its ground value; the same appears to be true also of Mars. In the first case the tropopause lies on the average at about 10 miles in the equatorial regions and at 5 miles above the poles. In the second the mean height of this transitional layer, when the temperature at the ground is 0°C., will be about 20 miles.[3] In both cases this is half the maximum theoretical height of the adiabatic atmosphere.

The odd thing is that this height is wholly independent of the density of the air at the ground level, so that if the amount of our air were doubled, or conversely reduced by half, the tropopause would still be substantially where it is now.[3] This is a counterpart of Maxwell's Law and may be expected to remain true within a wide range of variation in density or total mass, though not indefinitely.

Otherwise the maximum height of the adiabatic atmosphere and so of the actual tropopause are both directly proportional to the absolute temperature at the base of the atmosphere and are also determined by the force of gravity, the molecular weights of the constituent gases and by the ratios of their specific heats (specific heat at constant pressure divided by specific heat at constant volume).

All this should remain valid for the lunar atmosphere, though one cannot be certain that the lunar tropopause would also correspond to a drop in pressure (or density) to a quarter of the ground value. It may lie somewhat lower, as the ascending currents on the Moon will be very sluggish owing both to the small mass of the gases involved and the low force of gravity (the motive force is provided by the difference in specific *weight* between the gas at different temperatures). We will return to this anon.

On the Earth, the situation in the actual stratosphere is to begin with close enough to the theoretical isothermal model, the temperature dropping but slowly with increasing altitude. But at about 30 miles up the apple-cart is upset by the appearance of ozone, a heavy gas of molecular weight 48 which is yet able to maintain itself above the lighter gases owing to its capacity to absorb ultra-violet rays, whereby it becomes heated up to above the boiling point of water. This results in the establishment of an officially unrecognized second convective zone[1] with a consequent re-mixing of gases which have just begun to settle according to their molecular weight.

At 50 miles up the atmospheric temperature drops to 0°C. or so, and this is the farthest reach of the stratosphere, the last 20 miles of which depart considerably from the definition of isothermal atmosphere. Higher up there is more trouble. Oxygen is broken up into single ionized atoms, which become greatly agitated and attain high temperatures, the air going through a kind of heat spasms, known as D, E, F_1, and F_2 layers. These ionized layers strongly reflect radio waves of some wavelengths and attain temperatures up to 2,500° K., though direct exploration of the upper air by rockets would indicate generally lower temperatures than those obtained from theory.[1]

The ionosphere peters out at about 300 miles, but occasional aurorae still disclose traces of gas at 600 miles above the Earth's surface. This outermost part of the atmosphere is called exosphere. It is possible that segregation according to weight takes place here and hydrogen and helium are the predominant constituents, as required by theory, but there exists no evidence in support of this view. The theoretical temperature of the exosphere has been put as high as 10,000° K., which is more than the temperature of the Sun's radiating layer but represents the orbital velocity of individual molecules between the less and less frequent collisions (*vide* Chapter 2). It is thus devoid of the usual thermal connotation of the term. Once again, however, rocket data suggest that this estimate is greatly exaggerated, and according to D. R. Bates the exospheric temperatures may exceed 1,500° K. but rarely.[1]

On Mars, where oxygen is scarce, there may be neither an ozonosphere nor an ionosphere comparable to ours, so that his atmospheric structure would approximate much more closely to the simple theoretical model considered by Jeans.[3,10] On Venus, on the other hand, with an abundance of carbon dioxide, which occurs on the two other planets only as a small admixture, this gas appears to have been sorted out into the stratosphere through being heated by the absorption in the infra-red*, just as ozone has been in ours by the absorption of ultra-violet radiations. Thus we would have yet another possible atmospheric structure.

On Mars and the Earth water vapour will be frozen out at the tropopause, which forms a so-called 'cold trap', and will be unable to penetrate into the stratosphere in any quantity.[3]

The lunar atmosphere may represent an exaggeration of the Martian situation. As we have seen, the height of the tropopause is substantially

* V. A. Firsoff: 'The Earth's Twin', *Science News*, No. 52, 1959.

independent from the density at the ground level but may be somewhat lower for tenuous atmospheres. The temperature of the stratosphere, on the other hand, is here of vital importance; for it will be seen that this can never be lower than that of the tropopause. Otherwise the air from the stratosphere will sink below the tropopause and this boundary will cease to exist. On the Earth the isothermal part of the stratosphere preserves a steady temperature of $-54°$C. or $219°$K.; and had there been no oxygen or photodissociation this would be the temperature throughout the stratosphere up to extreme limits of rarefaction where the molecular-spray halo of the exosphere begins. The Moon lies at the same distance from the Sun as does the Earth, so that, unless the lunar atmosphere consists predominantly of carbon dioxide, which, as we shall see, appears unlikely, the daylight stratospheric temperatures of both bodies should be about equal. As already mentioned on p. 136, A^{40}, the heaviest and most common of the three isotopes of argon, is produced by the radioactive decay of potassium K^{40} (atomic weight 40 but atomic number 19 as against 18 for argon—the reaction is the emission of a positron), which must be present on the Moon. Argon is an inert, monatomic, heavy and sticky gas, singularly elusive to study, for it has no absorptions in the visible part of the spectrum at planetary temperatures, does not readily ionize and thus affect radio waves and has a low refractive index to boot, which makes it difficult to detect by refraction at the occultations of stars.

Thus the temperature of the lunar stratosphere by day should be roughly the same as that of our own stratosphere. Indeed, by a somewhat devious method (*see* p. 200) I have obtained a tropopause temperature of $-63°$C. for argon and of $-60°$C. for a mixture of heavy gases, as against the terrestrial figure of $-54°$C. Seeing, however, that the lunar day is nearly 30 times as long as ours, one must expect the lunar stratosphere to be a good deal colder by night than by day. The temperature of the tropopause, or uppermost layer of the troposphere, will vary in any case and can drop below that of the stratosphere, though not *vice versa*.

However, putting the temperature at the base of the atmosphere at $0°$C. ($273°$K.) and that of the lunar tropopause at $-60°$C. ($213°$K.), I have calculated the height of the tropopause for a mixture of heavy triatomic gases with a mean molecular weight 50 at $20\frac{1}{2}$ miles and for argon at 14 miles. In the first case the density at the tropopause comes out at about a third and in the second at about a half of the ground density. At night the heavy gases would be largely or wholly frozen out of the atmosphere and would in any case behave as vapours, no longer obeying the gas laws on which my calculations are based, so that argon alone remains an eligible atmospheric component. With a base temperature of $145°$K. an argon tropopause would lie 7 miles up and have a temperature of $113°$K., or $-160°$C. At this temperature even oxygen and nitrogen are vapours only,

140

as it lies below their respective critical temperatures ($-118°$C. and $-147°$C.). It is sufficient for all water vapour to be frozen out of the atmosphere even under a pressure of less than one thousand-millionth (10^{-9}) of an atmosphere, and we shall recall that the ascent to the argon tropopause involves a drop to only one-half of the ground density and so pressure. COS and SO_2 should likewise be totally precipitated, but perhaps not necessarily the whole of CO_2, as this gas has high vapour pressures, though these decline rapidly below $-150°$C.,[6] so that a fluctuation of a few degrees may be decisive in this case. In any event this would explain Dollfus's failure to detect CO_2 at a height of 100 miles above the night hemisphere near the poles.[2]

It is quite probable that the base temperature, especially in the polar regions, will be even lower than postulated here, for on the Moon the atmosphere must be expected to be much colder than the ground, as is often the case even in the dense atmosphere of the Earth. On Mars, which provides a closer comparison with the Moon, 'the temperature of the atmosphere near ground level is, during the day, possibly as much as 20 degrees or 30 degrees lower than that of the surface itself' (de Vaucouleurs).[10] If the lunar atmosphere consists largely of revaporized precipitates this effect should be very strongly marked, as vaporization requires the absorption of latent heat, which, however, would again be returned to the atmosphere at the re-precipitation by night. In any case, gases, apart from carbon dioxide and water vapour, will absorb practically none of the obscure heat radiated by the lunar rocks, whilst the absorption of solar heat will likewise be inappreciable, except for ozone. Convective currents will be very sluggish, both by reason of low gravity and low pressure and in the case of argon also of high viscosity. Conduction of heat in rarefied gases is an extremely slow process.[9] All this will prevent the atmosphere from keeping pace with the temperature of the ground, which, though hot, has a low thermal capacity.

Indeed in lunar conditions, where many of the atmospheric gases would be frozen out by night, the tropopause should have a composition different from that of the higher atmosphere, these gases being perpetually locked in circulation between the ground and the tropopause and contributing very little to the stratosphere. We have a similar situation in our atmosphere so far as water vapour is concerned: this is almost entirely concentrated within the lowermost 5 miles and occurs even at the tropopause only in minute quantities (variable).

With this duality of composition, combined with the general tenuity, of the atmosphere, the troposphere of the Moon may have a density totally unrelated to that of the stratosphere, contrary to the theoretical model and the terrestrial example.

However, let us take the daylight situation and the tropopause at

141

$-60°$C. According to the Smithsonian Physical Tables,[8] the pressures of saturated water vapour over ice close to this point are: $-50°$C.: : 0·0295 mm. Hg; $-55°$C.: : 0·0157 mm. Hg; $-60°$C.: : 0·0081 mm. Hg. If now Lipski's figure for lunar ground-level pressure of 0·0001 of ours is correct, as it well may be, this will amount to about 0·076 mm. Hg; so that the pressure at the tropopause, which is for argon half of the ground value, will become 0·038 mm. Hg. In other words, one must expect a fair proportion of the ascending water vapour to be frozen out below the tropopause even in daytime over most of the lunar disk.* Thus the ascending water vapour will be precipitated below the tropopause in the form of microscopic crystals, evaporating again before they touch the surface rocks, in a kind of thin perpetual snowstorm, rising over the ground as soon as this is warm enough for the hoar-frost to evaporate (in the present conditions there can be no liquid water on the surface of the Moon) and gradually working its way higher and higher up till it begins to sink again with the approach of the evening.

This might have been a mere mental exercise except for the various observations recorded in the previous chapters, for a perpetual snowstorm of this kind would account for the reddening of light at the terminator with a simultaneous absence of a clear twilight arc that a high conventional atmosphere could not fail to produce, as well as for the 'blue caps' round the poles and the brilliance of the limb in blue light, a brilliance which is less marked in the violet (*see* Chapter 10), since the supposed crystals, being larger than molecules, would have their maximum scattering power in the blue.

People brought up on Jeans's theory may find these conclusions startling; but we have seen that there is nothing in the theory of gases or physics of water to prevent such a situation. In the long run the Moon may be losing her water, but this loss need not be rapid so long as there is a little gas to provide the inescapable minimum of cover.

On the other hand, water vapour is subject to photodissociation and breaks up in short ultra-violet light into its constituent gases.[6] Both hydrogen and oxygen would escape from the Moon in due course, hydrogen fairly soon, oxygen somewhat more slowly. But they must first reach the escape level. We do not know how high exactly this will lie. Yet the outermost stretch of our own stratosphere is 300 miles, and the lunar atmosphere will extend *ceteris paribus* 6 times as high (the total mass of the gas is here very nearly irrelevant), or to 1,800 miles above the surface (Pickering's figure is 3,300 miles). Diffusion of gases is a slow process and it will take many lunar days before any of the liberated atoms will get half-

---

* Ice point occurs where vapour pressure draws level with atmospheric pressure. This is the same as dew-point on the Earth where pressures are high enough for the liquid phase to exist.

way up. At night there will be no ultra-violet radiations, so that water molecules will tend to re-form and resume the downward trek. Our own noctilucent and mother-of-pearl clouds may be due to the same mechanism.

Furthermore, the Le Chatelier Principle operates here. It says that whenever any factors tend to upset the existing equilibrium further change is opposed by its own products. Here, too, the liberated oxygen in the presence of ultra-violet rays will be transformed into ozone, which by absorbing the ultra-violet rays at a high level will shield the lower atmosphere from these radiations and so slow down the process of dissociation. It may be objected that in the rarefied lunar air the ozonosphere would lie close to the ground, but this is not so, for we have seen that a tropopause for heavy triatomic gases would be at 15 miles or so above the surface, and ozone, being hot, would certainly climb there and have no tendency to drop back again. Monatomic oxygen, too, provides a shield against the ultra-violet rays.

Thus water on the Moon has several lines of defence and even photo-dissociation does not appear to be too formidable a threat to its continued existence. In the presence of carbon dioxide it might combine with it to some extent to form formaldehyde, which itself would become polymerized, as suspected to be the case on Venus.[6]

Apart from the conventional high-lying atmosphere, we must also consider the ground gas skin. This exists on the Earth and is of some biological importance, but in lunar conditions it will, in some respects, be more important than the whole overlying gas halo, and this for two reasons.

The atmospheric pressure is so low that many substances which are solid or liquid on the Earth will become partly or even totally vaporized in the heat of the lunar day. Among the elements there are several more or less common ones with low melting points: Mercury, $-38 \cdot 86°$ C.; Bromine, $-7 \cdot 3°$ C.; Caesium, $28 \cdot 4°$ C.; Gallium, $29 \cdot 8°$ C.; Rubidium, $39°$ C.; Phosphorus, $44 \cdot 1°$ C.; Potassium, $63 \cdot 6°$ C.; Sodium, $97 \cdot 6°$ C.; Sulphur, 113–$120°$ C.; Iodine, $113 \cdot 7°$ C. All these would show considerable evaporation and some would boil readily under the reduced pressure. Even lead, bismuth, and tin could form appreciable vapours at the subsolar point. Most of these substances, however, are chemically active, and, apart from sulphur, may not occur much in the pure state. It is interesting to note in this connection that the yellowish colouring discernible to the north-east of Aristarchus and tentatively attributed to sulphur sometimes bears the appearance of a thin mist.

Sulphur may melt where it occurs on strongly insolated ground, and, having a high coefficient of volume expansion ($3 \cdot 4$ per cent per degree C.),[11] it could be very effective in eroding lunar rocks.

To return, however, to our vapours; of compound substances halides volatilize easily at moderate temperatures, especially aluminium chloride

(AlCl$_3$),[8] stannic chloride, which has a vapour pressure of 1 mm. Hg at
−22·7°C., and sulphuric chloride attaining the same pressure at −7°C.
All these are quite likely to be found on the Moon. Rock salt is more
recalcitrant, but could produce noticeable vapours if present in quantity,
as it may be. It will be recalled in this connection that the absence of liquid
water will favour the occurrence of soluble salts among the surface formations of the Moon—this is true to some extent even of our deserts. In fact,
if the reasoning in Chapter 7 be admitted such compounds may account
for a fair share of the superficial lunar rocks, perhaps especially among the
lunarite highlands.

Be this as it may, such vapours would be very heavy and trail low over
the ground. Indeed, the intensification of the violet element in the maria
with the progress of the lunation, noted in Chapter 10, may be due to them,
and the green sheen noticeable in the morning could likewise arise from a
kind of salt hoar-frost. The mobility of these vapours must needs be highly
restricted, so that this gas skin will differ greatly from place to place. In
some localities it may, though need not, be poisonous; in others, mixed
with carbon dioxide and water vapour, the gas skin may provide sustenance to plants evolved on the pattern of certain bacteria. It will also have a
sheltering effect both on such life as there may be and on such more
readily volatilizable deposits as water snow, if and where this is found,
partly by directly screening the sunlight and partly by increasing the local
atmospheric pressure, perhaps even to the point (4·6 mm. Hg)[8] where
liquid water could form. For the vapours would naturally flow down into
concavities and, if trapped in a cleft or deep crater, could build up to
considerable depth. And it must not be forgotten that the molecular weight
of, say, aluminium chloride is 133·5 (appr.). A vapour of this kind would
have a high specific weight. This, however, does not affect the general
proposition that liquid water cannot ordinarily exist on the surface of the
Moon.

Yet this does not exhaust the problem of the ground atmosphere, for
there is a second reason for its importance, a reason which deserves a
chapter to itself. This is sorption by the highly porous or pulverous
materials of the lunar surface. Such solids drink gas as a sponge does water
and yield it most grudgingly to the heat.

REFERENCES

1. BOYD, R. L. F. and SEATON, M. J. (Eds.). *Rocket Exploration of the Upper Atmosphere.* Pergamon Press, London, 1954.
2. DOLLFUS, AUDOIN. 'Nouvelle Recherche d'une Atmosphère au Voisinage de la
Lune.' *Comptes Rendus de l'Académie des Sciences*, 234, 1952.
3. FIRSOFF, V. A. 'Does Water Vapour Escape from Mars?' *J.B.A.A.*, Vol. 66, No. 2,
1956.
4.   'The Air of Other Worlds.' *The Journal of the British Interplanetary
Society*, Vol. 10, No. 5, 1951.

5. JEANS, J. H. *The Dynamical Theory of Gases.* Cambridge University Press, 1925.
6. KUIPER, G. P. (Ed.). *The Atmospheres of the Earth and Planets.* 2nd Edn. University of Chicago Press, 1952.
7. MEE, A. J. *Physical Chemistry.* Heinemann, London, 1943.
8. *Smithsonian Physical Tables, The.* 8th Edn., Washington, 1954.
9. UBISCH, H. VON. 'Conduction of Heat in Rarefied Gases.' *Applied Scientific Research,* Vol. A2, The Hague, 1951.
10. VAUCOULEURS, GÉRARD DE. *Physics of the Planet Mars.* Faber, London, 1954.
11. WALLACE STEWART, R. and SATTERLEY, JOHN. *A Textbook of Heat.* Clive, London, 1930.

14

WHEREIN THE ANSWER LIES

ALTHOUGH GAS MOLECULES have little cohesion between themselves in a state of temperature and pressure far removed from the critical point, they can yet be quite sticky and cling tenaciously to other substances, liquid or solid.[4,5,6]

The adhering gas may form only a superficial layer, in which case we speak of adsorption; or else its molecules may get in among those of the other body, becoming dissolved in it (solutions can be solid, as well as liquid: for instance, most alloys are solutions of metals in other metals) or entering with it into chemical combination. This is physical and chemical absorption respectively.

If we have physical adsorption or absorption, jointly or separately, the gas continues to be taken up by the ad- or absorbing body until the saturation point, appropriate to the temperature and pressure, is reached. In adsorption the amount is determined, other things being equal, by the area of contact; in absorption by the mass of the absorbent. In chemical absorption the Laws of Constant and Multiple Proportions are observed and the maximum amount of gas absorbed is fixed by weight in relation to the weight of the absorbent.

Proper chemical combination, such as, say, of hydrogen and oxygen into water, is between atoms, and its products are, generally speaking, stable. In the case of chemical absorption, however, we usually have a weaker second-grade bond between the substances, not involving a break-up of their molecules into atoms. The mass ratios betray this by being multiples of molecular as against atomic weights. The change is less thorough, and on the principle of 'easy come, easy go' such molecular compounds are less stable.

Thus the metal palladium sorbs chemically the gas hydrogen, with which it forms a molecular compound. Similarly many minerals combine with water into molecular compounds. Such water of hydration separates from them fairly easily under the influence of heat. Opal and chalcedony are some of the hydrated forms of silica, or oxide of silicon (SiO_2), most commonly occurring as quartz.

Important differences exist between these processes.

All of them are naturally expedited as the number of gas molecules impinging upon the body increases, that is to say, as the partial pressure of the gas rises. The total atmospheric pressure also plays a part here, since it hinders the escape of the gas from the body. Yet if we have a mixture of gases the amounts ad- or absorbed are less than the combined pressure would warrant, though somewhat above those if each gas were present alone at the same pressure as its partial pressure.

Whereas, though, superficial adsorption depends on the stickiness of the gas, which increases with falling temperature, the amount of gas held in solution increases with rising temperature.

Perhaps, oddly, glass is not a proper solid but a kind of very tough liquid[5] and an excellent gas solvent. Water vapour, carbon dioxide, nitrogen, oxygen, and some other gases, dissolve greedily in hot glass. In cooling it gives off the surplus it is no longer able to retain. Decrease in pressure has a comparable effect. Thus, if molten glass heated to 1,200° C. (Washburn) is exposed to vacuum (or near-vacuum) it immediately swells into a frothy mass as the occluded gases strive to escape and are imprisoned in the hardening bubbles.[4] Something similar will have occurred in the lunar lavas poured out on the surface.

Even cold glass contains in solution between 20 and 110 p.c. of gas by volume under the normal conditions of temperature and pressure, or NTP for short, which, it will be recalled, comprise 0° C. and 760 mm. Hg.

Parallelly with this, glass adsorbs gases, and water vapour in particular, high temperatures being required to drive it off. In Bunsen's experiments glass wool continued to yield water to phosphorus pentoxide until the temperature of 503° C. was reached.

This behaviour is typical of adsorption, which, as shown by Dewar and others, increases rapidly below the critical temperature, where gas molecules begin to adhere to one another, so that multiple layers are formed on the adsorbing surfaces.[4,5] Water vapour with its internal association through hydrogen bridges is especially susceptible to this. The effect is intensified as the temperature continues to fall, though it is checked somewhat if pressure is likewise decreased.

The pressure factor, however, enters into the formula for the adsorbed mass under a root sign, the exponent being usually about five, so that it is not nearly so important as is the temperature. In *The Sorption of Gases and Vapours by Solids*[4] MacBain writes (pp. 34–5):

'The fact that the sorption curve is continued down to the lowest pressures is of great practical significance. This is forcibly illustrated by considering the effect of diminished pressure upon the sorption of vapour for which $n=5$; that is, the sorption varies as the fifth root of the pressure. To halve any given value of sorption, the pressure would have to be diminished 32-fold. To reduce a given value of x/m* to 0·1 p.c. of its previous value, the pressure would have to be diminished in the proportion of 10^{-15}-fold, an operation which cannot be accomplished experimentally. . . .'

Chemical sorption, of which hydration is an example, in general also increases with falling temperatures, though it may not begin until a certain

* Ratio of sorbed gas to the mass of sorbent.

temperature is reached and persist into very high temperatures. Platinum and tungsten retain the oxygen absorbed by them even at white heat, while glass holds on to some of its water, by whatever means this may be, when red-hot.

The theoretical distinctions between the various mechanisms by which gas is held by solid are clear enough and on paper it is easy to lay down the law. In practice, on the other hand, all the different processes may be, and usually are, going on simultaneously, where, moreover, the solid will be to some extent permeable, the gas molecules slipping through visible or microscopic pores into its mass, so that persorption takes place, it is wellnigh impossible to distinguish between adsorption, absorption in solution or by chemical combination. For this reason the term *sorption* has been coined to cover all these variants without prejudice.

Some solids have a special affinity for this or that gas. Charcoal will absorb carbon dioxide more readily than it does water vapour, a situation which is reversed in silica jelly. Platinum sorbs oxygen more efficiently than it does other gases, whilst palladium shows a similar preference for hydrogen.

A general rule is that if we have two substances one of which dissolves in the other when that is liquid, either of them will be energetically sorbed as gas or vapour by the other in the solid state. We know from everyday experience the hygroscopic properties of salt and sugar which dissolve in liquid water and so, too, absorb the invisible water vapour from the air. Carbon dioxide, which readily dissolves in liquid water, will likewise be strongly sorbed by ice, and so on.

It is, further, clear that all sorption and adsorption in particular will be expedited if the sorbing surface is increased. Thus a rough surface will sorb more gas and will sorb it faster than a smooth one of the same material, and the maximum sorbing capacity will be attained by porous, spongy, or frothy bodies. Finely divided matter, such as dust, small crystals, and threads will also be highly adsorbent, as exemplified by, say, cotton wool, which sorbs invisible moisture just as greedily as it does water.

These conditions are admirably satisfied by the lunar surface, which, as we have seen in Chapter 11, approximates closely to terrestrial pumice overlaid by a thin pellicule of dusty or fragmentary matter. It will likewise be recalled that the best fit between the observed thermal behaviour of lunar rocks and terrestrial materials is secured by pumice *in air*,[7] that is to say, as it would be imbued with gas under atmospheric pressure on the Earth, though the covering dust would appear to be more or less de-gassèd, in day-time at any rate.

This shows that sorption is actually taking place, and that on a grand scale, for if this lunar 'pumice' can hold as much gas under the extremely low atmospheric pressures obtaining on the Moon in the blistering heat of the subsolar point as our pumice does under 760 mm. Hg., it must indeed be a far more efficient sorbent than any rock, however bubbly, known on Earth.

As much is, no doubt, to be expected considering the conditions in which lunar rocks have consolidated. Washburn's glass froth would probably be a good deal better approximation to the structure of these formations than any of our volcanic scoriae, which have set under the restraining forces of an atmospheric pressure amounting to $14\frac{3}{4}$ pounds per square inch and a gravity six times the lunar. The thermal behaviour of such glass froth, however, has not been studied in this connection. In general the approach of most investigators trying to match lunar conditions has always suffered from lack of imagination.

The amount of gas imprisoned in lunar 'pumice' may also indicate that this gas is more sticky in specie than our atmospheric gases, which has, in fact, been inferred from other data in Chapter 13.

However this may be, it can be stated without recourse to any hypotheses that the high gas content of lunar surface rocks gives a clear answer to the question posed in the preceding chapter: What has become of the atmosphere allowed to the Moon by theory? *This is simply held captive in the lunar soil*, only a thin envelope stretching high up over the ground in the hours of darkness and a denser layer of gas being released by the heat of sunrays during the day, a layer which begins to develop into a proper conventional atmosphere but can never complete the process. The importance of this situation for lunar ecology cannot be over-emphasized.

Water vapour should form a substantial proportion, perhaps the bulk, of this lower gas layer because it is one of the gases to which the substances occurring on the Moon's surface should be especially partial and because of the high critical temperature of water ($374°C$.), which is much above those of most of the common gases. The vapours of low-boiling solids would likewise be energetically sorbed.

Among the efficient absorbers of water must be listed silica, various silicates, including pumice and zeolites, volcanic glasses, silica gel (partly dehydrated jelly of silicic acid), alumina, and other oxides and salts of metals. Ice and dry ice, if present, and especially if finely divided or frothy in structure, could also hold large quantities of water vapour and carbon dioxide by sorption.

To indicate the ratios in which atmospheric gases are sorbed by a typical silicate, we may take Schmidt's data[4] relating to one of the zeolites (i.e. hydrous calcium–aluminium silicates), chabasite. He found that at 20°C. and pressure of one atmosphere this mineral sorbed the following multiples of its own volume:

H_2	A	O_2	N_2	CO	CH_4	CO_2	NH_3	H_2O
3·3	28·1	34·3	52·2	74·5	80·4	282·0	567·0	702·0

Schmidt 'pointed out that if various inert sorbing materials such as chabasite, chromic oxide, uranium oxide, vanadium oxide, and dehydrated gypsum were compared at any definite temperature and pressure, the relative amounts of the various gases were much the same in each case, so that the various solids differed by a roughly constant factor' (MacBain, p. 173).

Alumina is not so efficient as sorbent of carbon dioxide but it clings to water vapour most tenaciously.[4] At a pressure near vacuum, at $-20°C$. it still retains 100 cubic centimetres of water vapour at NTP for each gram of its mass (not *weight*, as on the Moon a mass of one gram would weigh only one-sixth of a gram, but this will not affect sorption, which is a molecular property independent of gravity). Alumina is an oxide of aluminium (Al_2O_3), which is one of the principal elements in the *Sial* layer of the Earth. It is a common mineral and may be even more common on the Moon owing to the expected preponderance there of elements of low atomic weight. It may, therefore, play an important part as a reservoir of atmospheric water vapour, some of which it would yield during the day.

From Chapter 7 it will be recalled that salts and silica gel may be the main constituents of lunabase, the dark rock of the maria. The behaviour of silica gel as sorbent is, accordingly, of considerable interest to us. This is summarized as follows in W. D. Bancroft's *Applied Chemistry* (p. 330):

'A dilute jelly may contain about 300 mols [a mole—*mol* is the American spelling—is the molecular weight of the substance expressed in grams] of water to one of silica (1 p.c. SiO_2). Such a jelly flows together again when broken to pieces. When the water content is only 30–40 mols (10 p.c. SiO_2), the jelly can be cut and will stand alone. With 20 mols. (14 p.c. SiO_2) the jelly is stiff, and it is brittle when the content is 10 mols. . . . At 6 mols can be pulverized and the powder is apparently dry. The vapour pressure is practically that of pure water down to a water content of 6 mols per mol of silica. On further dehydration the vapour-pressure curve drops continuously with no sign of the existence of any definite compound. When the water content drops to somewhere usually between 1·5 and 3·0 mols (60 p.c. silica) . . . jelly becomes opaque and chalky but clears up again when the water vapour reaches 0·5–1·0 mol (80 p.c. silica). . . . Owing to the action of capillarity, the water which evaporates from the outer surface of the capillaries is at once replaced from the inside of the jelly, leaving a vapour space in the centre of the jelly. This produces an opacity which lasts until the pores are free from capillary water. The balance of the water, 0·5–1·0 mol, is probably adsorbed.'

Even at 0·1 mm. Hg, at 0°C., the amount of water adsorbed by silica is about 0·05 gm. per gram of silica, and will rise steeply with falling temperature.

The described changes in the constitution and appearance of silica jelly may be of some importance in the circulation of subsurface moisture and could affect to some extent the albedo of the surface where the overlying materials are transparent. The efflorescence of salts, which turn white and fall to powder upon losing their water of hydration,[5] as could be the case in the hot regions of the Moon, must also be considered as a possible explanation of the brightening-up of surface features under a high Sun recorded in Chapter 9.

This naturally leads to the problem of erosion. Sorption results in the distension of molecular lattices in crystals. Some metals can be reduced to powder by absorbing water vapour (Gurwitsch).[4] Sorption and desorption will be constantly at work on the Moon, these processes being particularly rapid during lunar eclipses, which should have a shattering effect on the rocks with the production of finely fragmented or dust-like debris. This is a far more likely form of heat erosion than flaking, suggested among others by Whipple.[12] Thus taluses of coarse scree would be lacking, as is indeed shown by the examination of isolated peaks, say, in Mare Imbrium (Spurr).[10] Here and there landslides and large-scale shattering are found, but these appear to have been due to volcanic and tectonic stresses, or possibly to meteoritic impact, rather than to anything resembling our weathering. On the other hand, the presence of fine granular or dusty matter has been inferred from the thermal properties of the surface formations and the polarimetric data,[7,12] which is in good accord with the interpretation given above.

This would mean that the ancient formations could have been worn down and destroyed without the intervention of magmatic heat, remelting and other igneous paraphernalia, as envisaged among others by Spurr;[10] though neither does it necessarily follow that these have been totally absent. Sorption could also have cemented together some of the debris into more or less compact deposits. For if at any time, say, water vapour had been absorbed in any locality up to a point of deliquescence of siliceous jellies or salts, the resulting paste could have bound together the fragments. In other words, sedimentary formations need not be totally absent from the Moon, and the smoothing down of ancient crater floors may be partly due to the accumulation of such deposits.

This, however, is merely a superficial effect. Sorption will extend far below the lunar *soil*—which is in fact a strict counterpart of our soil—into the depths of those bubbly rocks.

There will be persorption even within seemingly compact solid rocks. The outward appearance of the Moon, however, shows clearly what simple theoretical considerations lead one to expect—that the lunar crust is honeycombed with systems of caves, crevices, and hollows of all sizes. We will also remember that only a few feet below the surface there is a permafrost layer,[7] while farther below the temperature must rise again owing to

L

the evolution of radioactive heat. The atmospheric gases are sorbed at the surface, beginning with simple adsorption, which is almost instantaneous[5] but will intensify with falling temperature, and thence passing into sorption by solution or chemical binding. These will draw off the first sorbed molecular layers and make room for more within the innumerable pores and bubbles of the frothy rock. By degrees the sorptive process will spread farther and farther down into the region of low temperatures and increased pressures, thus intensifying with every step. At the permafrost level there will be a kind of seal that water vapour may find impossible to force and where other gases may likewise be delayed, though some will probably percolate below it into the sphere of rising temperature, where higher pressures will be built up. Sooner or later in this sequence a pressure sufficient for the liquefaction of ice will be reached and, as soon as the ambient temperature exceeds 0°C, liquid water will form.

In other words we shall have a circulation similar to that of phreatic water in our limestone districts,[2] but beginning with gas 'syphoning' by sorption and gradually working up to a liquid stage.

The syphoning should be a very efficient means of depleting the external atmosphere, which would be kept in equilibrium by the reverse process of escape of gases from under the cold seal, partly through volcanic action and partly through simple erosion resulting in the opening up of vents similar to our swallets. In fact, in these conditions it may become difficult to distinguish between vulcanism proper and escape of gas through desorption and decompression, which will take place on a smaller scale within the upper rock layers in the cycle of the lunar day. This gives proper meaning to Pickering's statement that lunar 'vulcanism' does not manifest itself till two or three days after sunrise.[8]

There should also be upward erosion through infumigation by relatively hot gases and vapours (these need not be actually hot by our standards but only sufficiently hot to thaw their way through the permafrost seal) from the invisible underground watercourses. Thus those chains of small and not-so-small craters we find in many parts of the Moon need not be volcanic at all.

The surface rocks above the cold seal will form a kind of 'gas marsh', in which the concentration of gas will increase towards the permafrost layer, with a periodical fluctuation in the course of the lunar day as the soil and subsoil become heated by the Sun with partial desorption and emission of gas, to be followed by a reversed process with the coming of the night. In places a gas marsh of this kind may even pass into a proper marsh, capillary water forming below the surface and possibly some soluble constituents being brought to the point of deliquescence. Water, if holding salts in solution, could remain liquid below the ice point. For instance, a solution of sal ammoniac freezes at −18°C., or 0°F., so that a slight increase in pressure could suffice to keep it liquid. In other words, the name *palus* (marsh) given to some lunar features may not be quite so fanciful, after all.

The depth of the gas marsh layer will, no doubt, vary from place to place, depending on the structure and thermal properties of the rock, selenographic latitude, and daily insolation. Locally the permafrost layer may be right on the surface, but in warmer regions it will be some feet below the surface, as indicated by the radiometric data.[7]

To return, however, to sorption as such; this is accompanied by evolution of heat, for the sorbed molecules in losing their mobility pass their kinetic energy on to the sorbent. This heat must again be supplied to expel the sorbed gas from the sorbent, as has, in fact, been tacitly implied above. The heat of sorption is usually much higher than the heat of vaporization, though there are some exceptions to this rule; for instance, in the case of water vapour sorbed by charcoal.[4]

Tompkins and Young[11] have examined the adsorption of gases by finely divided caesium iodide, a halide that may occur on the Moon and would, incidentally, be subject to considerable evaporation in the midday heat of strongly insolated places. Thus, it would itself be adsorbed by the pumice-like rocks, then adsorbing the lighter gases, in a kind of concentric arrangement where a smaller box is found inside a larger one and so on, though not *ad infinitum*. Water ice would similarly sorb carbon dioxide, which upon freezing would adsorb lighter gases. The compound heats of sorption and vaporization could be very considerable.

However, Tompkins and Young studied the adsorption of CO, N_2, A, and O_2 by caesium iodide between $65 \cdot 5°$ K. and $91 \cdot 6°$ K. (CO_2 and H_2O are almost entirely solidified at such temperatures and have negligible vapour pressures) and pressures below and up to 1 mm. Hg for carbon monoxide, 2 mm. Hg for nitrogen, and 5 mm. Hg for oxygen and argon. At $90°$ K., $24 \cdot 5$ grams of sorbent adsorbed no less than 2×10^5 moles of CO under the pressure of $0 \cdot 5$ mm. Hg—an enormous amount if it is realized that a mole of CO is 27 grams! Nitrogen, with a lower critical temperature, was not adsorbed quite so strongly, but at about $80°$ K. and pressures between $0 \cdot 1$ and $0 \cdot 5$ mm. Hg the same sorbent adsorbed something like 5×10^4 moles of N_2.

The rise of pressure affected the sorption but little, and so, too, its fall in the direction of lunar atmospheric pressures could not have had any far-reaching effects. The temperatures of the lunar night are, of course, a good deal higher than in these experiments; but their results give us an idea of the intensity of sorption at such low temperatures. When temperature differences are not too great the amounts of different gases sorbed by the same neutral sorbent are in the first approximation the same for equal differences between the temperature of sorption and the critical temperature of the gas in question. Thus carbon monoxide, with a critical temperature of 134°K., will compare at 90°K. to carbon dioxide, whose critical temperature is 242°K., at about 198°K. (−75°C.). The critical point of water is 647°K., so that to draw a parallel we should have to take water vapour at 603°K., which is a good deal above the temperature of any portion even in the subsolar area of the Moon. Here, though, this simple relationship cannot be upheld.

Tompkins and Young[11] have found that a monolayer of adsorbed gas, that is to say a layer one molecule deep containing one mole of the gas, covers between 2 and 3 square metres. In the case of comminuted and highly porous matter this contact surface may be comprised within a comparatively small volume. For example, human lungs, which are spongy in structure, have an internal area of some 1,000 square feet, or 85 square metres in metric measure. At low temperatures multiple adsorption layers will form.

The heats of simple adsorption by neutral materials have been found by these investigators to be about 3,000 gram-calories per mole, in good accord with the results obtained by Magnus and collaborators for silica gel.[4] But the latter's figures for carbon dioxide and ammonia are 7,200 calories and 12,000 calories respectively. The figure for water vapour is not given but this should be about a third higher than for ammonia. On charcoal, a less efficient sorbent of water vapour, it is 6,100 calories at −78°C.

This should suffice to indicate the vast amounts of heat required to remove gas sorbed by lunar rocks, and with compound sorption mentioned above the figures have to be considerably increased. This is of great importance in considering the ability of the Moon to retain her water and its occurrence on her surface, which form the subject of the next chapter.

Sorption will also give rise to electrical phenomena,[4,5] but too little is known about this aspect to attempt conclusions. In any event it is possible that some of the glows occasionally reported on the Moon are of electrical origin, similar to silent discharge, and may be connected with sorption and desorption of gases, or thermo-electric phenomena more generally. Bad conductors of heat are equally bad at conducting electricity, so that high local charges may accumulate on the Moon. Where conduction occurs electricity will naturally tend to concentrate at the summits of isolated peaks, such as Piton in Mare Imbrium, on which something in the nature of electric discharges has been observed.[3]

Pickering[9] was the first to suggest that electrostatic winds may have been responsible for spreading the matter of the crater rays, which he believed to be snow.

REFERENCES

1. BANCROFT, W. D. *Applied Chemistry*. McGraw-Hill, New York, 1926.
2. CULLINGFORD, C. H. D. (Ed.). *British Caving*. Routledge, London, 1953.

3. DAVIDSON, M. *Astronomy for Everyman*. Dent, London, 1953.
4. MACBAIN, J. W. *The Sorption of Gases and Vapours by Solids*. Routledge, London, 1932.
5. MEE, A. J. *Physical Chemistry*. Heinemann, London, 1943.
6. PARTINGTON, J. R. *An Advanced Treatise on Physical Chemistry*. Longmans, Green, London, 1951.
7. PAWSEY, J. L. and BRACEWELL, R. N. *Radio Astronomy*. Oxford, 1955.
8. PICKERING, W. H. 'Meteorology of the Moon.' *Popular Astronomy*, Vol. 23, 1915.
9.   *The Moon*. Doubleday, Page and Co., New York, 1903.
10. SPURR, J. E. *Geology Applied to Selenology* (4 Vols.), 1944–9.
11. TOMPKINS, F. C. and YOUNG, D. M. 'The Adsorption of Gases on Caesium Iodide.' *Transactions of the Faraday Society*, Vol. 47, London, 1951.
12. WHIPPLE, F. L. *Earth, Moon and the Planets*. Churchill, London, 1946.

15

WATER AND SNOW

In chapter 13 we have seen that there exists no sufficient reason why water as substance should be absent from the surface of the Moon, although this is porous, highly adsorbent, and probably permeable, which will make for the steady depletion of the gas mantle. Water, owing to its comparatively high critical point, will not only readily solidify in the low temperatures which occur during a part of the climatic cycle; for the same reason it will also be intensively sorbed, especially by silica gels, volcanic glasses, salts, alumina, and some other common minerals which will assume a frothy texture. This gives water some additional protection against photodissociation and molecular dissipation, but it will also tend to remove it underground.

At a sufficient depth, progressively larger bodies first of ice, then of liquid water may be expected to have formed, with a kind of 'sunless sea' or seas on the boundary between the lighter pervious rocks above, which should also be specifically less dense than water, and the heavier impervious formations below. This will be a strange world of 'caverns measureless to man', hardly paralleled on the Earth, except on a small scale in her limestone districts;[3,10] although subterranean lakes and rivers are said to have been discovered beneath the parched sands of the Sahara.*

A liquid boils when the partial pressure of vapour over it becomes equal to the atmospheric pressure. If the two pressures draw level below the point of liquefaction (fusion), as, say, is the case of iodine or camphor on the Earth, the solid will 'boil' without melting and pass directly into vapour. This is called sublimation. The point of fusion for water is 0° C. and 4·58 mm. of mercury. If the pressure is less than this no liquid phase appears: there can be only solid ice and vapour. Under lower pressures ice sublimes at lower temperatures: at 3 mm. Hg, −5° C.; 2 mm. Hg, −10° C.; 0·48 mm. Hg, −20° C.; 0·29 mm. Hg, −30° C.; 0·10 mm. Hg, −40° C.; 0·05 mm. Hg, −45° C.; 0·03 mm. Hg, −50° C.; 0·016 mm. Hg, −55° C.; 0·008 mm. Hg, −60° C.[17]

0·10 mm. Hg corresponds to about 1/10,000 of our sea-level air pressure and is the figure usually attributed to the ground air pressure on the Moon. It will also be seen that below this point the temperature of sublimation drops only gradually as the decrease in the pressure of saturated water vapour becomes very rapid. Thus 0·008 mm. Hg represents a rarefaction to one millionth of our atmosphere, but the sublimation point is depressed by merely a further 20° C. In any case, on the most optimistic reckoning the

* A B.B.C. talk by St. Barbe Baker.

lunar atmospheric pressures are hopelessly too low for liquid water to form on the surface of the Moon as a matter of course, the more so as even above the ice-point pressure of 4·6 mm. Hg the existence of the liquid phase will be extremely precarious and the water produced in the melting would evaporate almost instantaneously: one would have to double this pressure before liquid water could be obtained in any quantity worth speaking of.

This, however, though undoubtedly true, refers to an abstract situation and in reality other factors often intervene to spoil the neat mathematical picture obtained under laboratory conditions. Thus, in defiance of Dalton's Law of Partial Pressures, the presence of a neutral gas, such as argon, will depress the partial pressure of vapour in equilibrium with the liquid or solid phase,[6] which here stand for water and ice respectively, so that the boiling or sublimation point is raised. When atmospheric pressures are high the effect is inappreciable, but if these are reckoned in millimetres and fractions of millimetres of mercury the difference may be considerable. This is one more reason why the formation of small amounts of liquid water at the bottom of hollows filled with heavy vapours, such as sulphur, appears possible. The water vapour itself over any large body of ice or snow, if such exist, could generate local excess pressure.

Briny pools will not freeze till some $-15°$C. of frost is reached, so that if salt deposits are brought to the point of deliquescence by sorbing water vapour a pressure of about 1·3 mm. Hg may suffice for the liquid to appear, which should be readily attainable at a small depth below the surface and exceptionally perhaps even on the surface. Furthermore, in certain conditions pure water can be cooled in large amounts down to $-26°$C. and in droplets down to $-72°$C. without freezing. Haines, who accompanied Byrd on his first Antarctic expedition, observed fogs composed of water droplets at temperatures as low as $-44°$C. In Greenland and the Antarctica fog bows have been seen at $-34°$C. and $-30°$C. respectively.[5] Yet, while water can *remain* liquid at such temperatures, which straddle the lunar sublimation point, if cooled gradually in the absence of dust, electrified particles, or mechanical disturbance, it must first be there to be cooled; it cannot form to begin with.

The required conditions may occur on the Moon and it is within bounds of possibility that mists of liquid droplets are emitted from volcanic vents or crevices in communication with underground reservoirs at higher temperatures and under higher pressures. Capillary condensations could easily exist inside the porous rocks and, as suggested in the preceding chapter, a briny bog could form in the subsoil beneath a cake of porous pumice.

Still, if liquid water occurs at all on the surface of the Moon it will be only exceptionally and in small quantities, which may be important biologically but could leave hardly any visible mark on the landscape. It is possible, on the other hand, that in the past ages, especially in periods of

STRANGE WORLD OF THE MOON

marked volcanic activity, the atmosphere of the Moon was denser as a whole, so that water vapour could liquefy at least locally in considerable amounts. Spurr[18] thought that the radial gully systems round such craters as Autolycus, Aristillus, and Theophilus, had been produced by water erosion when clouds of steam emitted by these 'lunavoes' condensed into torrential rains under the cover of local 'atmodomes' of superior density. This indeed seems to be the most reasonable explanation of such features.

There is also some evidence for more widespread rainfall in the region of Mare Imbrium. To the north-west of Eratosthenes where one of the main Apennine valleys debouches on Mare Imbrium its dark lunabase is over-laid by a fan of light-coloured lunarite debris which is difficult to account for unless it has been brought there by the agency of running water, though the light colouring has alternatively been attributed to rays from a small crater. (See also Plate XII.) One may find a few other instances of apparent water action on the surface of the Moon. Crater glacis and mountain faces are often seamed by gullies, which again are inexplicable without a spell of water erosion. These features, however, if not exactly rare, are comparatively inconspicuous, which is not at all surprising on the inter-pretation of the lunar surface advanced in these pages.

W. H. Pickering[12] favoured the view that the central cones of many ring mountains have been dismembered by ice erosion at a time when glaciers used to coat their sides and come down sliding out on to the floors, where the sides of the gullies can often be seen prolonged by low ridges, inter-preted by him as lateral moraines.

This conception is a little difficult. On the Earth the glaciers owe their compactness, flow, and erosive power to gravity, which would be of little account on the Moon. The ice, formed by the precipitation of hoar-frost, in low temperatures and under low atmospheric pressures and once more under reduced gravity, would be spongy and rigid, with little tendency to flow. True, below $-110°$C. water fails to crystallize and ice assumes a vitreous structure,[2] but it reverts to crystalline habit as soon as the tem-perature is raised, and with a denser atmosphere night temperatures, at least in low latitudes where many of these features are found, would hardly have sunk as low as that. It is also doubtful if even in her palmiest days the Moon had enough surface water for really large glaciers, though it is unwise to be dogmatic.

The gullies rending the sides of the central crater peaks, probably volcanic in origin, have U-shaped profiles, which on the Earth denotes ice erosion. Still, if ice action is involved, one would imagine this to have been by shattering, due to alternate thawing and regelation, rather than brute bulldozing. Comparatively thin snow-fields would suffice for that. The pseudo-morainic debris at the foot of the gullies could in this case have been deposited by the streams from the melt-waters and simply by sliding over the snow, as is often the case in our British mountains, where no glaciers exist.

Further, Pickering speaks (*The Moon*,[14] pp. 42–3) of 'a new kind of rill' discovered during the study of the Moon in the clear air of the Andes, at Arequipa:

'From its resemblance to a terrestrial watercourse it was named a river-bed, and it differs from the rills proper described in the 1st chapter in several important respects. In the first place, these minute rills or riverbeds are always wider at one end than at the other. Secondly, the wide end always terminates in a pear-shaped craterlet, Thirdly, their length is composed almost entirely of curves of very short radius, giving them a zigzag, winding appearance exactly resembling a terrestrial river as drawn upon a map. Fourthly, one end is nearly always perceptibly higher than the other. But here we come to a very marked distinction from the terrestrial rivers, for in the lunar rill the apparent mouth is always higher than the source. What this means, of course, is that if formed by the action of water, as seems from their appearance probable, the lake flowed into a river, and not the river into a lake.

'Nor, when we come to think of the matter, is this result surprising. The pressure of the lunar atmosphere must always have been slight, and evaporation from the sunny side of the Moon extremely rapid.'

Some rivers in our desert regions also peter out in the sands and thus reproduce to some extent the appearance of these lunar features, probably the most typical of which is found on the slopes of Mt. Hadley in the Apennines. It must, in fact, be admitted that it does look extremely like a meandering mountain stream. The largest of all—Schroeter's Valley—makes a less convincing 'river'.

On the evidence of the general characteristics of the lunar surface the existence of ordinary surface watercourses seems very doubtful, even if it be granted that the radial gullies of Aristillus are proper drainage channels. For there is some difference between a temporary channel dredged by a sudden downpour and a permanent or semi-permanent 'river'. One would expect the latter soon to open out for itself a way under the ground and disappear, without having time to cut out a valley. On the other hand, having established itself at a depth where it could flow more freely, reasonably secure from excessive evaporation and excessive sorption, an underground river would continue to erode the overlying rocks by infumigation and reprecipitation, combined with, possibly, frost shattering. Our own Cheddar Gorge largely owes its existence to this process.[3] In this way in localities where the emission of water was particularly abundant, as would appear to have been the case in Cobra-Head below Herodotus, where Schroeter's Valley originates, a sinking watercourse could have come into being at a higher level than usual for such lunar features and worn out a canyon upwards in the vaulting rocks. If so, the initial stages of the process would manifest themselves on the surface as a line of sinkholes or swallets—in fact, a crater chain.

Many lunar clefts show signs of such origin, although as a rule they are too linear to be assimilated to a winding watercourse. They would rather fit the explanation by gas seepage along deep-seated tectonic fractures. But in the case of Schroeter's Valley erosion by an underground watercourse seems a feasible proposition. Fractures may have intervened here, too: there are certainly some in the vicinity.

So much for the past. But how about the present?

Pickering[13,14,15] firmly believed that the white haloes, as well as the bright rays round the younger craters, were snow, more or less sparsely distributed at the bottom of small hollows, which made it invisible under oblique illumination. He even maintained that the great rays of Tycho were analogous to our cirrus clouds, only lying close to the ground.

His ideas have often been met with ridicule, and he added oil to the fire by his unfortunate knack of using controversial terms, such as the already mentioned 'riverbed', 'canal', 'run', speaking of the 'melting' of lunar snow-fields, although he was well aware that snow could not melt on the Moon. Possibly his worst 'offence' was the hypothesis that the irregular changes observed by him in the 'runs' or Eratosthenes represented seasonal movements of swarms of small animals. This provided handy ammunition to those who wished to see him as a crank not to be taken seriously. Regrettably, the argument was sometimes demagogical rather than scientific—aiming at arousing suspicion, creating prejudice and ill-will rather than at eliciting the truth. Thus the work of the dedicated life of a highly skilled and painstaking observer has been almost totally dismissed, if perhaps not entirely forgotten.

'Jeans has shown that there could be no water on the Moon', said the critics. Or 'How can there be snow on the Moon if the midday temperature of the ground is 20°C. above the boiling point of water?'

At first sight and on small knowledge such statements are convincing, and somehow or other neither Pickering himself nor his opponents have ever submitted the matter to a thorough physical examination. Perhaps the information made use of in this book was not available at the time of the controversy, but it seems more to the point that the minds of the profession were set in certain grooves which they found difficult to leave—a common human failing.

We have already seen that Jeans has *shown* nothing of the sort. All he did was construct in his mind and represent mathematically on paper the theoretical model of an atmosphere and substitute in his equation derived from it the numerical value of lunar gravitation for the g symbol. In the words of Einstein: 'In so far as mathematics applies to reality it is not

certain and in so far as mathematics is certain it does not apply to reality.'
So, too, with Jeans's theory: it was certain with reference to its own sym-
bols but not with reference to planetary atmospheres as they actually are,
and the lunar atmosphere in particular. It permitted an increased understanding of the problem, or provided an approximation to reality. In my
analysis, by including various factors left out of account by him and his
followers, I have tried to make this approximation closer, and from the
result it follows that there is no valid reason for denying the possibility of
the presence of water vapour in the lunar atmosphere, while, on the contrary, there may be valid reasons for expecting the lowermost lunar atmosphere to consist overwhelmingly of water vapour.

This eliminates the main objection to the presence of snow on the Moon.
The second objection is even more hollow than the first.

In Chapter 11 we have seen that the quoted temperature is attained only
exceptionally for a short time within a small area lying in the tropical belt
of the Moon, 3 degrees of latitude in width. Even within this small area the
quoted figure stands merely for the average, and, while it will be locally
exceeded, at other places the actual temperature must also fall below it.
Round the poles the thermometer never rises above the ice point, except
again locally, on the hill-sides facing the Sun. This provides for an almost
unlimited scale of variation in the midday temperature, from close to the
absolute zero in the depths of such rings as Newton, which never see the
Sun, to perhaps 200° C. in especially exposed parts of the equatorial belt.

True, some of Pickering's 'snow-fields' are so situated as to get the full
blaze of the midday Sun, so that if this were the whole of the story at least
some of the criticism would stand.

But it is not.

The thermocouple temperatures refer only to a thin, though perhaps
variable, skin of dusty or comminuted material (*see* Chapter 11), which
has a very low thermal capacity, that is to say, contains little heat. And it is
heat, not temperature, that counts in this case. The Sun certainly does
shine for nearly 15 days at a stretch, but he also does not shine for an equal
period of time. Just as certainly the sunshine is unobstructed, or practically
unobstructed; but the thinness of the lunar air cuts both ways. In the first
place, the air will be a good deal colder than the ground[19] and a difference
of 50° C. in their temperatures appears not an unreasonable estimate. In
the second, owing to the very low thermal conductivity of rarefied gases,
matched by the excellent insulating properties of the surface materials,
neither conduction nor convection of heat need be considered. Virtually all
heat traffic will be by radiation and absorption. In other words, the snow
could draw only on the heat supplied to it directly by the sunrays.

It can be shown that the heat received at a level horizontal surface one
square centimetre in area in the course of the lunar day is equal to a little

less than two-thirds of the product of the Solar Constant into the daylight period expressed in minutes and the cosine of the selenographical latitude of the place, or, strictly speaking, the latitude as counted from the line along which the Sun passes through the zenith (*see* Appendix). Disregarding here the latter correction, which is irrelevant for our purposes, we may say that at the equator this maximum of the available solar energy will be equal to half the Solar Constant times the day-time in minutes, for here the latitude is zero and the cosine of zero degrees is unity. Further, the Solar Constant is 1·97 gram-calories per square centimetre per minute; and taking this as 2 to make assurance doubly sure, we get $1\frac{1}{3}$ gram-calories per minute, or roughly 28,530 calories altogether.

This may sound a lot, but in terrestrial conditions it would suffice to evaporate in round figures 50 grams of water. In other words, this heat could vaporize a pool 50 cm., or some 20 inches, deep. This would not be too devastating for a substantial mountain *névée*.

On the Moon, however, water does not boil. It is the ice that sublimes at a temperature of −50°C. or so, depending on the figure adopted for the ground pressure of the lunar atmosphere, though, as we have seen, this temperature is not greatly affected by rarefaction beyond 0·0001 of one atmosphere (760 mm. Hg). The change of state or phase involves the absorption or liberation of a considerable amount of heat, the so-called latent heat, which does not affect the temperature of the substance undergoing the transformation. The latent heat of sublimation is equal to the sum of the latent heats of fusion and vaporization. This heat increases with falling temperature, in the case of water rather rapidly.

The Clapeyron–Clausius Equation[11] gives the latent heat of sublimation for 223°K. (−50°C.) as 757 gram-calories per gram of snow. Lunar snow, however, precipitated during the night, will be a good deal colder than −50°C.; in fact, −200°C. appears to be a reasonable estimate of its temperature. Further, being at this low temperature, it will become a natural recipient of other precipitates, and of carbon dioxide more particularly. The latent heat of vaporization of carbon dioxide is only about a tenth that of water, but its heat of sorption will be at the very least in the region of 800 gram-calories per gram. Thus nearly a thousand gram-calories will have to be supplied to steam a gram of dry ice off a deposit of water snow. Not knowing how much carbon dioxide there would be, the effect is difficult to estimate, but it will not be inconsiderable. On the other hand, the specific heat of ice within the envisaged range of temperature is known[4] and averages about one-third small calorie per gram per 1°C.; a more accurate computation (*see* Appendix) shows that some 50 gram-calories will be required to bring one gram of our snow to the sublimation point,[2] leaving out of account the changes of crystalline habit, which involve absorption of heat. This snow will have the form of loosely packed hoar-

162

frost, which will energetically sorb the liberated water vapour and the heat of sorption exceeds the heat of vaporization. No data are available here, but, since nothing can have greater affinity to water than water, the heat of sorption of water vapour by water ice or snow will be high. The average heat of sorption is some 3,000 gram-molecules per mole, the latter being 18 grams in this case, so that the lower limit for the heat of sorption would be 167 gram-calories per gram. Sorption of gases would double the figure and putting the total amount of heat required to vaporize one gram of lunar snow emerging from the night at 1,200 gram-calories should be a conservative estimate.

Oddly enough, the figures for the pressure of saturated water vapour over ice indicate that the more rarefied the lunar atmosphere the more difficult these snow-fields will be to vaporize, though at a certain stage molecular evaporation will intervene to redress the balance.[11]

If the whole of the heat of the sunrays could be utilized for sublimation the result, though not particularly impressive, would be appreciable. Yet pure snow reflects about 80 per cent of the incident radiation; it is also an efficient radiator in the low infra-red,[6] so that it will be losing some of the acquired heat in this way. Disregarding this loss, which may not be of much account at such low temperatures, let us stick to 20 per cent. This cuts down the available fortnightly supply of solar heat to about 5,670 gram-calories per square centimetre and will suffice for vaporizing 4·73 grams of snow only on the most optimistic reckoning.

At the latitude of 45 degrees, half-way to the pole, this amount is reduced to $3\frac{1}{3}$ grams, and evaporation will effectively cease before the pole is reached.

If this snow were in the form of compact ice, the deposit evaporating during the daylight hours would be, on the equator, about 5·3 cm., say, $2\frac{1}{4}$ inches, thick. But, being very loosely packed, it could easily be two or more feet in depth, though still containing the same amount of matter. This applies to level ground. If the snow were lying on a slope facing due north or south, at right angles to the Sun's path in the sky, the effect of the inclination would be exactly the same as that of increased latitude. A slope of 45 degrees would then get sufficient sunshine for evaporating a layer containing 3·3 grams of snow to the square centimetre. A precipitous mountain face could affect polar conditions, and if the snow were additionally contained at the bottom of hollows it would be virtually immune to evaporation, even on the equator.

We must also consider the possibility that any water, whether vapour or solid, on the surface of the Moon would consist wholly or largely of heavy water. Under the low atmospheric pressures all surface water will have undergone a slow process of fractional distillation for many millions of years, the more volatile components being gradually lost.

Deuterium water (there are also the tritium, hydrogen–deuteride, and other intermediate waters) has a somewhat higher latent heat of sublimation than ordinary water; but the difference is not significant for such low temperatures, about 10 calories to the gram.[9] On the other hand, its melting point is 3·8°C., as against 0°C. for ordinary water, which has a vapour pressure about 1¼ of the corresponding vapour pressure of heavy water within this range of temperatures. This ratio increases as the temperature continues to drop and becomes 1·41 for 220°K. (−53°C.). This will raise its point of sublimation by 2 degrees to 3°C., so that light water will tend to evaporate first. The concentration of heavy water in any permanent snow deposits must, therefore, be very high. Heavy water will also be able to become and stay liquid under lower pressures, though the difference is not such as drastically to affect our estimates, unless possibly it were all tritium water (tritium is a still heavier isotope of hydrogen with an atomic weight 3), which is very rare, radioactively unstable, and for which no data are at present available. Heavy water will be somewhat more effectively sorbed, though it is less active chemically than the light kind.

However this may be, the above analysis shows conclusively that snow-fields need not be unduly massive to be able to withstand the heat of sun-rays through the lunar day even on level ground at the equator. Thus Pickering has the last laugh, although this does not, admittedly, establish that the white haloes *must* be water snow. They may be that or they may be something else. It is, nevertheless, very likely that at least some of them are at least partly snow. The total amount of water vapour in the atmosphere of Mars must be a good deal higher than in that of the Moon. Yet no water absorptions have been found in the spectrum of Mars as a whole, and only slight traces in that of the polar caps.[6,19] No attempt has ever been made to examine the spectrum of, say, the white cauldron of Aristarchus. It must also be borne in mind that snow on the Moon will be at a much lower temperature than on Mars, so that the corresponding absorptions will be very weak. There are some further difficulties in the way which will emerge from the discussion of the problem given below. And yet Kuiper's infra-red spectrum of the Moon referred to in Chapter 12 appears to indicate an excess of water over that of Mars!

At this stage it is of great interest to examine the theoretical behaviour of snow deposits in lunar conditions, for this will differ considerably from what we are familiar with on the Earth.

The first point of importance is that as water is gradually frozen out of a thin quiescent atmosphere under a low gravity molecule by molecule these will seek out positions of lowest energy.[2] In other words they will sink as low as possible in the gravitational field, so long as this does not involve a rise in temperature, and otherwise stick to the coldest surfaces. Thus if snow were evaporating on a sunward slope of a ring mountain, the vapour, which would be at a very low temperature, say, −45°C., would creep low over the ground and become immediately reprecipitated upon reaching the still shaded, or obliquely illuminated, slopes, where the temperature of the ground may be expected to be below −100°C., even if not snow-bound, and less if under snow. This would cause a kind of migration of the thinner deposits round the clock.

Otherwise the general tendency will be for the hoar-frost to accumulate at the bottom of hollows, large, small, and microscopic, which may account for the dazzling whiteness of the floors of the lunar clefts or rills and the cauldrons of such minor craters as the 'Wash Bowl' in Cassini,[20] which may be assumed to emit water vapour. This tendency could also explain the invisibility of many white areas until the Sun is some 20 degrees to 30 degrees above the horizon and can penetrate inside the hollows where hoar-frost, or for that matter any other vaporizable deposit, has formed. The principle, however, cannot account for the existence of bright rays unless it is assumed that these run along invisible surface fractures where gas seepage from the interior is in progress. The tangential distribution of these features relatively to such craters as Tycho or Proclus militates against this hypothesis in general. In some cases, though, there exists an undeniable connection between white streaks, craterlets which become brilliant under a high Sun, and crevices showing in the same positions under oblique illumination. The floor of Gassendi may serve as an example here. (See Plate VIII.)

Another consequence of the general principle that the precipitation will seek out the loci of lowest energy is that the existing deposits of snow, rime, or ice will tend to be replenished from the atmosphere at nightfall, as their temperature will be a good deal lower than that of the clear ground from the start. This will be true even if the deposit has entirely evaporated, for the underlying ground will not only hold a good deal of vapour by sorption but will also have been chilled in the process of evaporation and/or desorption. In other words a deposit, once formed, will tend to perpetuate itself even without any local emission of vapour, which may be invoked to explain the persistence of the rays.

The sorbed water will be held mainly inside the rocks or the overlying fragmentary matter at a very low temperature. Thus the rising Sun will quickly remove the thin frosting of snow or gases from the surface, but as the heat of sunrays begins to penetrate underground—a slow process owing to the bad conductivity of the surface materials—the sorbed vapours will migrate upwards. Such migration will require energy, so that the ground will be chilled once more, and if there is enough vapour may be brought below the sublimation point. The result will be a curious phenomenon of hoar-frost appearing under the influence of sunlight.

This has actually been observed. In particular in the craters with bright rims the most brilliant patch often appears exactly opposite the Sun and follows him round the clock. The same, of course, would also be true of any other volatile substance.

The delay in geyser-like volcanic activity and its cessation with the coming of the great frost is readily understandable on this interpretation,[13,14,15] But the seeming occurrence of snow on the summits of high mountains, such as the Apennines, whose highest peaks are not only absolutely the brightest in all colours but show a very strong green reaction indicating snow or hoar-frost, obviously requires a different explanation. At first sight it flatly contradicts the principle of minimum energy.

Since lunarite is generally more porous than lunabase, this structure may intensify with altitude and its sorbing capacity increase accordingly, in which case the highest peaks will be intensely imbued with gas and may grow hoar-frost 'fur' in the heat of sunrays. This, however, is merely a guess. On the other hand, we will recall from Chapter 13 that ascending water vapour would soon become chilled down to ice point at no great height, so that it may be re-precipitated on the high mountain tops, at a level where a kind of thin 'violet layer' may be expected to form, possibly somewhere between 2 and 5 miles above the surface of the Moon.

This is the approximate altitude of the highest Apennines, which are thus well placed to receive some of the precipitate. It may also account for the 'Alpine glow' I observed on these mountains at sunset on 22 July, 1954.

Ice has several crystalline habits depending on the temperature, but the studied transitions[7] fall above the expected lunar sublimation point and consequently are of no interest to us here. In 1935, however, Burton and Oliver showed that below $-110°C$. under atmospheric pressure and at somewhat higher temperature if the pressure is reduced ice fails to crystallize and assumes an amorphous vitreous structure.[2] If heat is supplied the molecules quickly arrange themselves in hexagonal crystal lattices and revert to the amorphous state if this is withdrawn. The latent heat of the transformation has not been measured, but does not appear to be large. Even so, strictly speaking, it should have been taken into consideration in computing the energy of vaporization of lunar snow, which must in any case be regarded as only the lower limit.

Now I have often noticed the glazed appearance of the ring terraces at sunrise, an appearance which does not endure for more than a day or two and, significantly, seems to be absent at sunset. This could easily be explained by a precipitation of glassy frost which is later transformed into crystalline rime, thus losing its sheen.

All lunar snows must, of course, have this structure during the night and in such portions as are not exposed to sunshine even during the day. Thus the first step in the process of evaporation will be the change from amorphous to crystalline state, and so from the specular to diffuse reflection of light. This in itself should enhance their visibility sometime after sunrise.

As the process of evaporation goes on more vapour molecules are liberated on the now-rough crystalline surface of the snow at the sublimation temperature. Their energy will, of course, be very low and they will not be able to gain anything from the thin and chilly air above. In other words, these molecules will have just enough zip to climb a little way up and build up crystal lattices, extending higher and higher up. In the absence of wind and under a low gravity one must expect long feathers of hoar-frost to sprout out of the icy glass like some strange plants and stretch up towards the Sun. This again may have something to do with the observed rotation of white areas on the crater rims. The hoar feathers may grow many yards long in a ghostly jungle, trapping between them the accumulating vapour and thus delaying the onset of vaporization, both by increasing the receiving area and so thinning out the sunshine and by sorbing such vapour as has already formed.

Something of this kind happens on the Earth, too, especially on high mountains, where the snow in clear frosty weather develops a crystalline cover, as though of glassy grass, upon exposure to sunshine.

Gradually, however, the little air there is will get warmer and the sluggish vapours will begin to rise. In fact, these vapours will be intensely cold ($-50°$C. or less) to begin with and adiabatic expansion will chill them even further,* soon bringing them again below the sublimation point, causing the snow to fume.

In the greatly rarefied atmosphere any local evolution of vapour and such suspension of crystals, or dust, as it may contain may appreciably affect the barometric pressure, with a concomitant rise in the sublimation point, which will further hinder evaporation. The mist of ice crystals will soon screen the snow against sunshine, so that its disappearance will proceed much more slowly than the bare count of calories would seem to show.

The white icy veils observed over the polar snows of Mars must be of a similar nature.

Step by step the mist will rise higher and higher if there is enough snow to sustain it, developing eventually into a kind of low-lying cirrus cloud, precisely as suggested by Pickering,[13] Wilkins and Mee,[1] on observational evidence, for the great ray systems of Tycho and Proclus respectively (*see* Chapter 8).

Pickering[13] and Rawstron[16] have also observed an appearance resembling a snowstorm sweeping over the adjacent part of Mare Imbrium as the putative snow-fields of Pico and Pico B reached the climax in the process of evaporation. In all probability this was not a ground deposit but merely an icy mist spreading above the dark plain.

* If the evolving water vapour expands adiabatically to twice its original volume its temperature will drop over $85°$C. below the sublimation point of $-50°$C. (*see* Appendix).

The suggestion that electric forces—to be precise electrostatic repulsion —may have been responsible for spreading the white material of the rays of Tycho is due to Pickering.[14] Indeed, it is known that condensation of vapour is accompanied by production of high electric charges, so that this may well be the true explanation of these surprising features. Simple projection or radial fracturing of the crust are ruled out by the circumstance that the large ray system of the Tycho type are tangential to the central crater. They also appear to be picking up the white matter from the smaller craters on the way, which is suggestive of wind, or possibly a line of force, for the bright-rayed craters seem often to be connected with the great ray system of the 'metropolitan crater of the Moon', as Tycho has been dubbed. Menelaus is a case in point. It continues one of Tycho's rays across Mare Serenitatis.

The great double ray traversing the eastern mare complex passes through several bright craters and its line is continued by Kepler and Aristarchus. By prolonging the rays emerging from the invisible side of the Moon over her north limb to their meeting point, Wilkins has found that there must exist another powerful ray centre exactly antipodal to Tycho.[20] If, therefore, the electromagnetic nature of these features be admitted, one is naturally led to the conclusion that Tycho and Anti-Tycho may represent the magnetic poles of the Moon. In this context the nature of the mechanism responsible for the formation of the rays may be similar to that of our auroral streamers.

Too little is known about the latter to warrant any definite or even tentative conclusion. Yet this line of thought appears to offer reasonable prospects of solution of one of the greatest mysteries of our satellite's enigmatic face.

Thus this enquiry into the physics of the Moon is closed. There remains only one problem to consider—the problem of life.

REFERENCES

1. BRITISH ASTRONOMICAL ASSOCIATION, THE. *Tenth Report of the Lunar Section*, Vol. 36, Part 1. London, 1947.
2. BURTON, E. F. and OLIVER, W. F. 'The Crystal Structure of Ice at Low Temperatures.' *Proceedings of the Royal Society of London*, Vol. 153, Series A, 1935.
3. CULLINGFORD, C. H. D. (Ed.). *British Caving*. Routledge, London, 1953.
4. GIAUQUE, W. F. and STOUT, J. W. 'The Entropy of Water and the Third Law of Thermodynamics. The Heat Capacity of Ice from 15 to 273° K.' *Journal of the American Chemical Society*, Vol. 58, No. 7, 1936.
5. KISTLER, S. S. 'The Measurement of "Bound" Water by the Freezing Method.' *Journal of the American Chemical Society*, Vol. 58, No. 6, 1936.
6. KUIPER, G. P. (Ed.). *The Atmospheres of the Earth and Planets*. 2nd Edn. University of Chicago Press, 1952.
7. MASON, B. J. 'The Growth of Ice Crystals in a Supercooled Water Cloud. *Quarterly Journal of the Royal Meteorological Society*, Vol. 79, January, 1953.
8. MEE, A. J. *Physical Chemistry*. Heinemann, London, 1943.

9. MILES, F. T. and MENZIES, A. W. C. 'The Vapour Pressure of Deuterium Water from 20 to 230°.' *Journal of the American Chemical Society*, Vol. 58, No. 7, 1936.
10. NORTH, F. J. *Limestones*. Murby, London, 1930.
11. PARTINGTON, J. R. *An Advanced Treatise on Physical Chemistry*. Longmans, Green, London, 1951.
12. PICKERING, W. H. 'Evidences of Erosion on the Moon.' *Popular Astronomy*, Vol. 24, 1916.
13.   'Meteorology of the Moon.' *Popular Astronomy*, Vol. 23, 1915.
14.   *The Moon*. Doubleday, Page and Co., New York, 1903.
15.   'The Snow Peaks of Theophilus.' *Popular Astronomy*, Vol. 25, 1917.
16. RAWSTRON, G. O. 'Lunar Changes in the Neighbourhood of Pico and Pico B.' *Popular Astronomy*, Vol. 45, 1937.
17. *Smithsonian Physical Tables, The*. Washington, 1954.
18. SPURR, J. E. *Geology Applied to Selenology* (4 Vols.), 1944–9.
19. VAUCOULEURS, GÉRARD DE. *Physics of the Planet Mars*. Faber, London, 1954.
20. WILKINS, H. P. *Our Moon*. Muller, London, 1954.

LIFE?

IN THE PRECEDING CHAPTERS we have considered the situation on
the Moon as this is today, with some reference to the past, in the light
of observational evidence and the available information on the relevant
physical problems. The latter, while it does not directly establish the reality
of the controversial observations, yet makes these intrinsically probable,
providing a general picture which is consistent within itself and reconciles
the seemingly contradictory data.

Thus, while it is not possible to say at this stage that the white substance
forming the variable areas of the Moon is water snow, this is not at all
unlikely and indeed the most natural solution. Likewise unproven but
highly probable is that beneath the outer very tenuous atmospheric
envelope the Moon possesses a shallow layer of denser gas, evolving during
the day under the influence of solar heat and precipitating again or being
sorbed by the dust-covered or porous rocks with the coming of the intense
cold of the night. Occasional haziness of outlines in this or that lunar
locality, which is out of step with the visibility of the rest of the disk, local
mists and obscurations, the blue light behaviour of stars at occultation as
observed by myself, the brilliance of the limb in the blue, as well as the
reddening of the light at the terminator, all indicate that such an inner
atmosphere actually exists. The change of colour emphasis in the maria
from green to violet with the progress of the lunation also favours this
interpretation. But the strongest support for this view comes from the
microwave thermal data pointing to the high gas content of the subsoil
rocks.

Nothing is known about the composition of the lunar atmosphere, high
or low. The thinner external halo may, however, be largely composed of
argon with, perhaps, a proportion of nitrogen. Water vapour, carbon dioxide, as well as the heavy vapours of comparatively volatile substances,
such as sulphur and certain halides, may be the main constituents of the
ground atmosphere. In fact, there is some indication of a sulphur mist in
the diamond-shaped area north-east of Aristarchus.

Theory of sorption and radiometric data concur in attributing a high gas
content to the porous lunar rocks, which will form a kind of 'gas marsh',
whence the lower atmosphere is periodically replenished and which
accounts for the thinness of the outer air halo. The permafrost layer of the
lunar subsoil acts as a cold trap which will effectively seal most of the gas,
and water vapour in particular, contained in the interior, except where the
seal is broken by tectonic movements, volcanic vents and erosive tunnelling.

Vulcanism in these circumstances will be mainly of the geyser type, some 'eruptions' being simple superficial discharges of compressed gases released by erosion and the heat of sunrays. One must expect a kind of inverted erosion from below, by infumigation, partial liquefaction and frost shattering, which may be responsible for crater chains and such features as Schroeter's Valley.

Owing to the lower mean density of the Moon, it is probable that her surface materials are specifically lighter than those of the Earth's crust, with greater abundances of lighter elements which are biologically important and often form soluble compounds. The virtual absence today and great scarcity in the past of liquid water on the surface will have allowed these soluble compounds to remain there, whereas on the Earth they are immediately washed away by the rains and become concentrated in the oceans. Thus the outermost rocks of the Moon may be composed to a great extent of light soluble matter, which would dissolve in hot water into a muddy jelly, and there are indications that lunar lavas may have been largely of this type, rather than the conventional outpourings of fused silicates. Such, too, may be the material of which the maria were formed, possibly at the time of capture of the Moon by the Earth, which may have been geologically recent, although this particular conception is not necessary to maintain the overall picture painted here.

In any event, lunar rocks, which by general consensus resemble pumice in texture and are, no doubt, a good deal more bubbly than the terrestrial variety, will be lighter than water (our pumice is), and will overlie it in a natural stratification according to specific gravity. This, together with the general porosity, both macro- and microscopic, of the ground, leads one to expect large bodies of liquid water, as well as gas, to occur at the meeting of the outer formations with the lower impervious rocks, on the lines of H. G. Wells's fantasy in *First Men in the Moon*. A situation of this kind is not unknown on the Earth where permeable surface strata are found, even though these are specifically heavier than water.

There is some selenological evidence to indicate that these underground water and gas cushions may have discharged on the Moon the duty of our glassy basalt in maintaining the isostatic equilibrium of the surface relief by responding to the changes of pressure and tidal forces. Indeed even now, despite the tied-up rotation of the Moon, there will be tides in such underground waters, caused by the librations, the changing distance of the Moon from the Earth and solar gravity. The compound effect of these tides may be considerable, having erosive and volcanic repercussions.

The temperatures of the underground water basins will be high as compared with the surface sublimation point of $-40°$ C. to $-50°$ C., they will also be greatly compressed, so that this water will undergo explosive decompression upon reaching the surface.

The low force of gravity, one sixth of the terrestrial, will leave its mark on things large and small.

I have been constantly referring to 'lunar pumice'. In reality, though, the surface rocks of the Moon, especially in the lunarite highlands, will be more like meerschaum or glass froth formed upon exposure of molten glass to the vacuum. Such rock foam may have considerable mechanical strength and should be able to withstand heat erosion by exfoliation, despite its low thermal conductivity. But the porous structure will expose it to erosion by sorption, which is probably the main denuding force on the Moon. Sorption, too, may have led to some sedimentation, especially on the crater floors and in the maria.

The inclination of the equator to the plane of the ecliptic is only $1\frac{1}{2}$ degree, so that there will be hardly any seasonal changes of the type we are accustomed to. The polar and tropical zones will be 3 degrees wide each and here some fluctuation in temperature will occur in the course of our year; but the climatic cycle of the Moon is governed by its slow rotation, expressed in the lunation period of $29\frac{1}{2}$ days. about equally divided between night and day. Apart from eclipses and volcanic emissions, there can be no weather on the Moon.

This great climatic regularity and absence of seasons make changes on the Moon intrinsically difficult to notice: there is no proper spring, summer, autumn, or winter; they are all parts of the sunlight cycle, entwined in the play of light and shadow as the Sun rolls slowly across the dark sky.

Yet seasonal changes there certainly are: some markings darken, others become paler, expand or contract, with a variation of hue,[2] in the course of the lunar day; nor are these changes symmetrical as between evening and morning. The temperatures of the topsoil are in step with the phase. Most of the seasonal changes, on the other hand, lag behind the Sun two or three days, keeping pace with the subsoil temperatures. This shows that they do not depend on superficial alterations but have their seat some way below the ground. Such indeed would be the behaviour of vegetation sending long taproots down into the gas marsh.

The amplitude of temperature fluctuations on the surface attains nearly 300°C. in the tropical regions, but the mean daily variation for the whole disk at a moderate depth of 2 feet is only 80°C. The mean surface night temperature is, according to the latest data, 145°K. or −128°C., but it will be less locally, whilst snow deposits may approach the absolute zero. Portions of the surface at the subsolar point may exceed 400°K. (+127°C.), but such temperatures will be skin-deep and severely localized.

In the virtual absence of conduction and convection of heat, nearly all heat transfer will be by radiation, reflection, and absorption, and great climatic inequalities will be found within a very small compass, owing to the rugged relief and frequent differences in albedo.

172

The lower, atmosphere, perpetually balancing between precipitation and evaporation, sorption and desorption, will never reach high altitudes and, with water vapour predominating, may be confined within not more than 5 miles above the ground, ending up in a kind of thin 'blue cloud' of minute ice crystals. Vapours of sulphur and other volatile solids will be trailing low over the ground.

Thus local climates and local atmospheres will develop, like some sealed aquaria, within walled enclosures, clefts, and hollows, in the depressed portions of the maria, and other, less-well-defined, volcanic regions. Within these life may have secured a foothold. This life will probably be of a low order, although it may have evolved on some unexpected lines. The differences of shade and hue between neighbouring areas, sometimes disregarding vertical relief, look suspiciously like a growth of some kind.

As much has been mooted by many astronomers, but with the information collected and sifted in this volume we are on somewhat firmer ground as regards the fundamental necessities of life.

To take a few examples. Radial bands can often be seen overrunning the crater walls and it has been suggested by Moore[6] that they may be due to some kind of vegetation springing up along invisible fractures which exude life-sustaining vapours. The dark markings in and about Eratosthenes show equally little respect for the configuration of the ground in their movement and distribution, so that even though it is highly doubtful if they can represent 'small animals' moving at a rate of 6 inches per hour,[7] these changes may be due to some kind of biological activity. There are other less publicized and less conspicuous craters which display similar phenomena.

Near the centre of the Moon are several dark spots which show a faint bottle-green hue. The largest of these spots overruns a range of hills and it can be seen from the comparison with the parts of the hills beyond the spot that these are of a lighter hue than the adjacent mare, so that the colouring is definitely due to something on the surface of the rocks; vegetation seems to be a reasonable answer. Wright's filter photographs[13] show clearly the spread of the conspicuous green area, dark in extreme red and pale in ultra-violet, in Mare Tranquilitatis even within the brief span between the gibbous and full phase. This area has been recorded as greenish or green by many observers and its ultra-violet pallor may be an indication of gas. Whether or no vegetation is present, we seem to have here a clear case of a localized climatic zone covering the low parts of this Mare and the adjoining low portions of Maria Serenitatis and Foecunditatis. It is possible that the whole effect is only a few feet deep.

Thus we have at least one objective record of a seasonal change on a considerable scale, which, moreover, confirms my observations of the intensification of the shorter wavelengths of light in the reflection from the maria with the progress of the lunation.

However this may be, once the bar to the presence of water, if only as ice and vapour, has been removed and the occurrence of carbon dioxide, at least locally, is admitted as a definite possibility, there can be no chemical reason for denying that some species of plants may live on the Moon. There exist bacteria which can thrive on sulphur and some other unlikely substances, such as boracic acid.[5,9,10] On the Earth such environments may be unusual and offer little scope for development; but some of the local lunar atmospheres may have provided excellent conditions for evolution along this line and produced complicated organisms built on the same plan.

In assessing the possibility of life on other worlds we are greatly handicapped by having only one example—the Earth—to draw upon. The fact that terrestrial organisms may be unable to survive in the surroundings of another planet is by itself no more significant than that the fishes and other marine animals die when exposed to the air. From their point of view air is uninhabitable because they have failed to equip themselves with lungs. Life on the Earth has developed certain adaptations through millions of years of trial and error in response to the requirements of this particular habitat. It is unreasonable to expect it to cope with quite different surroundings. The conquest of dry land, the air, high mountains and polar regions was not achieved in a day. It is sometimes mooted, though this is only a hypothesis, that in the past geological ages the composition of the air was different, with little oxygen and large amounts of carbon dioxide, since buried in the sedimentary rocks as limestone and coal. If so, early animals will have had different respiratory organs.

So highly developed a form as an amphibian with external gills can adapt itself quickly to environments, poor or rich in oxygen, by reducing or expanding the size of these organs.[9] Deep-ocean fish live in total darkness and pressures going into hundreds of atmospheres.

If, on the other hand, terrestrial creatures of whatever kind would be able to survive on another world, taking the principle of uniformity of nature for a guide, we may regard this as definite evidence that life exists there.

The range of temperature variation on the Moon, even taken at its maximum span, which, after all, is atypical, is not prohibitive to life as we know it. H. Strughold[9] puts the 'band of temperatures' suitable for life at 110° F., or barely 60° C., but this applies to active life only, as against latent life, where the limits of tolerance are far wider. Even so, this appears to be too narrow a trench. According to Tikhov,[10] in northern Siberia, the Christmas rose (*Helleborus niger L.*) blossoms under the snow, while the scurvy grass (*Cochlearia arctica*) which grows on the shores of the Arctic Ocean can withstand without harm 46° C. of frost.[10] Our own roundleaved wintergreen (*Pyrola rotundifolia*) has been found hale and unfrozen at zero Fahrenheit (−18°C.).[4] Some arctic lichens live permanently in temperatures below −5°C. and continue to perspire down to −10°C. and to synthetize sugar from carbon dioxide and water down to −35°C. (Tobler),[5] although but slowly. Highly developed mammals living in cold climates survive long periods of temperatures as low as −50°C., so that this resistance of plants to cold is perhaps not very surprising. The answer is, of course, largely that they are able to maintain a body temperature which is above that of their surroundings.

Becquerel has shown that mosses, lichens, and algae can be immersed in liquid air (−109°C.) for several weeks without harm, and, when dry, for as long as six years. More surprising still, their dried spores retained their full vitality after being plunged in liquid helium (−271·15°C.) and exposed to vacuum.[3,10]

Some of the animalculae, such as rotatoria, and the tardigrades, distant relatives of the spiders, show equal resistance to cold as do the lichens among which they live. Normal skin can survive exposure to −150°C.

At the other end of the scale we encounter an equal degree of tolerance to heat and desiccation. Up to 100,000 microbes have been found in a single gram of dry sand in the Sahara. Vareschi[11] records that houseleek, a soft vascular mountain plant, can stand up to temperatures up to 50°C. 'Houseleek rosettes have been put in a herbarium, pressed, and left without light for 18 months. When looked at, the rosettes had sprouted, making stalk, leaf and flower. . . .' (p. 24, *Mountains in Flower*).[11] Some protozoa live permanently in hot springs at temperatures up to 90°C. and can withstand for short periods as much as 150°C., if desiccated. Spores are equally resistant to heat.

Thus the fluctuations of temperature encountered on the Moon are not in themselves prohibitive to life, the more so, as owing to the peculiarities of the lunar atmosphere and the low conductivity of lunar rocks it could easily have evolved suitable protective devices. Vital parts of perennial plants may be hidden underground, as in the espaliers of our mountain shrubs, the creeping azalea (*Loiseluria procumbens*) and dwarf willow (*Betula nana*). The generation of heat by plants is demonstrated by sphagnum moss, which I have often found moist and unfrozen while the surrounding ground was set hard with several degrees of frost. Snowdrops and other early flowers can melt their way through the snow and emerge on the surface. Tikhov records that 'early in spring in the mountains of central Asia natural hotbeds are observed in the shape of ice domes covering spaces of several score square metres. Plants and their flowers grow on these hotbeds.'[11]

Apparently, although in our latitudes normal greenery appears snow-white in photographs taken through an infra-red filter, which appears to

175

indicate that plants not only reject the infra-red but also reradiate in this region, some of the absorbed solar energy of shorter wavelengths (fluorescence), in cold climates the same species change their behaviour and, like Martian plants, no longer shine in the infra-red, storing up instead the heat dissipated in this way.[11]

The insulating properties of the lunar surface rocks ought to be of great importance to any living organisms existing there. They should also be able to store up rare or intermittently available materials, say, water, oxygen, and carbon dioxide, within their bodies. Terrestrial bog plants retain in their underwater parts oxygen produced in the photosynthesis to prevent their suffering from anoxia, for plants also breathe. Strughold[9] and others[10] have suggested that the Martian plants may have recourse to similar tactics. Water storage is, of course, common among desert and mountains plants, such as the already mentioned houseleeks and cacti. All bulbs represent storage of food against the lean and active times.

Less is known about the ability of living organisms, otherwise than in the embryonic or latent state, to achieve accommodation to low atmospheric pressures, for this is an adaptation that is obviously not required on the Earth. The danger of exposure to near-vacuum lies in increased evaporation, reduction of the boiling point which this entails, and the excess of internal over external pressure.

This, however, applies to organisms developed under comparatively high pressures and does not necessarily imply that life under low pressures is impossible. Lunar plants may be suitably insulated, by, say, spongy adsorbing surfaces, or tough impervious skins, against the loss of body fluids through evaporation. The reduced gravity may be helpful here, for their external tissues could easily support thick coats of insulating matter in which the surface of the Moon abounds.

Lunar plants may not depend on the supply of gas from the atmosphere at all, or only to a small extent, obtaining all or most of their needs from the gas marsh below and reaching out beyond it only for the energy of the sunrays required for photosynthesis or other similar processes. On the other hand, it is possible to conceive a system of membranes with pores which would capture atmospheric gases at the time of evaporation and concentrate them by adsorptive organs until sufficient pressure was obtained for the capillary condensation of water, thus securing the necessary moisture. Sorption, whether chemical or physical (organic charcoal is one of the most powerful sorbents, especially of carbon dioxide, which is so vital to plant life) and bubbliness would be the natural vital themes of the Moon.

In this connection the low atmospheric pressure has something to offer, for thanks to it effective protection against excesses of temperature becomes possible on the vacuum-flask principle. Imagine an external skin of dead vacuum cells, possibly lined with metallic reflecting material (chrysalids of small tortoiseshell butterfly display this feature) for protection against ultra-violet irradiation. Spaced among these cells are pores, which open out to suck in gas in the morning at the time of vaporization and desorption and close up again in the arid hours of midday and the night's cold.

Hairy or cobwebby growths likewise come to mind as possible means of defence against excesses of cold and heat, as well as to trap vapours and gases. Suitable pigmentation is a further possibility. The lichen *Verrucaria Hookerii* is almost snow-white, and some of the white features on the Moon may be organic. Lichens have a capacity to produce pigments to shield them from harmful radiations.[5] Some of the high-growing mountain plants affect a bluish or purplish hue, which may be a means of reflecting excessive ultra-violet rays.

The violet tinge of, say, the dark changeable markings of Eratosthenes may represent a similar protective device of a vegetable growth responsible for them. Pickering notes that lunar vegetation is not green but grey or violet-grey.[7] Yet some of the changeable areas definitely show green, brown, or yellow, at least for part of the lunation. Changes from one colour to another have likewise been reported. Thus the German group for the study of lunar colours organized by Kaiser has found that the floor of Ptolemaues changed from grey in the morning to olive-green and thence to a yellowish tone towards the evening.[2] This would be the normal sequence of changes if green assimilating plants were present.

One must expect great differences between the local climates and atmospheres, and any plants growing within one or another of these would be adapted to the special conditions obtaining there. Such adaptation may be very far-reaching, so that alongside of photosynthetizing plants with green chlorophyll we may also have photoreducing plants endowed with purple bacterial chlorophyll. Nor is there any definite reason for believing that these two types must necessarily exhaust the possible variants of chlorophyllic pigments. However, by the same token it is impossible to predicate about the unknown, but the known purple chlorophyll occurs in organisms which, instead of assimilating carbon from carbon dioxide, obtain energy from the oxidation of compounds of hydrogen, sulphides, and sulphur, for which, though, they require oxygen. It has been suggested by James Franck that this process may become important in environments where water is scarce or absent, as may be the case on Mars.[5] It is possible that local conditions on the Moon favour a similar line of development, and the suspected purple vegetation of Eratosthenes and some other craters may be a case in point. If, further, lunar plants resemble our lichens, these vary very greatly in pigmentation, depending on exposure to sunshine, humidity, and other factors, even within one and the same species.

The dangers of exposure to ultra-violet radiations have become something of a cliché. The phrase is being repeated parrot-wise in and out of season. Yet it is true enough that ultra-violet rays by breaking up living molecules can be fatal to living matter, and on the Moon terrestrial organisms would run great risks on this score. On the other hand, the energy of this radiation may be turned to good account by any Moon-grown plants (or animals, if any), which may also have acquired appropriate defences against its excess, say, by surrounding themselves with ozone-filled cells. After all, our own ozonosphere amounts to a partial pressure of 2·5 to 3 mm. Hg, which under lunar gravity will have to be reduced to one-sixth of this amount.

The early life stages of lunar organisms may be completed underground. There are, in fact, hosts of possibilities of minimizing this particular threat.

But the thing to be borne in mind is that even if the theoretical ground-level barometric pressure (discounting the temporary day-time atmosphere) corresponds to ours at a height of 40–50 miles, this does not mean that ultra-violet exposure on the Moon is the same as in that layer of our stratosphere because under a six-times-lower gravity the overlying lunar air must contain six times as much gas to produce the same pressure. Molecular scattering increases with the shortening wavelength of radiation, so that the ultra-violet rays will be the most affected. If, moreover, the gas is monatomic argon, this not only absorbs some ultra-violet, but by offering a smaller molecular cross-section to the rays it will scatter the shorter wavelengths even more efficiently than diatomic gases. The ground atmosphere, too, will have a shielding effect, and we have seen that this may even develop a faint replica of the violet layer of Mars.

Low gravity has another biological consequence. On the Earth a large proportion, if not most, of the energy required for life is dissipated in fighting gravity. On the Moon the corresponding requirements will be cut down to a sixth of ours, so that the energy needed to sustain life will be reduced in proportion.

To sum up, there does not seem to be any sufficient reason why plants, even of a highly organized type, should be unable to exist on the Moon, though probably only in isolated oases of life, the highlands being almost entirely barren, as they appear to be on Mars. This does not prove that they are actually there, but, being given this possibility, there is no apparent reason why it should not have been used. We have also seen that conditions on the Moon may have been more favourable to life in the past ages, so that, having arisen then, it would have had ample time to adapt itself to increasing rigours.

As for animals, these are admittedly somewhat difficult to conceive in lunar conditions, for, unlike plants, they cannot depend much on the gas marsh. However, perhaps they could derive the reduced energy necessary for locomotion entirely from plant matter. One would expect such creatures to be small and sluggish.

This survey leaves out of account the possibilities of the Moon's underground world, which are incalculable, for here water, the vital gases, congenial temperatures, and increased pressures will all be present. Only sunlight is absent. This excludes the normal assimilating plants, on which terrestrial life is based. True, our oceanic depths are also plunged in Stygian darkness, but they are in contact with the higher waters, whence they will be receiving a constant accretion of organic substances derived from photosynthesis. The same is in some measure true of the living world of our limestone caves.[1]

Possibly a similar interdependence exists on the Moon, but, if so, any life orders based on it must needs be severely restricted in scope. Perhaps heat of volcanic origin may provide the energy required by the plants for the production of organic substances from inorganic matter, thus allowing a fuller scale of life. If so, however, there is no present indication of this on the Earth, though neither is there an underground world comparable to that envisaged on the Moon.

Chemautotrophs are able to obtain sustenance direct from the inorganic world without sunlight, but they require oxygen, the supply of which in underground cavities may present serious difficulty. Possibly it could be drawn down into them by sorption, having been first produced on the surface by photosynthesis or directly by photodissociation of water vapour or carbon dioxide,[5] or else by their combination into formaldehyde and its polymers, in which oxygen is liberated. If so, for which again there is no present evidence, Wells's[12] intuitions may come nearer truth than any purely scientific speculation could.

The object of this book, however, is not to spin fanciful yarns, interesting as these might be, but to draw conclusions from observational data and known scientific facts. The first are sometimes uncertain, the second are not exhaustive; the conclusions themselves may be mistaken in part or in full. Still, I feel that they cannot be easily refuted and present a consistent reasonable picture of the Moon as a living world which is far more convincing than the conventional idea of a ball of terrestrial rocky desert raised to a high atmospheric level and made to revolve once a month. In fact, there can be little doubt that this view is wrong on many counts.

No, the Moon is a mysterious and wonderful world, which may yet hide many surprises. Modesty becomes man well, for his knowledge is truly small.

REFERENCES

1. CULLINGFORD, C. H. D. *British Caving*. Routledge, London, 1953.
2. HAAS, W. H. 'Does Anything Ever Happen on the Moon?' *The Journal of the Royal Astronomical Society of Canada*, Vol. 36, No. 7, 1942.

3. JAMES, P. F. 'The Limits of Life.' *The Journal of the British Interplanetary Society*, Vol. 14, No. 5, 1955.
4. KISTLER, S. S. 'The Measurement of "Bound" Water by Freezing Method.' *Journal of the American Chemical Society*, Vol. 58, No. 6, 1936.
5. KUIPER, G. P. (Ed.). *The Atmospheres of the Earth and Planets*. 2nd Edition, University of Chicago Press, 1952.
6. MOORE, PATRICK. 'Life on the Moon?' *Irish Astronomical Journal*, Vol. 3, No. 5, 1955.
7. PICKERING, W. H. 'Life on the Moon.' *Popular Astronomy*, Vol. 45, 1937.
8.   *The Moon*. Doubleday, Page and Co., New York, 1903.
9. STRUGHOLD, HUBERTUS. *The Green and Red Planet*. Sidgwick and Jackson, London, 1954.
10. TIKHOV, G. A. 'Is Life Possible on Other Planets?' *J.B.A.A.*, Vol. 65, No. 5, 1955.
11. VARESCHI, V. and KRAUSE, E. *Mountains in Flower*. Drummond, London, 1942.
12. WELLS, H. G. *First Men on the Moon*.
13. WRIGHT, W. H. 'The Moon as Photographed by Light of Different Colors.' *Publications of the Astronomical Society of the Pacific*, Vol. 41, No. 241, 1929.
14. FIRSOFF, V. A. 'Lunar Occultations Observed in Blue Light and the Problem of the Moon's Atmosphere.' *J.B.A.A.*, Vol. 66, No. 7, 1956.

APPENDIX I

Relating to Chapter 2

PAGE 5 *et seq.*

Ideal gases obey the equation $PV = RT$, which is a combination of Boyle's and Charles's Laws known as Clapeyron's Formula and states that the product of the pressure exerted by a gas into its volume is proportional to the absolute temperature of this gas, the coefficient of proportionality R being called the Gas Constant, equal to $8 \cdot 314 \times 10^7$ ergs per degree per mole.

Now gas pressure is due to the innumerable impacts of gas molecules on the opposing surfaces. The molecules move with various velocities, but very large numbers of them are involved, so that the pressure remains steady and in a gas of uniform composition they behave as though all of them were animated with the same velocity C, called mean square root velocity, always directed at right angles to the surface which is exposed to pressure by the gas.

Let us take a volume of gas within a cube with edges l inches long. The molecules will strike the 6 faces of the cube as if they were all moving with the velocity C perpendicularly to these faces. In other words all their movements can be resolved into three components parallel to the three edges of the cube meeting in the same corner. If there are n molecules altogether one-third of them, i.e. $n/3$, will always be moving along each of these three axes.

Each molecule in each of the three equal sets will strike the same face $\frac{1}{2}C/l$ times per second and rebound upon impact in the opposite direction. The gas being of uniform composition, every molecule has the same mass m. The surface of one face of the cube is equal l^2 and it will be struck by $n/3$ molecules $\frac{1}{2}C/l$ times per second. The momentum of the molecule is mC. After striking the bounding surface of the cube the molecule will bounce back elastically with the same velocity C in the directly opposite direction, i.e. its momentum will be $-mC$. This means that it has received a total momentum of $-2mC$, for $mC - 2mC = -mC$. But, since action must be equal to reaction, the face of the cube will have received the same momentum of opposite sign, i.e. $2mC$. In other words the momentum received by the whole face l^2 from $n/3$ molecules per second will be

$$\frac{MC}{\text{sec.}} = 2mC \times \frac{n}{3} \times \tfrac{1}{2}C/l.$$

C/sec is the measure of acceleration and acceleration times mass measures force. Force per unit area is pressure p. The area of the face is l^2 so that the force per unit area will be l^2 times less, or

$$p = \frac{nmC^2}{3l^3} = \frac{nmC^2}{3v},$$

for l^3 is the volume v of the cube. Thus

$$pv = \tfrac{1}{3} nmC^2 \text{ (Boyle's Law).}$$

According to Avogadro's Law n is the same for all gases for the same volume v in the above equation. $PV = RT$, and, n being constant, C^2 is directly proportional to T and inversely to m, or molecular weight.

R is referred to the mole* and thus $1/n$ is incorporated in it, so that this relationship can be written:

$$C^2 = \frac{3RT}{m}.$$

PAGE 7

Escape velocity U is obtained from the equation of orbital motion:

$$\tfrac{1}{2}v^2 = GM.\left(\frac{1}{r} - \frac{1}{2a}\right),$$

where G is the universal gravitational constant, M mass of the planet (in the present case), r radius vector at the point at which the velocity of the orbiting body is v, and a semi-major axis of the orbit, by putting $a = \infty$, or $\frac{1}{2a} = 0$. Then the orbit becomes a parabola and $v = U$.

$$\tfrac{1}{2}U^2 = \frac{GM}{r} \text{ and } U = \sqrt{\frac{2GM}{r}} \tag{I}$$

For the surface of the planet $r = R$, radius of the planet, and $\frac{GM}{R^2} = g$, superficial gravity, so that the equation becomes

$$U = \sqrt{2gR}.$$

On the other hand, $M = V.\rho$, volume × density, and volume varies as R^3, so that it will be seen from (I) that U is directly proportional to $R\sqrt{\rho}$.

PAGE 8 *et seq.*

Jeans[6] considers a theoretical atmosphere in isothermal equilibrium (same temperature throughout) at its upper limit where, assuming uniform rotation throughout, the centrifugal force balances gravity. He shows that gas at this theoretical limit will behave as though all of it were streaming away with a uniform velocity equal to $\tfrac{1}{4}C$ (see ref. to p. 6). The same situation will obtain in the actual atmospheric layer where molecular collisions can be neglected if the mean excess of molecular velocities over the velocity of escape is substituted for the mean molecular velocity C in the previous case. This can further be represented as the escape of the same

---

* A mass of any substance which expressed in grams equals the molecular weight of this substance. The volume of one mole of any gas at N.T.P. is 22.415 litres.

amount of gas from a uniformly condensed layer having the mass of the entire atmosphere and placed at the lowermost level of the isothermal atmosphere, i.e. the tropopause, through a system of orifices allowing just this amount to pass. To this extent it is immaterial at which actual level the dissipation occurs.

From such considerations through intermediate mathematical stages (which can be found in his original work) Jeans derives a formula for the time t_1 in which an isothermal atmosphere of a given gas will be totally lost by a planet with a mean radius a and superficial gravity g:

$$t_1 = \frac{C^3}{2g^2a} \, e^{\frac{3ga}{C^2}},$$

where C is the mean square-root molecular velocity of the gas and e the base of natural logarithms (see p. 196).

It will be recalled that $C^2 = \dfrac{3RT}{m}$, so that the formula is highly sensitive to the absolute temperature of the atmosphere.

Taking the values of a and g for the Earth as unity, Jeans gives the following table of C for which t_1 for the Moon ($a = 0.273$, $g = 0.165$) becomes 1,000, 100,000, and 1,000,000,000 years respectively

$$6.1 \times 10^4; \; 5.4 \times 10^4; \; 4.8 \times 10^4 \text{ cm. sec.}^{-1}.$$

A table of mean square-root molecular velocities for various gases, derived from the same source, reads as follows:

Gas	for —100°C.	0°C.	300°C.	
H_2	1.47×10^5	1.84×10^5	2.66×10^5	cm. sec.$^{-4}$
He_2	1.04×10^5	1.31×10^5	1.90×10^5	
H_2O	4.9×10^4	6.1×10^4	8.8×10^4	
N_2	3.9×10^4	4.9×10^4	7.1×10^4	
O_2	3.7×10^4	4.6×10^4	6.7×10^4	
A	3.3×10^4	4.1×10^4	5.9×10^4	
CO_2	3.1×10^4	3.9×10^4	5.7×10^4	

Jeans's avowed aim was to determine the time of dissipation only as to order of magnitude, so that perhaps the point that he overlooks the convective atmosphere below the tropopause, which contains in the case of the Earth and apparently also of Mars about four-fifths of the total air mass, and limits his considerations to the overlying supposedly isothermal atmosphere cannot be fairly taken in evidence against him. But, unfortunately, his atmospheric model bears little resemblance to actuality. For one thing the temperature at the escape level is very much higher than at the tropopause; for another he neglects the association of water molecules and the fact that O_2 and partly also CO_2 will exist as vapours and not as

N

gases proper in the assumed conditions. Finally, various physical and photo-chemical processes intervene at different atmospheric levels and upset the theoretical applecart.

The problem of lunar atmosphere is considered in more detail in Chapters 12 and 13.

Relating to Chapter 3

PAGE 24

The effects of changes in the period of axial spin of the Moon, whether due to shrinkage or other causes, can be assessed quite easily on certain simplifying assumptions.

No significant error is introduced if the present orbit of the Moon is considered a circle and the Moon a sphere of homogeneous density.

The angular momentum of her orbital motion is simply given by the expression MRv, where M is her mass, R the radius of her orbit and v orbital velocity, assumed to be circular and equal to her actual mean orbital velocity. $v = 2\pi RP^{-1}$, where P is the period of orbital revolution, so that the orbital angular momentum A will be:

$$A = 2M\pi R^2 P^{-1} \tag{1}$$

Angular momentum is the product of moment of inertia into angular velocity, the latter being most conveniently expressed in radians per second. The moment of inertia of a sphere of uniform density is given by the expression $M\dfrac{2r^2}{5}$, where M is the mass of the sphere and r its radius.

Angular velocity in radians is equal to $\dfrac{2\pi}{P}$, P being once more the period of one complete revolution. Therefore the angular momentum A' of a sphere rotating with uniform velocity will be:

$$A' = \frac{4M\pi r^2}{5P} \tag{2}$$

Comparison of (1) and (2) is instructive. In the case of the Moon P is the same in both expressions and equal to $27^{\text{d}}.32$, $R = 240,000$ miles in round figures and $r = 1,080$ miles.

$$\frac{A'}{A} = \frac{2}{5} \cdot \left(\frac{r}{R}\right)^2 \sim \frac{1}{123,200}, \tag{3}$$

whence it follows clearly that no significant change in A can result from any partial transfer to it of A' at the present stage of the Moon's orbital revolution. If, however, the Moon's orbit was at one time substantially smaller than at present, her radius much larger and period of rotation shorter such a readjustment of angular momentum could affect her orbit more. This is also and particularly true if, after her assumed capture by the

184

Earth, the Moon pursued an elongated elliptical orbit, resembling that of Nereid about Neptune, the accelerating tidal action of the Earth at the close perigee (point nearest to the Earth), combined with the volcanic emission of gas and the attendant shrinking of the lunar globe, could have easily driven the Moon away from the Earth, especially as planetary perturbations would be strong at the apogee.

The elliptical case, however, is very difficult to deal with.

From the alterations in the shape of the oldest rings Spurr[17] infers a contraction of the lunar radius by 400–500 miles since the Proteroselene and by about 125 miles since the Mesoselene, when Mare Imbrium was formed (Chapter 7, p. 68) to the present figure of 2,160 miles.

A contraction of the radius by a third would reduce the period of rotation by a factor of $\frac{4}{9}$, as can be easily seen from the equation (2), i.e. in the present situation to some 12 days $3\frac{1}{2}$ hours. The tidal action of the Earth would soon deprive the Moon of this excess rotation and bring her back to the tied-up state. The orbit would be somewhat wider and the month longer but only slightly so (3), so that in the first approximation the latter may be taken not to have changed. Thus by referring to (2) we shall see that she would have lost about $\frac{5}{9}A'$, this amount having been added to A.

Yet the ratio (3) does not tell the whole story; for, although A is so much larger than A', it also varies less with the change of R, in other words, a comparatively small change in the value of A will react strongly on R.

From Kepler's Third Law P varies as $R^{3/2}$, so that A will vary as $\sqrt{R}$. only (1).

Thus, if we now take the remote period when the radius of the Moon's orbit R' was equal to $\frac{1}{9}R$ and her axial period P' to, say, $0.2P$, as could easily have been the case with an independent planetary body of her size, the ratio (3) will have to be multiplied by 150 and we shall have:

$$\frac{A'}{A} = \frac{1}{180}.$$

so that the envisaged changes will be correspondingly more telling.

A one-third reduction in radius will still alter the axial period by a factor of $\frac{4}{9}$, so that this period P'' will become[2] $\frac{4}{9} \times \frac{1}{50} P = \frac{1}{225} P$. Thus the axial angular momentum of the Moon A'' will be 225 times as large as now; $A'' = 225A'$. Her orbital angular momentum A_1 on the other hand, will represent only one-third of the present figure A; $A_1 = \frac{1}{3}A$.

At the end of this transformation the Moon will have her present radius and, neglecting the increment of orbital momentum derived from the slowing down of the Earth's spin, the whole of the difference between the axial angular momentum as it was then and is now will have been added to the orbital angular momentum as this was then. In other words, the resultant orbital angular momentum A'_1 will be:

$$A'_2 = \tfrac{1}{3}A + 224A' \text{ and}$$

(1)(2) $\quad A'_1 = \dfrac{2M\pi R^2}{3P} + \dfrac{896M\pi r^2}{5P} = \dfrac{M\pi}{15P} \cdot (10R^2 + 2{,}688r^2)$

$$= \dfrac{M\pi R^2}{15P}\left(10 + 2{,}688 \cdot \dfrac{r^2}{R^2}\right)$$

(3) $\quad \dfrac{r^2}{R^2} = \dfrac{1}{123{,}200} \times \dfrac{5}{2} = \dfrac{1}{49{,}280}$

$$A'_1 = \dfrac{10{\cdot}055 M\pi R^2}{15P}$$

This represents a small increase in the orbital angular momentum by a factor of 1·0055. To obtain the corresponding increase in R, this factor must be squared, as A varies in proportion to $\sqrt{R}$ and so R in proportion to A^2. $1{\cdot}0055^2 = 1{\cdot}0110$, i.e. the increase in R is still only 1·1 per cent. There would also be a reciprocal action of the Moon on the Earth, whose rotation would likewise be slowed down and the angular momentum lost by her added to the orbital momentum of the Moon, so that the resultant widening of the orbit would be more marked. It is, nevertheless, clear that any great change in the orbit of the Moon could arise from this source only if the orbit were an eccentric ellipse with a close perigee.

Relating to Chapter 4

PAGE 28

Oblateness e is defined as the difference between the equatorial and the polar diameters divided by the equatorial diameter. It is the result of the centrifugal force of rotation f, which increases from the poles to the equator and partly counteracts the force of gravity $g \cdot g = GMr^{-2}$, where G is the gravitational constant, M mass of the planet and r its radius. But M also equals volume $\times$ density (ρ), so that

$$g = \tfrac{4}{3}G\pi\rho r.$$

To obtain the centrifugal force at the equator, we need know the acceleration that would be imparted to an unattached body (in absence of gravity) at the distance r (equatorial diameter) from the axis of revolution by the angular velocity ω, which, as we will recall, is equal to $2\pi/P$, P being the period of revolution. See Fig. 3.

ω is the angle through which the sphere turns in a unit of time, in which a point at the equator will describe an arc equal to the linear peripheral velocity v. If we now take an infinitesimal increment of time $\mathrm{d}t$ we shall have:

$$\mathrm{d}v = r\mathrm{d}\omega;\ \mathrm{d}\omega = \dfrac{-2\pi\dfrac{\mathrm{d}P}{\mathrm{d}t}}{P^2}\ \mathrm{d}t.$$

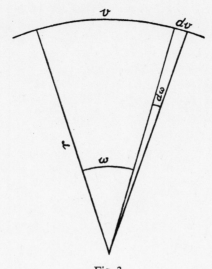

Fig. 3

Since the movement is uniform circular motion, $\dfrac{\mathrm{d}P}{\mathrm{d}t} = 2\pi$
so that

$$\mathrm{d}\omega = \frac{-4\pi^2}{P^2}\,\mathrm{d}t, \text{ whence}$$

the acceleration imparted to an unattached body of unit mass at the equator $\dfrac{\mathrm{d}v}{\mathrm{d}t} = -\dfrac{4\pi^2 r}{P^2}.$ This force is opposite in sign to gravity and oblateness e is proportional to the ratio of the absolute value of this force f to g, usually designated ψ.

$$\psi = \left|\frac{f}{g}\right| = \frac{4\pi^2}{P^2} : \frac{4G\pi\rho r}{3} = \frac{3\pi}{G\rho P^2}.$$

The coefficient of proportionality e/ψ depends on the distribution of mass inside the planet. If all of the mass is concentrated at the centre, as is very nearly the case of Saturn, $e/\psi = \frac{1}{2}$; for a homogeneous body, to which Moon is usually taken to approximate, it is $\frac{5}{4}$. The numerical result given on p. 28 has been obtained on this assumption.

Relating to Chapter 6
PAGE 51
Baldwin's[1] empirical equation reads:

$$D = 0\cdot1083d^2 + 0\cdot6917d + 0\cdot75,$$

where D is the decimal logarithm of the diameter in feet and d is the decimal logarithm of the depth in feet (p. 132–3).

As a matter of fact, this equation has been shown to be unsatisfactory at the lunar end of the curve where the craters are plotted and when I last communicated with him he was working on an improved statement of his relationship.

Yet another variant of the equation relates D_1, log diameter at ground level, to d_1, log depth below ground level, and reads:

$$D_1 = 0{\cdot}0638d_1{}^2 + d_1 + 0{\cdot}5545.$$

The latter equation has not been published to date and I owe the permission to reproduce it here to R. B. Baldwin's personal courtesy.

The matter, however, does not rest here, for, as has been pointed out by Jeffreys,[7] there is no reason to believe that craters produced by volcanic explosions would differ from those made by shells, bombs, or exploding meteorites. Moreover, Patrick Moore[14] gives the following comparison of the diameters and depths of three terrestrial meteoritic pits, two of the Richat structures and the lunar ring Theaetetus, chosen as a typical example of well-preserved formation of this type:

Crater	Diameter	Depth	Depth : Diameter
Coon Butte, Arizona (meteoritic)	4,150 ft.	550 ft.	1 : 7·5
Odessa 1, Texas (meteoritic)	550 ft.	14 ft.	1 : 39
Odessa 2, Texas (meteoritic)	70 ft.	17 ft.	1 : 4
Témimichat-Ghallaman (volcanic)	500 metres	34 metres	1 : 14
Ténoumer (volcanic)	1,800 metres	108 metres	1 : 16
Theaetetus (lunar)	16 miles	7,000 ft.	1 : 12

Copernicus, however, with a diameter of 56 miles and a depth of 11,000 feet, yields a ratio depth/diameter 1 : 31, which is close to Odessa 1 though nothing like Odessa 2 or Coon Butte, which is all rather out of joint.

Relating to Chapter 7

PAGE 66

The mean density of the Moon is 3·34 gm. cm.$^{-3}$. Owing to her small size, there will be but little increase in density with depth due to compression. Jeffreys[7] calculates that if the Moon were composed entirely of the same material her density would range from 3·28 on the surface to 3·41 at the centre, but adds that 'there are probably outer layers similar to those of the Earth'.

If, however, the material of the Moon were basalt a change in its crystalline habit under increasing pressure would cause it to condense to a density of 3·8 at a depth of only 35 km. below the lunar surface. If the degree of further compression were the same as in Jeffreys's estimate given above, the material at the centre of the Moon would reach density 4. Here a simple numerical calculation is highly instructive.

The mean radius of the Moon $R = 1{,}738 \times 10^5$ cm. The radius of the sphere shorn of the outer 35-km. layer will, therefore, be $R' = 1,703 \times 10^5$ cm. The density ρ within this radius cannot be less than 3·8 on the usual assumptions regarding the composition of the Moon. The mass of this inner sphere will be

$$M' = \frac{4}{3} \pi R'\frac{3}{\rho} = 7{\cdot}856 \times 10^{25} \text{ g}$$

Unfortunately, the whole mass of the Moon is only $7{\cdot}737 \times 10^{25}$ g, so that this result is obviously impossible and the assumptions must be wrong. Either there exists a layer of very light rocks considerably thicker than 35 km., or else a zone of lower density has formed at the core.

PAGE 73

The idea of a low density zone at the centre of a planet encounters much opposition. Yet when Bullen in 1936 proceeded to derive the distribution of densities inside the Earth from the known densities of the crustal rocks he found that the density at 35 km. underground should be 3·32 g./cm.[3], which would give 5 just outside the core at the depth of 2,900 km. On these assumptions the mass M' and moment of inertia C' of the core would satisfy the relationship

$$C' = 0{\cdot}57 \, M' \, r^2 \text{ (where } r \text{ is the radius of the core.)}$$

The coefficient 0·57 is very close to $\frac{2}{3}$, corresponding to a hollow shell. Jeffreys[7] finds this result 'wholly unacceptable', but I am not so certain about this, especially with a small mass, such as the Moon. The result obtained in the preceding section seems to point in this direction.

PAGE 68 *et seq.*

The origin and composition of tektites is of great interest in connection with this page and the main theme of Chapter 7 generally.

These meteoritic bodies, scattered in several distinct showers at widely separated points of the Earth's surface, such as Australia and Czecho-slovakia, have long been a puzzle to astronomers and geologists alike. Terrestrial origin has been suggested, but this seems to be impossible in the light of H. E. Suess's finding that the small amounts of gases found in the bubbles which are often present in tektites have a pressure of about 0·001 atmosphere.[18] Such pressure is consistent with the idea, first broached by Verbeek in 1897, that the tektites come from the volcanoes of the Moon. Urey does not believe in their volcanic origin but seems to favour the dynamically difficult view that the tektites were projected to the Earth by 'meteoritic splashes'.

Tektites have a density of about 2·5,[9] have a very high silica and alumina content, and have otherwise been found by Urey to be substantially identical in composition with the terrestrial sediments derived from the decay of igneous rocks. The low content of argon in the Australites and Philippinites, examined by Suess, Hayden, and Inghram, gives these tektites ages not exceeding 2×10^7 years,[18] whereas Urey puts the age of the tektites examined by him as low as one million years.[19] The youngest meteorites of other types have radioactive ages of about 200 million years.

In considering the possibility of lunar origin, Urey[19] writes:

'The assumption of an oxidizing atmosphere on the moon at any time . . . is unrealistic, and in a reducing atmosphere we should expect ammonia and carbon compounds to be present. Ammoniacal water solutions should dissolve silica and alumina, and, moreover, potassium would remain in solution in such solutions instead of being preferentially adsorbed as compared to sodium, as occurs in terrestrial weathering, since the ammonium ion can replace potassium in clay materials. The uranium content of tektites, 1·4–1·8 p.p.m., indicates that this element has been concentrated to a high degree in these objects, as it is in the igneous rocks of the earth or in terrestrial sediments. There seems to be no very certain way by which uranium could be concentrated by a solution process. . . . Heavy metals are known to form stable and soluble compounds with some carbon compounds, and uranium and thorium might be transported in some process of this kind. . . . Perhaps some properties of a tektite might be accounted for in this way, and some transport of potassium, silica, alumina, uranium, and thorium to the surface would occur.'

If, however, the tektites were formed on the Moon their age shows that this could not have been in any hypothetical past when she had a reducing atmosphere. They could, on the other hand, have been produced by processes in every way similar to terrestrial weathering, including oxidation, somewhere in the great honeycomb of the Moon's underground caverns and been conveyed to the surface by an uprush of volcanic waters. As Jeffreys has pointed out,[7] water would explode violently upon reaching the surface zone of low pressure, but there is no reason why ordinary volcanic processes should not have intervened and cases are known when matter ejected by terrestrial volcanoes reached velocities exceeding that of escape from the Moon.

If this interpretation is substantially correct, violent volcanic activity must have been in progress on the Moon in geologically recent times, the rocks underlying the sublunar hydrosphere are comparable to our surface formations, as one would otherwise expect, and, finally, their high content of the radioactive matter responsible for our own pockets of subterranean heat is consistent with the volcanic hypothesis.

PAGE 68

With regard to the problem of lunar underground cavities, H. P. Wilkins gives the following information in *Our Moon*[21] (p. 119):

190

'Long ago it was calculated that if the moon had contracted on cooling at the same rate as granite, a drop of only 180° F. would create hollows in the interior amounting to no less than 14 millions of cubic miles.'

The source of this information and the method used are unknown to me, but the degree of contraction found by Spurr from the 'oppression' and 'appression' experienced by the old lunar ring mountains makes it practically certain that extensive cavities have been formed in the subsurface layers of the Moon. The very low density of the uppermost portion of the lunar globe indicated by the considerations in the reference to p. 66 further corroborates this conclusion.

Relating to Chapter 11

PAGE 111 et seq.
The motions of the Moon are summarized in the three empirical laws established by Cassini:

1. The Moon rotates uniformly about an axis fixed within the lunar globe. The period of rotation is identical with the sideral period of the Moon's revolution in her orbit, which is 27·321661 days.
2. The pole of lunar rotation z makes a constant angle of 1° 35' with the pole of the ecliptic Z, which is a fixed point on the celestial sphere as seen from the Moon.
3. Owing to the nearly uniform regression of the lunar node on the plane of the ecliptic and the nearly constant inclination of the lunar orbit, equal to 5° 8', the pole of the lunar orbit P describes a small circle around Z in a period of 18⅔ years. Z falls within the arc of the great circle zP, whence it follows that the planes of the lunar orbit and of the lunar equator intersect on the ecliptic, the plane of the latter lying between the other two.

These laws are only approximately true, as all motions of the Moon are subject to considerable irregularities.

PAGE 112 et seq.
The Solar Constant at the distance of the Moon is 1·97 gram-calories per square centimetre per minute, or $1·37 \times 10^6$ ergs per square cm. per second.

If we now take an ideally 'black-body' which absorbs 100 per cent of all incident radiation, the energy E radiated by it *in vacuo* when its absolute temperature is T can be obtained from the Stefan–Boltzmann equation:

$$E = \sigma T^4,$$

where σ is the so-called Stefan's Constant and equals $1·37 \times 10^{-12}$ gram-calories per cm.^{2} per sec. or $5·75 \times 10^{-5}$ ergs per cm.^{2} per sec. Conversely if this energy E is supplied to the blackbody per cm.[2] per sec. its temperature will be raised from $0°$K. to $T°$K. In other words,

$$T = \sqrt[4]{\frac{E}{\sigma}}.$$

If we now substitute for E the Solar Constant and express σ in the same units we shall have the absolute temperature of the blackbody exposed at right angles to unobstructed sunshine *in vacuo* at the mean distance of the Earth–Moon system from the Sun, i.e. one astronomical unit = 93 million miles. A simple calculation gives the result as $392·9°$K. The mean temperature of a blackbody sphere, or black-sphere temperature, is obtained on the same principle and on the same assumptions comes up $277·6°$K.

The Moon, being nearly airless and absorbing 93 per cent of the incident sunlight, approximates fairly closely to the blackbody situation and the mean temperatures found from observation do not differ much from the theoretical blackbody ones. If, on the other hand, the lunar surface is taken in detail there will be great differences in its albedo, nor will it even be a 'grey body', another abstract which behaves as the blackbody multiplied by unity minus albedo, i.e. the absorbed fraction of the incident energy. For in actual fact the absorption will be selective, some wavelengths being absorbed more than others (Moon shows colour even as a whole and thus departs from the blackbody ideal). The energy, however, in the different parts of the Solar spectrum differs both because the Sun does not emit uniformly in all wavelengths and because the light quantum or photon is proportional to the frequency and so inversely proportional to the wavelength. Any physical or chemical action, such as adsorption or desorption of gases, evaporation, photodissociation, etc., will further alter the balance.

Relating to Chapter 12

PAGE 129 *et seq.*
The dimming of a star at the Moon's limb in blue light, which may but need not be analogous to the darkening of the disks of Jupiter and Saturn at the line of contact during occultations, can be due to various causes.

Molecular scattering is approximately proportional to λ^{-4} and would increase steadily with the increasing molecular concentration and thickness of the gas layer through which the light of the star has to pass as the star approaches the limb of the Moon. The same would usually apply to selective molecular absorption, unless for some reason the absorbing gas were concentrated in a thin layer above the surface.

In either case the effect is subject to Lambert's absorption law:[12]

$$I_d = I_i \cdot e^{-\kappa d},$$

where I_d is absorbed light, I_i incident light, κ absorption coefficient and d

thickness of the absorbing layer. Sometimes extinction coefficient a is used instead. This is the reciprocal of the thickness expressed in cm. of the layer which causes the incident light to be reduced to 0·1 of its original intensity.

$$a = 0·4343\,\kappa.$$

To apply this law to the present case the sphericity of the gas layer and the density gradient must be taken into consideration.

Obscuration by mist or haze will likewise be proportional to the effective thickness of the intervening layer, but is generally independent from λ. If, however, the mist-forming particles are very small they will scatter short-wave radiations more effectively than the long-wave ones. If, further, they are crystalline and magnetic or electrical forces are present the longer axes of the crystals will assume a definite orientation with regard to the field and the transparency of the mist will vary with the line of sight.

This appears to be the case with the Martian Violet Layer[3] (Firsoff) and probably also here, as the observed appearance could be due only to the presence of a thin obscuring shell of finely divided crystalline material.

Relating to Chapter 13

PAGE 134 *et seq.*
Jeans's equation will be found on p. 183. Lyman Spitzer, Jr.,[10] gives it the form:

$$t_1 = \frac{6C}{3g} \cdot \frac{e^Y}{Y},$$

where $Y = \frac{3ga}{C^2}$, the notation being otherwise as on p. 183. How 6 is obtained in the numerator, I do not see: it should really be 4·34; but otherwise the two forms are clearly equivalent. The point, however, is that Jones has found an error in Jeans's calculations, as a result of which the time t_1 does not correspond to the total dissipation of the gas in question but to a drop in its density by $1/e$ of the initial value, so that the real time of total dissipation will be $e \cdot t_1$. e is the base of natural logarithms and equals approximately 2·72, so that this correction does not affect the order of magnitude, but this is not the end of the story.

Jeans's theory is of fundamental importance and it may be as well to consider it step by step by referring to his original exposition in *The Dynamical Theory of Gases*, Cambridge University Press, 1925, page 343 *et seq.* with some amplification.

Here Jeans considers the surface of a sphere of radius R, corresponding to the escape level in the atmosphere of a planet of radius a and superficial gravity g. At this height molecular collisions are by definition so infrequent that they can be neglected and any molecule moving with the velocity of escape $U = \sqrt{2ga^2/R}$ or more away from the surface will never return to the planet's atmosphere. Now all molecular velocities can be resolved into three components along the axes at right angles to each other, two of which are tangential to our sphere at the point of origin and the third normal to it at this point. Let us call the three components u, v, and w respectively.

The rate of effusion of gas through an aperture (of unit area in unit time) is equal to

$$v \cdot \left(\frac{hm}{\pi}\right)^{\frac{1}{2}} \int_{o}^{\infty} e^{-hmu^2}\, u\,du, \tag{A}$$

where v is molecular density, i.e. the number of molecules per unit volume, m molecular weight, $h = 1/2RT$, and u is 'positive molecular velocity', that is to say, velocity so directed that the molecules moving with it at the level of the aperture will be able to pass out through the aperture.

In the present case this 'positive molecular velocity' will be any molecular velocity at the surface of the escape-level sphere away from it and fulfilling the condition

$$u^2 + v^2 + w^2 \geqslant \frac{2ga^2}{R},$$

so that the rate of effusion will become

(A) $\qquad v\left(\frac{hm}{\pi}\right)^{\frac{3}{2}} \int\int\int e^{-hm(u^2+v^2+w^2)}\; w\,du\,dv\,dw \qquad$ (B)

the integration being extended over all values of u, v, and w, where w is positive (away from the surface of the sphere) and the condition given above is satisfied. In other terms, any real molecular velocity c forming an angle θ with the axis of w and an angle φ with the plane uv will have components u, v, and w equal to $c.\sin\theta\cos\varphi$, $c.\sin\theta\sin\varphi$, and $c.\cos\theta$ respectively, and the limits of integration will become for θ from 0 to $\frac{1}{2}\pi$, for φ from 0 to 2π, and for c from $\sqrt{2ga^2/R}$ to ∞. The rate of dissipation at the escape level R will be, accordingly:

(B) $\hfill$ (C)

$$v\left(\frac{hm}{\pi}\right)^{\frac{3}{2}}\pi \int_{c=\sqrt{2ga^2/R}}^{c=\infty} e^{-hmc^2}\, c^3\, dc = \frac{v}{2\sqrt{\pi hm}}\, e^{-hm2ga^2R^{-1}} \cdot (1+hm^2ga^2R^{-1})$$

In an isothermal atmosphere, to which this reasoning refers, the density $\rho(=vm)$, and hence the molecular density v, obeys the relationship:

$$v = v_0\, e^{-2hmga\,\frac{R-a}{R}},$$

where v_o is molecular density at the base of the isothermal atmosphere. Thus substituting v_o for v in (C) we obtain:

$$\frac{v_o}{2\sqrt{\pi hm}}\, e^{-2hmga}\left(1 + hm\,\frac{2ga^2}{R}\right) \qquad\qquad \text{(D)}$$

This gives us the rate of dissipation (per unit area per unit time) in terms of the molecular density v_o at the base of the isothermal atmosphere.

The integration of expression (A) yields: $\frac{1}{2}\cdot\dfrac{v}{\sqrt{\pi hm}}$, and if we compare this with (D) we shall see, as Jeans points out, that 'the loss is exactly what it would be if gas from the base of the isothermal layer were streaming away freely into space, without any resistance, through a series of orifices of total area equal to $e^{-2hmga}\left(1 + hm\,\dfrac{2ga^2}{R}\right)$ times the surface of the sphere of radius R' (p. 343).[6]

The latter is, of course, $4\pi R^2$. Jeans, however, omits to multiply (D) by this surface. He takes instead v_o, which is the number of molecules contained in a cm.[3] at the base of the isothermal atmosphere, divides this by (D) and calls the result t_o.

$$t_o = \frac{2\sqrt{\pi hm}}{1 + 2hmga^2\,R^{-1}}\cdot e^{\,2hmga} \text{ seconds} \qquad\qquad \text{(E)}$$

This he describes as 'the time required for the planet to lose an amount equal to a layer one cm. thick of the gas in question at the base of its isothermal atmosphere' (p. 345).[6]

This, however, would appear to be made on the tacit assumption that $4\pi R^2 = 4\pi a^2$, i.e. that $R^2 = a^2$, for the number of molecules in the isothermal base layer one cm. thick is $4\pi a^2 v_o$ and the total loss per unit time is $4\pi R^2\times$(D). At a later stage Jeans does, in fact, equate R with a, which may be legitimate enough for a term $R - a/R$ but not for a square of the ratio of the two quantities, which in the case of the Moon will be in the region of $\frac{1}{4}$ and even for the Earth is, on Jeans's own assumptions, about $\frac{4}{9}$.

However, t_1 is obtained by multiplying t_o by the thickness H of what may be described as the 'equivalent isothermal atmosphere', i.e. a fictitious atmosphere containing the same gas mass as the whole of the isothermal atmosphere but having a uniform density and pressure throughout equal to their corresponding values in the base layer.

If now R is equated with a and $2hm$ is replaced by $3/C^2$, h being equal to $\dfrac{1}{2RT}$ and $C^2 = \dfrac{3RT^*}{m}$ (see page 182), equation (E) becomes:

$$t_o = \frac{4\cdot34}{C(1 + \frac{3ga}{C^2})}\, e^{\frac{3ga}{C^2}} \qquad\qquad \text{(F)}$$

---

* R stands in this case for the Gas Constant, not the radius of the escape sphere.

o

On these assumptions the pressure p_0 at the base of the isothermal layer, and so throughout the fictitious equivalent isothermal layer, will be

$$p_0 = v_0\, mgH, \tag{G}$$

which will be true of the mixture of gases composing the isothermal atmosphere, as well as of any of the constituent gases, p_0 and v_0 standing in the latter case for the partial pressure and partial molecular density of this gas respectively (Dalton's Law). By referring to our page 182 we shall also see that, using the present notation,

$$p_0\, v_0 = \tfrac{1}{3}\, v_0\, mC^2 \quad \text{(Boyle's Law).}$$

v_0 is number of molecules per unit volume, so that $v_0 = 1$, and

$$p_0 = \tfrac{1}{3}\, v_0\, mC^2, \quad \text{whence}$$

$$(G) \qquad\qquad H = \tfrac{1}{3} \cdot \frac{C^2}{g}, \quad \text{but}$$

$$t_1 = Ht_0 = \frac{C^2}{3g}\, t_0$$

$$t_1 = \frac{1{\cdot}45C}{g(1 + \frac{3ga}{C^2})} \cdot e^{\frac{3ga}{C^2}} \text{ seconds} \tag{H}$$

The formula given on p. 183 is obtained from (H) by omitting unity from the bracketed term in the denominator and putting $\tfrac{1}{2}$ for $\frac{1.45}{3}$, which is permissible within the present limits of accuracy. If Jones's and my own corrections are introduced we get:

$$t_2 = \left(\frac{a}{R}\right)^2 e\, t_1 \tag{I}$$

As a matter of luck rather than design, the two corrections very nearly cancel out and Jeans's original formula stands within his assumptions. There is, however, another point of especial interest for the Moon. The temperature of the atmosphere is assumed not to vary throughout the night-and-day cycle, which is very nearly true of our stratosphere. But, the Moon's night–day cycle being nearly 30 times as long as ours, considerable differences must be expected in the atmospheric temperatures at all levels as between the illuminated and the unilluminated part, so that the dissipation of the day atmosphere presents a separate problem from that of the night atmosphere. As a rough approximation all Jeans's values of t_1 may be doubled, which, though, provides but a partial answer, as processes of great complexity are involved, and it must be recalled that Jeans disregards the convective atmosphere.

To return to Lyman Spitzer, Jr., he writes:[10]

'. . . While the upper atmosphere at great heights is isothermal at the temperature T_c, the lower atmosphere has a temperature less than T_c, and the density at lower heights is correspondingly much increased over the density of the hypothetical atmosphere. This increase of density gives a total atmospheric mass much greater than that assumed, and the time required for a certain fraction of the atmosphere to escape is correspondingly increased. For correct results we must multiply t_1 by B, where B is the ratio between the actual mass of the atmosphere and the mass of the hypothetical atmosphere with a temperature T_c at all heights, and with a particle density n_{io} at the Earth's surface. Since the total mass is approximately proportional to the pressure at the Earth's surface, we have:

$$B = \frac{n_0 T_0}{n_{io} T_c} \qquad (23)$$

To determine the ratio n_0/n_{io}, we express this as the product of two ratios—n_0/n_{150} and n_{150}/n_{io}, where n_{150} is the actual particle density at 150 km., which we shall again set equal to $10^{12}/cm^3$. On the assumption that the atmosphere is stirred up to 150 km., n_0/n_{150} for each type of atom is equal to the observed ratio of the total particle densities, or $2\cdot7 \times 10^7$, if we take the observed ratio of the sea-level particle density to be $2\cdot7 \times 10^{19}/cm^3$ when T_0 equals $273°$. If the upper atmosphere is assumed to be isothermal and in diffusion equilibrium above 150 km., then the actual atmosphere above this height will be identical with the hypothetical model used in deriving equation (20), and, in particular, n_{150} will be the same for both the real and the hypothetical atmosphere. The ratio n_{150}/n_{io} is then found from equation (2) (i.e. $n(h) = n(O)e^{-h/H}$), with H the scale height of the isothermal layer for the particular type of atom under discussion. With these assumptions we find

$$B = 2\cdot7 \times 10^7 \left(\frac{273}{T_c}\right) e^{150/H} \qquad (24)'$$

From this equation Lyman Spitzer, Jr., has obtained the following table for the terrestrial conditions:

Correction Factor for Times of Escape

T_c (°K)	500	750	1,000	1,500	2,000
H (km)	28	42	56	84	110
B	$6\cdot9 \times 10^4$	$2\cdot8 \times 10^5$	$5\cdot1 \times 10^5$	$8\cdot2 \times 10^5$	$9\cdot7 \times 10^5$

Note: His equation (2) is equivalent to our $v = v_0\, e^{-2hmga\,\frac{R-a}{R}}$

This correction is difficult to apply in practice and there are good reasons to believe that the temperature of the upper atmosphere is much lower than expected.

PAGE 137 *et seq.*

In a convective atmosphere in the condition of adiabatic equilibrium the temperature T of the gas (on whatever scale) decreases steadily with height z. In other words $dT/dz = $ a constant. This is very nearly true of our air in settled dry weather. The constant is usually designated Γ and called adiabatic lapse. For a dry atmosphere $\Gamma = g/c_p$, where g is gravity and c_p specific heat of the atmospheric gas at constant pressure.[20]

Adiabatic changes are changes undergone by a constant mass of gas with a constant amount of heat, no heat being either supplied to the gas or withdrawn from it in the course of such changes. Adiabatic equilibrium is determined by the condition $pv^\gamma = $ a constant, p standing for pressure, v for volume, and γ for c_p/c_v, ratio of the specific heat of the gas at constant pressure to its specific heat at constant volume. γ depends on the structure of the molecule; it is approximately 1·67 for monatomic, 1·41 for diatomic and 1·26 for triatomic gases.

Since the mass of gas is constant in the course of adiabatic change, the density ρ is inversely proportional to v and the condition of adiabatic equilibrium may be represented thus: $p/\rho^\gamma = \kappa$, where κ is a constant.

In an adiabatic atmosphere the pressure gradient $dp/dz = -g\rho$, which means that pressure is directly proportional to g and ρ and decreases with height z. But $p = \kappa\rho^\gamma$, so that

$$\frac{d\,(\kappa\rho^\gamma)}{dz} = -g\rho$$

$$\kappa\gamma\rho^{\gamma-1}\,d\rho = -g\rho dz$$

$$\int_{\rho_0}^{\rho} \kappa\gamma\rho^{\gamma-2}d\rho = -\int_0^z g dz, \text{ where } \rho \text{ is the density at } z.$$

Hence $\dfrac{\kappa\gamma}{\gamma-1}\,(\rho_0^{\gamma-1}-\rho^{\gamma-1}) = gz$ \hfill (J)

Now Jeans[6] puts $\rho = 0$ to obtain the maximum height z to which an adiabatic atmosphere can extend and, substituting p_0 for $\kappa\rho_0^\gamma$, into (J) gets the equation:

$$z = \frac{p_0\gamma}{g\rho_0(\gamma-1)} \tag{K}$$

Where, however, both p_0 and ρ_0 are unknown, as is usually the case with bodies other than the Earth, it is more convenient to put $\rho_0 = 3p_0/C^2$, for $p = nmC^2/3v$ and $nm/v = \rho$ (see our p. 182). Thus

$$z = \frac{\gamma C^2}{3g(\gamma-1)} \tag{L}$$

C is a function of T and it will be seen that the limiting height of the convective atmosphere (if this could exist in isolation) does not depend on its mass, density, or ground pressure, but only on its composition, gravity, and temperature.[3]

In reality, before this limiting height z is reached, convection is stifled by viscosity and that the sooner the more rarefied the gas and the lower the gravity g because according to Maxwell's Law viscosity is substantially

198

independent from the density ρ, whereas the force of an ascending or descending air current is determined by the differences in specific weight of the gas at different temperatures. When this has happened there is no longer any convection. Conduction in rarefied gases is so slow a process that it can be neglected. As a result the atmosphere assumes an isothermal structure, i.e. it has the same temperature throughout and its density at any height is determined solely by the gravitational pressure of the overlying gas mass. The lower portions of our stratosphere satisfy these requirements fairly well.

In an isothermal atmosphere of sufficient height the constituent gases will become stratified according to their molecular weights, as if we had several atmospheres of different gases superimposed upon each other and extending upwards to different levels, which are the higher the lighter the gas. No segregation according to molecular weight has, however, been found in the atmosphere of the Earth up to 60 km.; the position above this height is at present unknown.

If we turn back to p. 198 we shall see that $\rho = 3p/C^2$, and, since $C^2 = 3RT/m$ and $h = 1/2RT$, $\rho/p = m/RT = 2hm$. In an isothermal atmosphere T is constant, R and m are also constant for each constituent gas and so long as the gas mixture remains unsegregated for this mixture as a whole as well.

The problem is to express ρ_z at a height z above the base of the isothermal atmosphere in terms of ρ_0 at the base, where $z = 0$.

Pressure is weight resting on a unit surface. Let us consider the change of pressure dp over an infinitesimal increase of z equal to dz, within which ρ may be taken to be constant and the divergence of the sides of the solid having the unit square area for its base and dz for its height may be neglected (these sides if prolonged indefinitely will converge at the centre of the planet). The weight of the solid thus defined is $g\rho\, dz$. The pressure will decrease with increasing height. Therefore:

$$-\mathrm{d}p = g\rho\, \mathrm{d}z = 2hmgp\mathrm{d}z, \text{ whence}$$
$$-\mathrm{d}p/p = 2hmg\mathrm{d}z.$$

Integrating this between the base of the isothermal atmosphere and the height z, where pressure is p_z, we have

$$-\int_{p_0}^{p_z} \frac{\mathrm{d}p}{p} = 2hmg \int_{o}^{z} \mathrm{d}z$$

$$\ln p_0 - \ln p_z = 2hmgz \text{ or}$$

$$\frac{p_0}{p_z} = e^{2hmpz}$$

$$p_z = p_0\, e^{-2hmgz} \text{ and, since } \rho/p = \text{a constant,}$$

$$\rho_z = \rho_0\, e^{-2hmgz} \tag{M}$$

199

This corresponds to Jeans's equation (*op. cit.* p. 338):

$$\rho = \rho_0\, e^{-2hmga\left(\frac{z}{a+z}\right)} \tag{N}$$

when z is small in relation to a and may be neglected in the denominator of the fraction.

PAGE 140 *et seq.*

Instead of regarding the atmosphere as composed of two distinct parts, the adiabatic troposphere and the isothermal stratosphere, as Jeans does, the two may be taken to be superimposed, as I have done in considering the problem of water vapour in the atmosphere of Mars.[3] If we disregard the complications arising out of viscosity and heat transfer by absorption and radiation, the adiabatic atmosphere should end at the level where its density becomes equal to that of the isothermal atmosphere, considered as extending all the way up from the ground all by itself. For the density of the adiabatic atmosphere has a flatter gradient and once the densities of the two atmospheres draw level with each other convection should cease.

Let T_o be the absolute temperature at ground level, T_z absolute temperature at the tropopause, and ρ_o and ρ_z gas densities corresponding to these two levels.

From the adiabatic equation we have:

$$\frac{\rho_z}{\rho_o} = \left(\frac{T_o}{T_z}\right)^{\frac{\gamma}{1-\gamma}} \tag{O}$$

(O) (M)
$$\left(\frac{T_o}{T_z}\right)^{\frac{\gamma}{1-\gamma}} = e^{-mgz/RT_o}, \text{ for in the iso-}$$

thermal atmosphere the temperature is the same throughout and if this atmosphere existed by itself its temperature would be T_o. We further have:

$$\frac{\gamma}{1-\gamma}(\ln T_o - \ln T_z) = -mgz/RT_o, \text{ whence}$$

$$z = \frac{RT_o\,\gamma}{mg(\gamma-1)}(\ln T_o - \ln T_z) \tag{P}$$

For the important practical case where $T_o = 273°$K. ($0°$C.), $\ln T_o \sim \ln e + \ln 100$, and the expression in brackets can be written:

$$(1 - \ln T_z/100),$$

which simplifies numerical calculation.

For the Earth this equation yields a result which is about $\frac{1}{4}$ too low, probably owing to the departure of our troposphere from the adiabatic ideal, as, on the one hand, the heat traffic involved in condensation and evaporation causes fluctuations of temperature which have not been provided for by the theory and, on the other, there is absorption of the heat of sunrays by the clouds and of the obscure heat of the Earth's both by the clouds and by water vapour and carbon dioxide. These factors should be substantially absent on the Moon.

We may consider two likely atmospheric compositions: (1) A mixture of heavy gases, say, CO_2, COS, O_3, and SO_2, having a mean $m = 50$ and $\gamma = 1.26$ (for triatomic gases); (2) Argon, a heavy, sticky inert gas of $m \sim 40$ and $\gamma = 1.67$ (monatomic). An air mixture resembling ours is unlikely on every reckoning.

Taking $g \sim 160$ cm./sec.[2], $T_o = 273°$K., $T_z = 213°$K., we get z equal to 33 km. (approximately $20\frac{1}{2}$ miles) and $22\frac{1}{2}$ km. (approximately 14 miles) respectively.

The weak point of this calculation is that T_z is unknown and is taken to be approximately the same as that of our stratosphere (219°K.), which seems to be a reasonable guess for the daylight hemisphere of the Moon, but is a guess only.

The accuracy of this assumption can be checked up to some extent by calculating T_z from the adiabatic lapse over z. Adiabatic lapse Γ for a dry atmosphere can be obtained from the equation: $\Gamma = g/c_p$. For argon, with $c_p = 0.127$ gram-calories per 1°C. per gram[2] (this has to be multiplied by Joule's Constant $J = 4.185 \times 10^7$ ergs, to bring the terms to the same units, whilst g is taken as the force acting on a mass of 1 gram) at N.T.P., $\Gamma = 3.01°$C./km. and $T_z = 205.33°$K., or 7.67 degrees less than assumed, which may be regarded as a wholly satisfactory degree of agreement. For the heavy triatomic gas mixture agreement is even closer. These gases have low values of c_p, which is 0.201 for CO_2,[2] likely to be predominant in the mixture. The corresponding values of Γ and T_z are 1.90°C./km. and 211°K. respectively.

Incidentally, Γ can be obtained from (J) by substituting p/ρ for $\kappa\rho^{\gamma-1}$.

(J)
$$\frac{\gamma}{\gamma-1}\left(\frac{p_o}{\rho_o} - \frac{p}{\rho}\right) = gz, \text{ and, since } p = \frac{\rho C^2}{3} \text{ (see our p. 198)}$$

and $C^2 = \dfrac{3RT}{m}$, (J) becomes:

$$\frac{R\gamma}{m(\gamma-1)}(T_o - T) = gz, \text{ whence,}$$

putting $z = 1$ km,

$$\Gamma = (T_o - T) = \frac{gm(\gamma-1)}{R\gamma} \times 10^5 \text{ °C./km.}$$

This equation gives slightly, but not significantly, higher values for Γ, which becomes for argon equal to 3.08°C./km. It is, therefore, possible that the calculated values of z are a little too high.

Another point of interest is the drop in density in the ascent to z.

This can be obtained from the isothermal equation:

$$\frac{\rho_z}{\rho_o} = e^{-mgz/RT_o}$$

For the heavy gas mixture the ratio is 0·38, or just over $\frac{1}{3}$, and 0·52, just over $\frac{1}{2}$, for argon. On the Earth it is $\frac{1}{4}$ and I have obtained a similar result for Mars.[3] On the Moon, however, one would expect the tropopause to be somewhat lower in proportion and argon has a high viscosity coefficient.

On the Earth this density ratio remains unchanged when the height of the tropopause varies depending on T_o. The same may be taken to be true of

the Moon. From the adiabatic equation we have: $T_z = \left(\frac{\rho_o}{\rho_z}\right)^{\frac{1-\gamma}{\gamma}} T_o$. so

that T_z will vary directly as T_o, at least when it does vary.

Water vapour can never behave as an ideal gas in lunar, or for that matter in terrestrial, conditions; at the assumed stratospheric temperature of 213° K., CO_2, with a critical temperature of 243° K., will likewise be a vapour, and in the temperatures of the lunar night all heavy gases will be either wholly or partly precipitated and can exist only as vapours, so that they will no longer obey the gas laws postulated here. Argon alone can be considered in these circumstances as a proper atmospheric gas.

$T_o = 145°$ K. yields for argon a $T_z = 113°$ K. with $z = 11$ km. (7 miles).

These results are, of course, true only within the limits of the assumptions made at the start, which approximate but roughly to the real situation, considerably affected by the processes described in the following chapter, as well as other factors which may be unknown or have been overlooked.

PAGE 141

It has been found that, contrary to Dalton's Law of Partial Pressures, the presence of an indifferent gas, such as argon would be, reduces the pressure of vapour in equilibrium with its liquid (or solid). 'Hence, for accurate work the boiling point of a liquid is defined as the highest temperature that can be reached by a liquid under a given pressure of its own vapour when heat is applied externally and evaporation occurs freely from the surface' (A. J. Mee: *Physical Chemistry*,[12] p. 232). The same applies to sublimation at temperatures below the freezing point of the liquid in question.

The *Smithsonian Physical Tables, 1954* include the following table (635) for the pressure of saturated water vapour at low temperatures over ice (it will be somewhat less in the presence of a neutral gas):

Temperature in °C.	Pressure in mm. Hg
−69	0·0023
−65	·0041
−60	·0081
−55	·0157

Temperature in °C.	Pressure in mm. Hg
−50	·0295
−45	·0540
−40	·0962
−35	·1675
−30	·2855
−25	·4790
−20	·7740
−15	1·239
−10	1·945
−5	3·010
0	4·580

Relating to Chapter 14

PAGE 147 *et seq.*

Sorption at a given temperature is a function of the partial gas pressure p and is expressed by an empirical formula:[11]

$$x/m = kp^{1/n}, \tag{Q}$$

where x and m stand for the mass of the sorbed gas and sorbent respectively, expressed in grams, and k is a constant depending on the substances, whilst n may vary between 1 and 10 and is frequently about 3. The values of k and n vary with the temperature, diminishing as this rises, n in particular tending towards unity.

This is the so-called parabolic equation of sorption.

In Schmidt's equation the amount of gas c sorbed by a porous body at the pressure of one atmosphere and any given temperature between 0°C. and 150°C. is represented as a linear function of the square root of the heat of vaporization of the gas λ (see also the following section)

$$\log c = k_1 \sqrt{\lambda} - k_2$$

where k_1 and k_2 are constant for each given specimen of sorbent.

According to MacBain[11] the heat of sorption is usually much higher than the heat of vaporization. Use has been made of it in the production of low temperatures; e.g. 6°K. has been obtained by pumping off hydrogen sorbed at the temperature of liquid air or liquid hydrogen.

'Heat of sorption is usually and most simply obtained by comparison of two isotherms. Comparing the pressure at two temperatures corresponding to any fixed value of x/m, that is, two points on the same isosthere, the heat of sorption follows from the equation, $d \ln p/dT = -q/RT^2$. This value of q refers to the differential or instantaneous heat for the addition of further small amounts to a surface by which x has already been sorbed, as distinguished from the integral heat of sorption where x is the total amount sorbed by the quantity m of sorbing material. q is the molar heat in each case, that is, the number of small calories per gram molecular weight of the gas of vapour sorbed. . . . Coolidge has shown that heats of sorption calculated from the isostheres have, as a matter of fact, a tendency to be somewhat less than those directly measured' (MacBain, *op. cit.*, pp. 400–1).

The free energy of sorption according to the same author is $RT \ln l/p$ for a gas and $RT \ln p_s/p$ for the vapour of a liquid with a vapour tension p_s.

q can be found by comparing the parabolic equation (Q) with the differential heat equation given above. From (Q): $p = (x/km)^n$. Substituting this into the differential heat equation we have:

$$d \ln \left(\frac{x}{km}\right)^n = -\frac{q}{MRT^2} \, dT,$$

where M is the mass of one mole of the sorbed gas, as x is expressed in grams. Thus:

$$\frac{n}{x} \, dx = -\frac{q}{MRT^2} \, dT, \quad \text{and}$$

$$n \int_{x_0}^{x} \frac{dx}{x} = -\int_{T_0}^{T} \frac{q}{MRT^2} \, dT$$

$$n \ln \frac{x}{x_0} = \frac{q}{RM} \left(\frac{1}{T} - \frac{1}{T_0}\right)$$

$$q = \frac{RMn(T_0-T)}{T_0 T} \cdot \ln \frac{x}{x_0} \tag{R}$$

The logarithmic form is somewhat unhandy, as x_0 cannot be equal 0, but (R) does give us q in terms of the drop in the temperature of the sorbed gas and the ratio of the additionally sorbed gas to the amount that has been sorbed at the beginning of the determination, both expressed in grams. It may seem at first sight that q does not depend on k, p, and m, but these enter into the relationship by way of x_0. This is, in fact, why x_0 is there.

Relating to Chapter 15

PAGE 162

The total solar energy received by a level element of lunar ground at the equator, or, strictly speaking, the line where the Sun passes through the zenith, which need not necessarily coincide with the equator, during the lunation can be obtained in the following way.

Let the Sun be at an arbitrary altitude x above the astronomical horizon. If we take a square area of side a cm. exposed perpendicularly to the sunrays the flux of solar energy through this area will be $a^2 \times S$ per minute, where S stands for the Solar Constant of 1·97 gram-calories per cm.^{2} per minute. On reaching the level ground the same flux will be spread over a rectangular area ab and every square cm. of this area will receive less solar

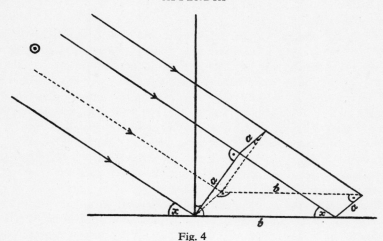

Fig. 4

radiation in the ratio $a^2 : ab$ or $a : b$. If we now put $a = 1$ and call dE the energy received in dt by a cm.^{2} of the rectangular area (see Fig. 4) we get:

$$dE = S \sin x \, dt.$$

In the course of the lunar day (period of daylight) of D minutes x (expressed in radians) will vary from 0 to π, so that

$$x = \frac{\pi}{D} \, t, \text{ so that}$$

$$dE = S \sin \left(\frac{\pi t}{D}\right) dt, \text{ whence}$$

$$E = S \int_O^D \sin \left(\frac{\pi t}{D}\right) dt$$

$$= S \left[-\frac{D}{\pi} \cos \left(\frac{\pi}{D} t\right) \right]_O^D$$

$$= -S \frac{D}{\pi} (-1 - 1)$$

$$= \frac{2SD}{\pi}.$$

Substituting numerical values and carrying out the operations, we obtain a figure of approximately 28,530 gram-calories per cm.^{2} of level ground at the equator (or locality where the Sun passes through the zenith) in the course of a lunation. A square cm. of level ground at the selenographical latitude φ (regarded equinoxially as above) will receive during the lunation this amount of energy multiplied by $\cos \varphi$.

PAGE 162 *et seq.*

It has been found that in the equilibrium systems for a pure substance involving two phases, solid and liquid (fusion–solidification), liquid and vapour (evaporation–condensation), or solid and vapour (sublimation–condensation), the pressure determining the equilibrium condition does not depend on the volume of the system but only on the temperature, provided that the effects of gravity, surface tension, electrification, and magnetism, and with the solid phase of torsion, are absent or disregarded.[15] In ordinary terrestrial conditions these factors can affect the equilibrium but little, but on the Moon, with very low temperatures and pressures, such influences should gain in relative importance; electrification in particular may affect evaporation considerably.

However this may be, the latent heat of transition from one phase to the other in any of the three equilibrium systems, and that of sublimation–condensation in particular, is not constant for a constant mass, usually taken to be one gram, and varies with temperature and pressure. The latent heat of sublimation l_s can be obtained from the Clapeyron-Clausius equation:

$$l_s = \frac{RT^2}{Mp} \cdot \frac{\mathrm{d}p}{\mathrm{d}T}, \qquad \text{(S)}$$

where R and T have their usual connotations, p is pressure in any units (these cancel out as between p and $\mathrm{d}p$), and M is the molecular weight of the subliming substance. This equation gives especially good results for low vapour pressures and hence low temperatures, where the behaviour of the vapour approximates more closely to that of ideal gas.

In our case we may take $T = -223°$K. $(-50°$C.$)$, which will be the sublimation point for an atmospheric pressure of 0·0295 mm. Hg (about one 25-thousandth of our sea-level pressure). The Smithsonian figures (see page 202–3) for the encompassing vapour pressures at $-55°$C. and $-45°$C. are 0·0157 mm. Hg and 0·0540 mm. Hg. respectively, so that

$$\frac{\mathrm{d}p}{\mathrm{d}T} = \frac{0·0383}{10} \sim 0·0038 \text{ mm. Hg per } 1°\text{C. } M=18,$$

$p=0·0295$, $R=8·314 \times 10^7$, and, in order to obtain l_s in gram-calories, (S) must be divided by Joule's Equivalent $J=4·185 \times 10^7$; otherwise the result will be in ergs.

Substituting the numerical values into (S) and carrying out the operations, we obtain

$$l_s = 757 \text{ gram-calories per gram.}$$

As the temperature at which sublimation occurs continues to drop l_s increases, and in lunar conditions the radiometric temperature of the ground is quite irrelevant for the temperature of any putative snow-field, which even on the Earth will be at freezing point on the hottest summer

206

day; so that, emerging from the shadows of the lunar night, any such snow-field could not be warmer, and would probably be much colder, than 145°K. In fact, considering that lunar snow would be chilled by its own evaporation, as well as by the evaporation and desorption of gas deposits upon it (dry ice and other precipitable gases), a temperature of the order of $-200°$C., or $73°$K., does not seem improbable. Water vapour pressures at such temperatures are, according to Kuiper, about $10^{-15\cdot0}$ mm. Hg for $100°$K. and $10^{-26\cdot6}$ mm. Hg for $70°$K.[10] Accurate calculation is difficult in these conditions, but it is clear that until this snow had been heated up to the sublimation point its evaporation would be negligible, however rarefied the lunar atmosphere may be.

PAGE 162

W. F. Giauque and J. W. Stout[4] give the following figures for the thermal capacity C_p cal./deg./mole of ice at low temperatures (the relationship is very nearly linear):

$T°$ K.	C_p	$T°$ K.	C_p
40	1·466	150	5·265
50	1·896	160	5·550
60	2·304	170	5·845
70	2·701	180	6·142
80	3·075	190	6·438
90	3·448	200	6·744
100	3·796	210	7·073
110	4·130	220	7·391
120	4·434	230	7·701
130	4·728	240	8·013
140	4·993	(M taken as 18·0156)	

Since the relationship is very nearly linear, $dC_p/dT = $ a constant. Thus, to compute the approximate amount of heat needed to heat up a gram of ice from $70°$K. up to $223°$K., we may take the gradient at the middle of the range, say, between $160°$K. and $150°$K., divide this by $M = 18$ and multiply by 153^2.

$$\frac{0\cdot0285 \times 153^2}{18} = 46\cdot67 \text{ gram-calories.}$$

PAGE 164

Few data are available for deuterium water and the other heavy waters, but F. T. Miles and A. W. C. Menzies[13] give a few figures and empirical formulae for deriving the vapour pressure and heat of vaporization of D_2O from the corresponding data for H_2O.

Pressure of D_2O in mm. Hg.

$T°$C.	$p\,D_2O - p\,H_2O$	$p\,D_2O$
10	$-1\cdot4_6$	$7\cdot7_5$
20	$-2\cdot4_8$	$15\cdot0_6$
30	$-4\cdot0_1$	$27\cdot8_1$

Comparison formula:

$$\log \frac{p\mathrm{D_2O}}{p\mathrm{H_2O}} = -16 \cdot 99867 + \frac{268 \cdot 8426}{\mathrm{T}} + 7 \cdot 4971604 \log \mathrm{T} +$$
$$-9 \cdot 761107 \times 10^{-3}\mathrm{T} + 4 \cdot 4288 \times 10^{-6}\,\mathrm{T}^2.$$

and for Latent Molar Heat of Vaporization:

$$L_{\mathrm{D_2O}} - L_{\mathrm{H_2O}} = 2 \cdot 303 \times \mathrm{RT}^2 \frac{\mathrm{dlog}(p_{\mathrm{D_2O}}/p_{\mathrm{H_2O}})}{\mathrm{dT}} = -1230 + 14 \cdot 90 \times \mathrm{T} +$$
$$-0 \cdot 04466 \times \mathrm{T}^2 + 4 \cdot 052 \times 10^{-5} \times \mathrm{T}^3.$$

For 40°C. L of D_2O exceeds that of H_2O by 300 gram-calories, the difference increases with dropping temperature.

The Smithsonian Physical Tables, 1954 give the latent heats of melting and vaporization of D_2O in kg.-calories per mole as 1·51 and 10·74 at 25°C., which compares with 1·44 and 10·48 for H_2O in the same conditions. The ice point of D_2O is given as 3·802°C. and the boiling point of D_2O at one atmosphere as 101·42°C.

PAGE 167

The relationship between volume V and temperature T in adiabatic change is expressed by the equation: $T_o V_o{}^{\gamma-1} = T V^{\gamma-1}$, whence

$$\frac{V}{V_0} = \left(\frac{T_o}{T}\right)^{\frac{1}{\gamma-1}}$$

For water vapour $\gamma = 1 \cdot 305 \sim 1 \cdot 3$, and if we put 2 for V/V_o we obtain the desired expansion in volume to twice the original volume V_o. Numerically

$$\frac{T_o}{T} = 2^{0 \cdot 7} = 1 \cdot 625, \text{ so that}$$

if we take the initial temperature equal to the sublimation point, assumed to be 223°K., we get $T = 137 \cdot 6°K$.—a drop of 85·4 degrees.

For an element inside a large snow-field volume expansion will be proportional to the height z reached by the vapour over the surface of the snow; and, since the specific heat of water vapour at constant pressure is high, $c_p = 0 \cdot 488$ gram-calories per 1°C. per gram,[2] it is clear that the evolving vapours and the 'violet layer' of fine crystals buoyed upon them will ascend but slowly in the course of the lunar day and may never reach any great height.

The same considerations will apply to CO_2 snow, only that its c_p is about one-fifth of that of H_2O and latent heat of vaporization is also about 10 times less than that of H_2O, so that the whole process will be much more rapid.

Jeffreys's classical equation for the rate of evaporation of a particle freely suspended in space, which is much used in meteorology, [5,8] reads:

APPENDIX

$$\frac{dm}{dt} = 4\pi k\rho C V_o, \tag{T}$$

where m is the evaporating mass (in grams), t time (in seconds), k molecular diffusion coefficient of the vapour in the ambient gas, ρ density of the ambient gas, C electrostatic capacity of the particle, which *ceteris paribus* is proportional to the linear dimensions of the particle (in *cm*), and V_o density of the vapour on the surface of the particle expressed as a fraction of the density of this gas, i.e. partial pressure of vapour/atmospheric pressure.

Jeffreys[8] assumes in (T) the concentration of the vapour at a sufficient distance from the particle to be 0. If it is not the last term becomes $V_o - V$, where V is vapour concentration in the ambient gas. If wind be present there will be a further velocity coefficient, usually represented as K_v.

(T) would be applicable to the evaporation of freely suspended ice or dry ice crystals in the lunar atmosphere. The dimensions of these crystals should be of the same order as those attributed to the particles in the Martian 'violet layer', i.e. between 0·1 and 1 micron (cm.$^{-3}$). k and ρ, however, are in doubt.

(T) deals with what may be described as spherical evaporation.

For an element of snow on the ground the evaporation will be hemispherical only. We may consider a small isolated circular area of snow of a radius a. The electrostatic capacity of a circular disk is $2a/\pi$; but, since evaporation takes place on only one side of the disk, the relevant capacity C will be a/π, so that

(T) $$\frac{dm}{dt} = 4\,k\rho a V_o.$$

For a similar area completely enclosed within a large snow-field, however, the evaporation becomes cylindrical, as it can proceed only vertically upwards.

Here the condition of steady flow is determined quite simply by the area, so that we have

$$\frac{dm}{dt} = \pi\,a^2 k\rho V_o, \tag{U}$$

or if a unit area is taken

$$\frac{dm}{dt} = k\rho V_o \tag{V}$$

on the previous assumptions.

It is immediately obvious that for a large snow-field the rate of evaporation at the perimeter will be higher than for the inside area where it will be (U). In fact, if a sufficiently small unit area is chosen the perimeter evaporation per unit area will be about twice as fast as in the enclosed part of the snow-field if the perimeter may be regarded as substantially recti-linear by comparison with the size of the elements under consideration. If marked indentations be present the rate of evaporation will increase, though it can never exceed the hemispherical rate.

From these considerations it is clear that the perimeter will tend to contract towards the minimum possible length in relation to the more slowly evaporating interior. In other words, any snow-field lying on even ground will tend towards circular shape, as the circle has the smallest perimeter in relation to its area.

The actual problem of evaporation in lunar conditions presents multiple difficulties. In the above reasoning it is assumed that the evaporating sur-face is smooth and even and it has been pointed out in the main text why the formation of feathery crystalline growths must be expected with rising temperatures. On the other hand, so long as the temperature stays suffi-ciently low for the ice to remain amorphous, the surface of the snow-field may be comparatively smooth, thus approximating to the situation envisaged in the mathematical argument.

Another difficulty lies in the correct evaluation of the diffusion coeffi-cient k.

Chapman and Cowling[22] give the following formula for k, which they call $D_{1,2}$, for a pair of gases of molecular weight m_1 and m_2 respectively diffusing in one another and the absolute temperature T:

$$D_{1,2} = \frac{3}{8n\sigma_{1,2}{}^2} \left\{ \frac{kT(m_1+m_2)}{2\pi m_1 \, m_2} \right\}^{\frac{1}{2}}, \qquad \text{(W)}$$

where n is the number of molecules per cm.^{3} of the mixture, k is Boltz-mann's Constant equal to $1 \cdot 380 \times 10^{-16}$ erg/degree C., and $\sigma_{1,2}$ the collisional diameter of the two gases for each other in cm. They further postulate that $\sigma_{1,2} = \frac{1}{2}(\sigma_1 + \sigma_2)$, or the arithmetical mean of the collisional diameters of the two gases taken separately. This is a somewhat crude assumption. Indeed, there is some discrepancy here between the values of the diffusion constants obtained from the kinetic theory of gases and those deduced from the broadening of the rotational spectral lines at low pressures of the order of 10^{-2} mm. Hg, especially for gases having a large dipole moment, such as CO_2 and NH_3 (Gordy, Smith and Trambaruls).[23] Theoretical or observational data for water vapour are generally lacking, except for the diffusion of pure water vapour in itself, which may be of interest in lunar conditions, as the local atmosphere in the vicinity of an evaporating snow-field would consist predominantly of water vapour. In this case $\sigma_{1,1} = 10 \times 10^{-8}$ cm.

Most of the data relate to the diffusion of ammonia in itself and in the common gases. Since, however, H_2O and NH_3 have very similar electric polarities, it may be assumed with fair approximation that their collisional diameters vary from CO_2 to A in the same ratio. Now the value of $\sigma_{1,2}$ obtained from line broadening and theory for NH_3 is:

in A $3\cdot73 \times 10^{-8}$ and $4\cdot04 \times 10^{-8}$ cm.
in CO_2 $7\cdot59 \times 10^{-8}$ and $4\cdot51 \times 10^{-8}$ cm.
in H_2 $2\cdot95 \times 10^{-8}$ and $3\cdot59 \times 10^{-8}$ cm.

respectively.[23] Diffusion being a kinetic problem, the figures in the second column might meet the case better. However, the Landolt-Börnstein *Physikalisch-Chemische Tabellen*[24] give the following figures of k $(D_{1,2})$ for water vapour at NTP in:

air $0\cdot198$ cm.^{2}/sec.
CO_2 $0\cdot132$ cm.^{2}/sec.
H_2 $0\cdot687$ cm.^{2}/sec.

From (W) it will be seen that $D_{1,2}$ varies inversely as the square of $\sigma_{1,2}$, so that the latter varies inversely as the square root of $D_{1,2}$.

We may now take for guidance the ratio of the collisional diameter of H_2O in CO_2 to that of H_2O in H_2 as computed from $D_{1,2}$ and compare this to the corresponding values for NH_3 in the same gases obtained by the other two methods. The corresponding figures are: $2\cdot28$; $2\cdot57$; $1\cdot23$. Thus it seems that the values obtained from the line broadening provide a closer approximation to the experimental data, after all. We may, therefore, take that $D_{1,2}$ (H_2O in A) $= D_{1,2}$ (H_2O in CO_2) $\times (\frac{7\cdot59}{3\cdot73})^2 = 0\cdot55$ cm.^{2}/sec.

All this is valid for NTP and from (W) it will be seen that *ceteris paribus* $D_{1,2}$ varies inversely as n and directly as $T^{\frac{1}{2}}$. From Boyle's Law n is directly proportional to the total atmospheric pressure p. Since, however, the rate of evaporation itself is directly proportional to the diffusion coefficient, it, too, will be directly proportional to $T^{\frac{1}{2}}/p$ and all results obtained with k for NTP will vary in this ratio with the changing conditions.

Three cases of evaporation will be of especial interest in the present context: H_2O in A, in CO_2 and in itself.

In a sufficiently large snow-field the differential rate of evaporation at the perimeter may be neglected and equation (V) applied as a fair average for the whole surface from which evaporation is taking place. Thus the rate of evaporation in grams per cm.^{2} per sec. will be

$$R = kp \, V_o.$$

k for H_2O in CO_2 at NTP is given as $0\cdot132$ cm.^{2}/sec., ρ,[24] density of the ambient atmosphere, is directly proportional to atmospheric pressure p and the molecular weight m of this atmosphere. Thus, if index $_1$ refers to the Earth and index $_2$ to the Moon, we have: $\rho_2/\rho_1 = p_2 m_2/p_1 m_1$. If we now put $\rho_1 = 1\cdot293 \times 10^{-3}$ g./cm.^{3}, $p_2 = p_1 \times 10^{-4}$, $m_2 = 44$ and $m_1 = 30$, we obtain $\rho_2 = 1\cdot293 \times \frac{44}{30} \times 10^{-7} = 1\cdot90 \times 10^{-7}$ g./cm.^{3} If it is further assumed that the snow is evaporating at $-50°$C. the partial pressure of vapour on the surface of evaporation will be $0\cdot0295$ mm. Hg. Thus, if we

P

call the atmospheric pressure P, the vapour pressure p and the molecular weights of gas and vapour M and m respectively, we shall have:

$$V_o = \frac{pm}{PM} \text{ and numerically}$$

$$V_o = \frac{2\cdot95 \times 18 \times 10^{-4}}{7\cdot6 \times 44 \times 10^{-4}} = 0\cdot1542.$$

The correction factor is $\left(\frac{T_2}{T_1}\right)^{\frac{1}{2}} + \frac{p_2}{p_1} = \left(\frac{223}{273}\right)^{\frac{1}{2}} \times 10^4 = 9\cdot036 \times 10^3.$

Therefore,

$$R = 0\cdot132 \times 1\cdot90 \times 10^{-7} \times 0\cdot1542 \times 9\cdot036 \times 10^3$$
$$R = 3\cdot495 \times 10^{-5} \text{ g. per cm. per sec.}$$

The result is 'per cm.' because electrostatic capacity is expressed in linear measure and in the present case, on the assumptions made above, this corresponds to an area of 1 cm.²

We have seen from the main text that to begin with the temperature of the snow may be as low as $-200°$C. and would gradually rise to the sublimation point, which for the assumed atmospheric pressure will be about $-42°$C. For the lowest temperatures within this range the rate of evaporation will be infinitesimal and it will be a little higher than the calculated value at the sublimation point itself, but it is easy to see that here the difference is small and will not affect the order of magnitude. The effects of sorption and adiabatic expansion, involving chilling and re-precipitation, have been left out of account, so that the rate of evaporation as calculated above will represent something in the nature of an upper limit, unlikely to be attained in practice.

There are 86,400 seconds in a day. The morning and evening temperatures will be very low, so that it appears legitimate to reduce the lunar day to 10 days (terrestrial) of effective sunshine during which evaporation on the assumed scale may be proceeding. The total mass dissipated by evaporation would, therefore, be $R \times 8\cdot64 \times 10^5 = 30\cdot20$ gr. per cm.² We have seen, however, from p. 163 that the total amount of solar energy available for vaporization during the lunar day will be sufficient for vaporizing in these conditions barely $4\cdot73$ grams of snow per cm.² In actual fact, the assumptions made here have been far too optimistic and the evaporation would be proceeding at a much lower rate because it is postulated above that the atmosphere in the vicinity of the snowfield is wholly devoid of water vapour, which is clearly impossible.

Argon as a somewhat lighter monatomic gas offers less resistance to evaporation and the value of R is correspondingly higher. $R = 1\cdot496 \times 10^{-4}$ g per cm.² per sec.

For evaporation in an atmosphere of water vapour—and owing to the very low density of the lunar atmosphere the atmosphere in the immediate vicinity of a lunar snow-field may be composed predominantly of water vapour—the value of $D_{1,2}$ must be obtained from (W), taking $\sigma_{1,2}=10^{-7}$ cm. n is Loschmidt's Number $= 2\cdot69 \times 10^{19}$ at NTP.[2] It is directly proportional to the pressure and must, therefore, be multiplied by 10^{-4} (the assumed ratio of the lunar and terrestrial atmospheric pressures). $m_1 = m_2 = 18$.

$$D_{1,1} = \frac{3}{8 \, n \, \sigma_{1,1}} \left(\frac{kT}{\pi m}\right)^{\frac{1}{2}} \text{ and numerically}$$

$$D_{1,1} = \frac{3}{8 \times 2\cdot69 \times 10^8} \left(\frac{1\cdot38 \times 10^{-16} \times 223}{3\cdot142 \times 18}\right)^{\frac{1}{2}}$$

$$D_{1,1} = \frac{10^{-16}}{8 \times 2\cdot69} \left(\frac{0\cdot69 \times 223}{3\cdot142}\right)^{\frac{1}{2}} = 3\cdot195 \times 10^{-17} \text{ cm.}^2/\text{sec.}$$

$\rho = 1\cdot1158 \times 10^{-7}$ g./cm.^{3}. $V_o = 2\cdot95/7\cdot6 = 0\cdot3882$. There is no correction this time and R becomes

$$R = 0\cdot3195 \times 1\cdot1158 \times 0\cdot3882 \times 10^{-24} \text{ g./cm.}^2 \text{ sec.}$$
$$= 1\cdot384 \times 10^{-25} \text{ g./cm.}^2 \text{ sec.}$$

This is, as might have been expected, a very much lower (in fact, infinitesimal) rate of evaporation than in either a CO_2 or an A atmosphere. It is also the more accurate as D is based here on the directly determined value of σ, and it has already been indicated why this case is of particular interest for lunar conditions.

Assuming once more (p. 212) that the total evaporation in the course of a lunation will be $R \times 8\cdot64 \times 10^5$, the total dissipation of mass per cm.^{2} of even surface will be equal to $1\cdot384 \times 8\cdot64 \times 10^{-20}$ or $2\cdot760 \times 10^{-19}$ grams, i.e. it will be practically nil. This is a significant result, for it shows that under low atmospheric pressures sublimation or vaporization of water snow will be most effectively hindered by its own products and may ultimately be brought to a complete standstill.

The conditions postulated in the above calculation are, no doubt, exaggerated and in reality the evaporation will begin in a situation close to that assumed in the first two cases, i.e. with the atmosphere totally devoid of water vapour, and gradually move towards the situation of the last case, without perhaps ever attained it in full. Even so it must be borne in mind that the rate of evaporation will be extremely low precisely in those initial (and final) stages and in progressing it will be increasingly stifled by the rising saturation of the ambient atmosphere with water vapour. In other words, it may well be that the Sun will never succeed in vaporizing even those 4·73 grams of snow per square cm., the heat energy for which is available in his non-reflected radiations.

213

The problem could also be tackled by considering the rate of incidence and evaporation of molecules at given partial pressures (partial pressure in the ambient atmosphere and on the surface of evaporation). The *Smithsonian Tables*[16] give the following equations for the rates of molecular incidence (evaporation):

$$v = 3\cdot513 \times 10^{22} P_{mm}/\sqrt{MT} \text{ cm}^{-2} \text{ sec.}^{-1}, \tag{X}$$

where v is the number of molecules, P_{mm} partial pressure in mm. Hg, M molecular weight of the gas in question, T absolute temperature; and

$$G = 5\cdot833 \times 10^{-2} P_{mm}\sqrt{M/T} \text{ g. cm.}^{-2} \text{ sec.}^{-1}, \tag{Y}$$

which expresses the same relationship in grams.

In this way a more accurate picture of the process of evaporation could be obtained by integrating the rates of evaporation and incidence over the various changes of P_{mm}; but the procedure would be rather involved and in the absence of any definite data its practical value would be limited. The discussion given above should suffice to set the approximate bounds to the rate and effect of evaporation in lunar conditions.

The conclusion appears to be that sufficiently large lunar snow-fields, once established, should be able to maintain themselves for long periods of time, if not indefinitely, with little loss of mass.

REFERENCES

1. BALDWIN, R. B. *The Face of the Moon.* University of Chicago Press, 1949.
2. CLARK, J. B. *Mathematical and Physical Tables* (New Edn. revised by A. C. Aitken). Oliver and Boyd, Edinburgh and London, 1950.
3. FIRSOFF, V. A. 'Does Water Vapour Escape from Mars?' *J.B.A.A.*, Vol. 66, No. 2, 1956.
4. GIAUQUE, W. F. and STOUT, J. W. 'The Entropy of Water and the Third Law of Thermodynamics. The Heat Capacity of Ice from 15 to 273° K.' *Journal of the American Chemical Society*, Vol. 58, No. 7, 1936.
5. HOUGHTON, HENRY G. 'A Preliminary Quantitative Analysis of Precipitation Mechanisms.' *Journal of Meteorology*, American Met. Socy., Vol. 7, No. 6.
6. JEANS, J. H. *The Dynamical Theory of Gases.* Cambridge University Press, 1925.
7. JEFFREYS, SIR HAROLD. *The Earth.* 3rd Edn. Cambridge University Press, 1952.
8. 'Some Problems of Evaporation.' *Philosophical Magazine*, No. 207, 1918.
9. KUIPER, G. P. 'On the Origin of the Lunar Surface Features.' *Proceedings of the National Academy of Sciences of the U.S.A.*, Vol. 40, No. 12, 1954.
10. (Ed.). *The Atmosphere of the Earth and Planets.* 2nd Edn. University of Chicago Press, 1952.
11. MACBAIN, J. W. *The Sorption of Gases and Vapours by Solids.* Routledge, London, 1932.
12. MEE, A. J. *Physical Chemistry.* Heinemann, London, 1943.
13. MILES, F. T. and MENZIES, A. W. C. 'The Vapour Pressures of Deuterium Water from 20° to 230°.' *Journal of the American Chemical Society.*, Vol. 58, No. 7, 1936.
14. MOORE, PATRICK. A lecture on the Moon delivered at the Manchester University, 1956.
15. PARTINGTON, J. R. *An Advanced Treatise on Physical Chemistry.* Longmans, Green, London, 1951.

APPENDIX

16. *Smithsonian Physical Tables, The*. Washington, 1954.
17. SPURR, J. E. *The Shrunken Moon*. Business Press, 1949.
18. UREY, H. C. *The Planets*. Oxford University Press, 1952.
19.   'On the Origin of Tektites.' *Proceedings of the National Academy of Sciences of the U.S.A.*, Vol. 41, No. 1, 1955.
20. VAUCOULEURS, GÉRARD DE. *Physics of the Planet Mars*. Faber, London, 1954.
21. WILKINS, H. P. *Our Moon*. Muller, London, 1954.
22. CHAPMAN, S. and COWLING, T. G. *The Mathematical Theory of Non-Uniform Gases*. Cambridge University Press, 1939.
23. GORDY, W., SMITH, W. V. and TRAMBARULS, R. F. *Microwave Spectroscopy*. Chapman & Hall, London, 1953.
24. LANDOLT-BÖRNSTEIN. *Physikalisch-Chemische Tabellen*. Julius Springer, Berlin, 1923–36.

APPENDIX II

The map below shows only the larger features on the Moon mentioned in this book. As in all the photographs the north is at the bottom, a convention due to the inversion of the image in most astronomical telescopes. (The naked-eye aspect is obtained by simply turning the photographs upside-down.)

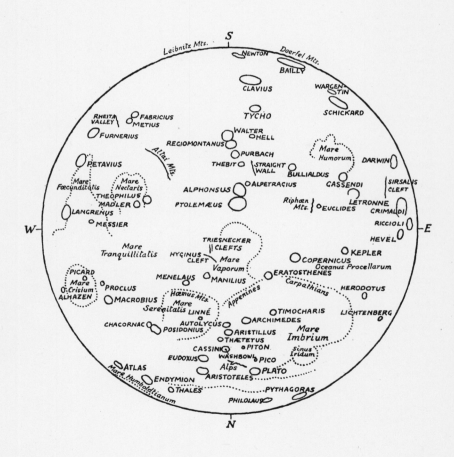

INDEX

217

Baum, R. M., 82, 109, 111
Beard, D. P., 47
Becquerel, P., 175
Beer, W., 30
Bellamy, H. A., 18
Bergquist, N. O., 19
Bessarion (crater), 83
Birt, W. R., 2, 104
blackbody, 114, 191, 192
'black desert', 71
black-sphere temperature, 192
Blackwelder, Eliot, 24
blowhole craters, 45
'blue caps', 95, 142
'blue clouds', see 'blue mists'
'blue flash', 129
'blue mists', 83, 109, 173
Boltzmann's Constant, 210
Bombon, Lake, 37, 48
bomb pits, 51
Bond, —, 30
Boneff, W., 47
Boon, J. D., 50
boracic acid, 174
bowl-craters, 45
Boyle's Law, 135, 181, 182, 211
Bracewell, R. N., 120
Britain, 48
British Astronomical Association, 2, 84
British Isles, 65
bromine, 143
Brownian movement, 74
bulge, tidal (or fossil), 27–29, 42, 67, 72
Bullen, K. E., 189
Bullialdus (crater), 60, 94, 96
bulwark plain (walled plain), 43
Bunsen, R. W. von, 147
Burton, E. F., 166

caesium, 143
caesium iodide, 153
calderas of collapse, 37, 51
Callisto, 67
Cambrian Ice Age, 23, 24
Cambridge, 133
camphor, 156
Canada, 50
'canals', 95
capillary water, 152, 157, 176
capture hypothesis, 20–23, 60, 63
carbon dioxide, 10, 12, 67, 90, 109, 128,
    131, 136, 139, 140, 141, 147, 148,
    153, 154, 170, 174–176, 183, 210,
    211, 213
carbon monoxide, 153
carbonyl sulphide, 136, 141

Carpathians, Lunar, 38
Carpenter, J., 49
Cassini (crater), 165
Cassini's Laws, 191
Caucasus, Lunar, 38
cavities, underground, 62–75, 190, 191
Celsius temperature scale, see Centigrade
Centigrade, 7
central-fountain hypothesis, 49
central peaks, 52
'Centrameridional Horst', 42, 59, 63,
centrifugal force, 15, 28, 186, 187
Chacornac (crater), 56
chalcedony, 146
changes on the Moon, 1, 2, 76–84,
    86–97, 177
changes, seasonal, 86–97, 177
Chapman, S., 210
charcoal, 148, 176
Charles's Law, 181
chemautotrophs, 179
chlorophyll, 177
Christmas rose, 174
circular velocity, 54
Clapeyron–Clausius Equation, 162, 206
Clapeyron's Formula, 181
Clavius (crater), 59
clefts, 39, 40, 45, 91
climate, 112–121, 156, 172, 204, 205
Cobra-Head, 81
Cochlearia arctica, 174
'cold seal', see 'cold trap'
'cold trap', 139, 152, 170
collisions, molecular, 6–8, 182, 193, 194,
    210
colongitude, 127
colour blindness, 98
colourings, 76, 82, 83, 86, 98–110, 122
    170, 173, 177
colour photography, 103
'Comet Tail', 72
compression, gravitational, 11, 188
Comstock, G. C., 125
concentric craters, 56
conduction of heat, 9, 73, 113, 141, 172,
    199
conical fracture, 37
convection of heat, 141, 137, 172, 197
convective atmosphere (*see also*
    troposphere), 137, 197
Cooke, S. R. B., 62
Coolidge, A. S., 203
cooling of lava, 66
Coon Butte, 50, 188
Copernicus (crater), 24, 31, 38, 44–46,
    56, 58, 59, 70, 72, 77, 82, 83, 89,
    94, 108, 188

218

INDEX

220

nitrogen, 6, 7, 10, 67, 147, 153, 170, 183
Nölke, F., 19
normal conditions of temperature and
    pressure, 7, 147, 150, 211

oblateness, 28, 186, 187
obscurations, 81, 193
obscure heat, 9
obsidian, 57, 71
Ocampo, S., 48
Ocean of Storms, see Oceanus Procel-
    larum
Oceanus Procellarum, 31, 42, 43, 60, 64,
    81, 102, 106
occultations, 126, 127, 129
Odessa 1, 188
Odessa 2, 188
O'Neill's Bridge, 72
Ophiucus, 133
Öpik, E. J., 105
'oppression', 191
'optical window', 10, 98
Orange Free State, 50
orbital motion, equation of, 182
orbit of Moon, 16–19, 111, 184–186
Our Moon, 105, 190
overthrust, 40, 41
oxygen, 6, 7, 10, 139, 143, 147, 153, 179,
    183
ozone, 136, 138, 141, 143, 201
ozonosphere, 143

Pacific Ocean, 19, 37
palladium, 148
Palus Nebularum, 91
parabolic equation of sorption, 203
partial pressure (see also vapours), 146,
    147, 157, 196, 202, 209, 214
Pawsey, J. L., 120
Peal, S. E., 47
penumbra, 35, 36, 90
Percy Mountains, 83
permafrost, 119, 151–153
Permo-Carboniferous (Permian) Ice Age,
    24
persorption, 148, 151
Petavius (crater), 56, 59, 80, 83
Pettit, Edison, 114, 116, 117, 119, 121
phases, effect of, 35, 36, 58, 113
Phillipines, 37, 48
Philolaus (crater), 82
Phocydides (crater), 90
phosphorus, 143
photodissociation, 136, 140, 143, 179
photoreduction, 177

photosynthesis, 175, 176, 179
Physical Chemistry, 202
Physikalisch-Chemische Tabellen, 211
Picard (crater), 81
Pic du Midi Observatory, 40, 128, 129
Pickering, W. H., 2, 19, 42, 47, 48, 50,
    57, 63, 79, 81, 89, 91, 92, 95, 104,
    107, 109, 124, 125, 142, 152,
    158–161, 167, 168, 177
Pickering (crater), 72, 91, 92
Pickering's experiments with slag craters,
    52
Pico, 71, 91, 167
Pico B, 167
Piddington, J. H., 116, 118, 119
Piton, 71, 91, 131, 154
planetesimals, 1
planets, 5, 6
plants (see also vegetation), 173–178
Plateau of Antrim, 65
Plato (crater), 31, 80–82, 104
'plats', 96
Pluto, 5, 11, 14
plutonic (volcanic) hypotheses, 55–75
polar axis of Moon, 26, 111, 191
'polar grid', 40
polarimetry, 100, 101, 119, 151
polarization, 100, 101, 103
Posidonius (crater), 56
potassium, 140, 143, 190
precipitation, 165, 166, 173
pressure, atmospheric, 11, 136, 144, 146,
    149, 176, 212
pressure of saturated water vapour over
    ice, 202, 203
Pretoria Salt Pan, 71
Proclus (crater), 58, 83, 89, 91, 165
Proctor, R. A., 48
Proteroselene, 68, 185
proto-Earth, 19, 22
protozoa, 175
pseudo-shadows, 96
Ptolomaeus (crater), 41, 53, 104, 177
Publications of the Astronomical Society
    of the Pacific, 102
pumice, 12, 66, 148, 149, 171
Purbach (crater), 40
Purkinje effect, 98, 103
Pyrola rotundifolia, 175
Pythagoras (crater), 90

quadrants, lunar, 31, 32
quarter phase, 35, 36, 58, 113
quartz, 70, 146
Quaternary Ice Age, 23
Quebec, Province of, 50

223